적중 100

영어 기출 문제집

중3

미래 | 최연희

Best Collection

구성과 특징

교과서의 주요 학습 내용을 중심으로 학습 영역별 특성에 맞춰 단계별로 다양한 학습 기회를 제공하여
단원별 학습능력 평가는 물론 중간 및 기말고사 시험 등에 완벽하게 대비할 수 있도록 내용을 구성

Words & Expressions

Step1   Key Words 단원별 핵심 단어 설명 및 풀이
         Key Expression 단원별 핵심 숙어 및 관용어 설명
         Word Power 반대 또는 비슷한 뜻 단어 배우기
         English Dictionary 영어로 배우는 영어 단어

Step2   실력평가 단원별 수시평가 대비 주관식, 객관식 문제풀이

Step3   서술형 대비 학업성취도 및 수행능력평가 대비 서술형 문제풀이

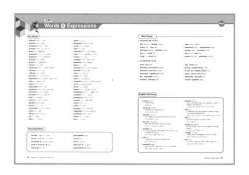

Conversation

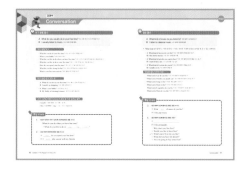

Step1   핵심 의사소통 소통에 필요한 주요 표현 방법 요약
         핵심 Check 기본적인 표현 방법 및 활용능력 확인

Step2   대화문 익히기 교과서 대화문 심층 분석 및 확인

Step3   교과서 확인학습 빈칸 채우기를 통한 문장 완성 능력 확인

Step4   기본평가 시험대비 기초 학습 능력 평가

Step5   실력평가 단원별 수시평가 대비 주관식, 객관식 문제풀이

Step6   서술형 대비 학업성취도 및 수행능력평가 대비 서술형 문제풀이

Grammar

Step1   주요 문법 단원별 주요 문법 사항과 예문을 알기 쉽게 설명
         핵심 Check 기본 문법사항에 대한 이해 여부 확인

Step2   기본평가 시험대비 기초 학습 능력 평가

Step3   실력평가 단원별 수시평가 대비 주관식, 객관식 문제풀이

Step4   서술형 대비 학업성취도 및 수행능력평가 대비 서술형 문제풀이

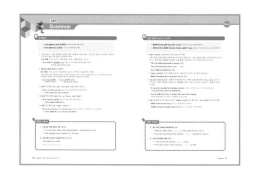

Reading

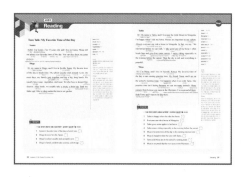

Step1   구문 분석 단원별로 제시된 문장에 대한 구문별 분석과 내용 설명
         확인문제 문장에 대한 기본적인 이해와 인지능력 확인

Step2   확인학습A 빈칸 채우기를 통한 문장 완성 능력 확인

Step3   확인학습B 제시된 우리말을 영어로 완성하여 작문 능력 키우기

Step4   실력평가 단원별 수시평가 대비 주관식, 객관식 문제풀이

Step5   서술형 대비 학업성취도 및 수행능력평가 대비 서술형 문제풀이
         교과서 구석구석 교과서에 나오는 기타 문장까지 완벽 학습

Composition

|영역별 핵심문제|

단어 및 어휘, 대화문, 문법, 독해 등 각 영역별 기출문제의 출제 유형을 분석하여 실전에 대비하고 연습할 수 있도록 문제를 배열

|단원별 예상문제|

기출문제를 분석한 후 새로운 시험 출제 경향을 더하여 새롭게 출제될 수 있는 문제를 포함하여 시험에 완벽하게 대비할 수 있도록 준비

|서술형 실전 및 창의사고력 문제|

학교 시험에서 점차 늘어나는 서술형 시험에 집중 대비하고 고득점을 취득하는데 만전을 기하기 위한 학습 코너

|단원별 모의고사|

영역별, 단계별 학습을 모두 마친 후 실전 연습을 위한 모의고사

교과서 파헤치기

- **단어Test1~3** 영어 단어 우리말 쓰기, 우리말을 영어 단어로 쓰기, 영영풀이에 해당하는 단어와 우리말 쓰기
- **대화문Test1~2** 대화문 빈칸 완성 및 전체 대화문 쓰기
- **본문Test1~5** 빈칸 완성, 우리말 쓰기, 문장 배열연습, 영어 작문하기 복습 등 단계별 반복 학습을 통해 교과서 지문에 대한 완벽한 습득
- **구석구석지문Test1~2** 지문 빈칸 완성 및 전문 영어로 쓰기

Contents

Lesson 6

Find Your Passion

🐦 의사소통 기능

- 불만족 표현하기
  I'm not satisfied with this T-shirt.

- 다짐 말하기
  I promise I won't be late again.

🐦 언어 형식

- 관계부사
  He wanted to create a place **where** people
  could try his innovative food.

- 접속부사 however, thus
  Some dishes were even decorated with flowers.
  Customers, **however**, were unhappy.
  He wanted to cook much more quickly and easily.
  Thus, he invented new machines for his kitchen.

교과서
Words & Expressions

Key Words

- **actor** [æktər] 명 배우
- **appreciate** [əprí:ʃièit] 동 진가를 알아보다, 고마워하다
- **arts high school** 예술 고등학교
- **blueberry** [blú:bèri] 명 블루베리
- **check** [tʃek] 명 계산서
- **complain** [kəmpléin] 동 불평하다
- **completely** [kəmplí:tli] 부 완전하게
- **creative** [kriéitiv] 형 창의적인, 창조적인
- **crush** [krʌʃ] 동 으깨다
- **customer** [kʌ́stəmər] 명 고객, 소비자
- **decide** [disáid] 동 결정하다
- **decorate** [dékərèit] 동 장식하다, 꾸미다
- **device** [diváis] 명 도구
- **dish** [diʃ] 명 음식, 요리
- **draw** [drɔː] 동 그리다
- **fantastic** [fæntǽstik] 형 환상적인
- **few** [fjuː] 형 소수의, 거의 없는
- **finish** [fíniʃ] 동 끝마치다
- **fix** [fiks] 동 수리하다
- **form** [fɔːrm] 명 서류
- **fresh** [freʃ] 형 신선한
- **gladly** [glǽdli] 부 기꺼이
- **grand** [grænd] 형 웅장한, 위대한
- **happen** [hǽpən] 동 일어나다
- **honestly** [ánistli] 부 솔직하게, 솔직히
- **inconvenience** [inkənví:njəns] 명 불편, 애로
- **innovative** [ínəvèitiv] 형 획기적인
- **inventor** [invéntər] 명 발명가
- **ma'am** [mæm] 명 (여성을 정중히 부르는 말) 부인
- **meal** [miːl] 명 식사
- **passion** [pǽʃən] 명 열정, 흥미
- **pay** [pei] 동 지불하다, 지급하다
- **promise** [prámis] 동 약속하다, 다짐하다
- **provide** [prəváid] 동 제공하다
- **pursue** [pərsú:] 동 추구하다, 추진하다
- **rare** [rɛər] 형 덜 익은, 살짝 익힌
- **real** [rí:əl] 형 사실적인
- **reason** [rí:zn] 명 이유
- **role** [roul] 명 역할, 배역
- **satisfied** [sǽtisfàid] 형 만족한
- **sell** [sel] 동 팔다
- **slice** [slais] 명 한 조각, 일부
- **successful** [səksésfəl] 형 성공적인
- **supper** [sʌ́pər] 명 만찬, 저녁 식사
- **surely** [ʃúərli] 부 확실히, 분명히
- **tank** [tæŋk] 명 (물 · 기름 등의) 탱크
- **throughout** [θru:áut] 전 ~ 동안 내내
- **unfortunately** [ənfɔ́:rtʃənətli] 부 불행하게도
- **uniquely** [ju:ní:kli] 부 독특하게
- **yet** [jet] 부 아직

Key Expressions

- **as a result** 결과적으로
- **be interested in** ~에 관심이 있다
- **be used to** ~에 익숙하다
- **do one's best** 최선을 다하다
- **feel like -ing** ~할 마음이 나다
- **fill out** 작성하다
- **have a bite of** 한 입 베어 물다
- **have a look at** ~을 살펴보다
- **not anymore** 더 이상 아니다
- **now that** ~이기 때문에, ~이므로
- **of all time** 역대, 지금껏
- **put ... in charge of ~** ~에게 …의 책임을 맡기다
- **put up** 내붙이다, 게시하다
- **scare away** 겁주어 쫓아내다
- **take charge of** ~의 책임을 지다, ~을 떠맡다
- **take a class** 수업을 듣다
- **take on** ~을 떠맡다
- **That's the reason why ~.** 그것이 ~하는 이유이다.
- **turn off** ~을 끄다

Word Power

※ 서로 비슷한 뜻을 가진 어휘

- [ ] **check** 계산서 – **bill** 계산서
- [ ] **complain** 불평하다 – **criticize** 비난하다
- [ ] **completely** 완전히 – **thoroughly** 철저하게
- [ ] **creative** 창의적인 – **original** 독창적인
- [ ] **decide** 결정하다 – **determine** 결정하다
- [ ] **fix** 수리하다 – **repair** 수리하다

- [ ] **happen** 일어나다 – **occur** 일어나다
- [ ] **provide** 제공하다 – **supply** 제공하다
- [ ] **pursue** 추구하다 – **seek** 찾다, 추구하다
- [ ] **reason** 이유 – **cause** 원인
- [ ] **supper** 저녁 식사 – **dinner** 저녁 식사
- [ ] **surely** 확실히 – **certainly** 확실하게

※ 서로 반대되는 뜻을 가진 어휘

- [ ] **completely** 완전하게 ↔ **incompletely** 불완전하게
- [ ] **fantastic** 환상적인 ↔ **realistic** 현실적인, 현실성 있는
- [ ] **convenience** 편리함 ↔ **inconvenience** 불편

- [ ] **rare** 덜 익은 ↔ **well-done** 잘 익은
- [ ] **satisfied** 만족한 ↔ **dissatisfied** 불만족한
- [ ] **sell** 팔다 ↔ **purchase** 구입하다

※ 동사 – 명사

- [ ] **appreciate** 진가를 알아보다 – **appreciation** 진가의 인정
- [ ] **complain** 불평하다 – **complaint** 불평
- [ ] **decide** 결정하다 – **decision** 결정
- [ ] **decorate** 장식하다 – **decoration** 장식

- [ ] **innovate** 혁신하다 – **innovation** 혁신
- [ ] **pay** 지불하다 – **payment** 지불
- [ ] **provide** 제공하다 – **provision** 공급
- [ ] **pursue** 추구하다 – **pursuit** 추구

※ 접두사 un-

- [ ] **clear** 명백한 – **unclear** 불확실한
- [ ] **creative** 창의적인 – **uncreative** 창의적이지 않은
- [ ] **easy** 쉬운 – **uneasy** 불편한
- [ ] **fortunate** 행운의 – **unfortunate** 불행한
- [ ] **happy** 행복한 – **unhappy** 불행한

- [ ] **natural** 자연스러운 – **unnatural** 자연스럽지 않은
- [ ] **real** 사실적인 – **unreal** 사실적이지 않은
- [ ] **successful** 성공적인 – **unsuccessful** 성공적이지 않은
- [ ] **usual** 흔한 – **unusual** 흔치 않은

English Dictionary

- [ ] **appreciate** 진가를 알아보다
  → to like something because one recognizes its good qualities
  어떤 것의 좋은 점을 인정하여 그것을 좋아하다

- [ ] **complain** 불평하다
  → to say that you are annoyed, not satisfied, or unhappy about something or someone
  어떤 것이나 누군가에 대해 짜증나거나 불만족스럽거나 불쾌하다고 말하다

- [ ] **crush** 으깨다
  → to press something so hard that it breaks or is damaged
  어떤 것을 세게 눌러서 깨지거나 손상되게 하다

- [ ] **customer** 고객, 소비자
  → someone who buys goods or services from a shop, company, etc.
  상점, 회사 등으로부터 상품이나 서비스를 구입하는 사람

- [ ] **decorate** 장식하다, 꾸미다
  → to make something look more nice by putting something pretty on it
  어떤 예쁜 것을 올려놓아 어떤 것을 더 좋아 보이게 만들다

- [ ] **fix** 수리하다
  → to repair something that is broken or not working properly
  망가지거나 제대로 작동하지 않는 것을 수리하다

- [ ] **form** 서류
  → an official document with spaces where you write information
  당신이 정보를 적을 여백을 가진 공식적인 문서

- [ ] **pursue** 추구하다, 추진하다
  → to make efforts to achieve a particular aim or result, often over a long period of time
  종종 오랜 시간에 걸쳐, 어떤 특정 목표나 결과를 달성하기 위해 노력하다

- [ ] **rare** 덜 익은, 살짝 익힌
  → cooked a short time; still red inside
  잠깐 요리된; 속이 아직 붉은

01 다음 짝지어진 단어의 관계가 같도록 빈칸에 알맞은 말은? (중요)

> check – bill : determine – _____

① complain ② cause ③ crush
④ device ⑤ decide

02 주어진 영어 설명에 맞게 문장의 빈칸에 알맞은 말을 쓰시오. (서답형)

> It is unnecessary to _____ the argument any further.

> <영어 설명> to make efforts to achieve a particular aim or result, often over a long period of time

➡ _____

03 다음 주어진 단어를 사용하여 자연스러운 문장을 만들 수 없는 것은?

> provide slice promise fix

① I'll see what I can do but I can't _____ anything.
② They're sending an engineer to _____ the phone.
③ I usually have a _____ of bread every morning.
④ Photographs of actors _____ the walls of the restaurant.
⑤ Teachers _____ a model for children to imitate.

04 다음 빈칸에 들어갈 알맞은 말을 고르시오.

> Find your _____ and follow your dreams.

① passion ② device
③ convenience ④ expression
⑤ contact

05 밑줄 친 부분의 의미로 알맞지 않은 것은? (중요)

① They managed to scare the bears away. (겁주어 쫓아내다)
② Could you fill out these forms? (작성하다)
③ I was not used to carrying a tray with one hand. (~에 사용되었다)
④ I don't feel ready to take on new responsibilities. (떠맡다)
⑤ To take the class, you have to be able to use a computer. (수업을 듣다)

06 다음 빈칸에 공통으로 들어갈 말로 알맞은 것을 고르시오.

> • You will take charge _____ the company.
> • To my thinking, he's one of the greatest comedians _____ all time.

① in ② of ③ with
④ at ⑤ for

01 다음 영영풀이에 알맞은 어휘를 〈보기〉에서 찾아 쓰시오.

┌── 보기 ──────────────────┐
　　form　　complain
　　customer　　appreciate
└──────────────────────────┘

(1) to say that you are annoyed, not satisfied, or unhappy about something or someone

　➡ _____

(2) someone who buys goods or services from a shop, company, etc.

　➡ _____

(3) to like something because one recognizes its good qualities

　➡ _____

(4) an official document with spaces where you write information

　➡ _____

02 다음 짝지어진 두 단어의 관계가 같도록 빈칸에 알맞은 말을 쓰시오.

(1) decide : decision = complain : _____

(2) completely : incompletely
　　= natural : _____

03 다음 우리말에 맞도록 빈칸에 알맞은 말을 쓰시오.

(1) 그것은 획기적인 디자인 덕분에 곧 인기 있게 되었다.
　➡ It soon became popular thanks to its _____ design.

(2) 나는 내 방을 꽃으로 장식하고 싶어.
　➡ I want to _____ my room with flowers.

(3) 그는 그의 어린 딸에게 안전장치를 만들어 주었다.
　➡ He made a safety _____ for his baby daughter.

(4) 그녀는 이 영화에서 주인공을 연기한다.
　➡ She plays the main _____ in this movie.

04 우리말에 맞게 한 단어를 추가하여 주어진 어구를 알맞게 배열하시오.

(1) 나는 패션에 대한 열정을 갖고 있다.
　(a, I, fashion, have, for)
　➡ _____

(2) 그 새 식당은 밝고 다채로운 간판을 세웠다.
　(the new restaurant, sign, and, bright, up, a, colorful)
　➡ _____
　_____

(3) 양해해 주셔서 감사드리며 불편을 끼쳐드린 점 사과드립니다.
　(we, you, your, understanding, and, inconvenience, thank, apologize, any, for)
　➡ _____
　_____

(4) 이제 겨울이니까, 나는 주말마다 스키 타러 갈 거야.
　(I'm, weekend, winter, it's, now, go, going, skiing, every, to)
　➡ _____
　_____

Conversation

1 불만족 표현하기

I'm not satisfied with this T-shirt. 나는 이 티셔츠가 마음에 들지 않아.

- 'I'm not satisfied with A.'는 '나는 A가 마음에 들지 않는다.'는 의미로 불만족을 나타내는 표현으로, 'I'm not happy with ~.'라고 표현하기도 한다. 불만족을 나타낼 때는 'not satisfied with ~', 'not happy with ~', 'not pleased with ~'와 함께 'unhappy with ~', 'dissatisfied with ~'를 사용하여 'I'm unhappy with ~', 'I'm dissatisfied with ~' 또는 'I don't like ~'라고 할 수도 있다.

- 불만족에 대하여 물을 때는 'Are you dissatisfied with ~?' 또는 'Are you unhappy with ~?(~이 마음에 안 드니?)' 등과 같은 표현을 사용한다.

- 고민이나 불만족의 원인을 물어볼 때는 'Is something worrying you?(무슨 걱정거리가 있나요?)' 또는 'Is there something bothering you?(뭔가 걸리는 일이 있나요?)', 'Is there anything wrong?(뭐 잘못된 일 있니?)', 'What happened?(무슨 일 있니?)'와 같은 표현을 사용하고, 무슨 문제가 있는지 물어볼 때는 'Is something wrong?(뭐가 잘못되었니?)' 또는 'What's wrong (with you)?(뭐가 잘못됐나요?)', 'Why are you disappointed?(왜 실망스러운가요?)'와 같은 표현을 쓸 수도 있다.

불만족 표현하기

- I'm not satisfied with ~. 나는 ~가 만족스럽지 않아.
- I don't like ~. 나는 ~가 안 좋아.
- I'm not happy with ~. 나는 ~가 마음에 들지 않아.
- I'm unhappy with ~. 나는 ~가 마음에 들지 않아.
- I'm dissatisfied with ~. 나는 ~가 불만스러워요.

핵심 Check

1. 다음 밑줄 친 (A)의 우리말과 일치하도록 주어진 표현을 이용하여 영어로 쓰시오.

   M: Hello, ma'am. How can I help you?

   W: I bought this phone only a week ago, but it sometimes turns off by itself.

   M: Oh, I see. May I have a look at it? (Pause) We're sorry for the inconvenience. It'll take a few hours to fix it.

   W: (A)그 휴대전화가 만족스럽지 않아요. (the phone, satisfied) I'd like a new one.

   M: Of course. I just need to fill out this form.

   ➡ _____

② 다짐 말하기

> **I promise I won't be late again.** 다시는 늦지 않겠다고 약속할게요.

- 'I promise to ~.'는 '~하겠다고 약속합니다.'의 뜻으로 확실하게 하겠다는 다짐을 나타내는 말이다. promise를 쓸 때는 to부정사나 'that 주어+동사'의 형태가 따라온다. 상대방에게 확실하게 '~하겠다.'는 의미로 확실성을 나타내는 'make sure(확실하게 하다)'를 사용하여 'I will make sure that 주어+동사 ~' 라고 할 수도 있다.

- 다짐이나 확실한 일을 나타내는 표현에는 sure(확실한), certain(확신하는), positive(긍정적인) 등을 사용하여 'I'm sure (that) ~.'이라고 하거나 'I'm certain (that) ~.' 또는 'I'm positive about ~.(나는 ~에 대해 확신한다.)'라고 할 수 있고, '맹세하다'라는 의미의 'swear'를 사용하여 'I swear I will ~.'이라는 표현을 사용할 수 있다.

- '확실하다'라는 의미로 'I'm 100 percent sure.(나는 100% 장담해.)' 또는 'It is obvious/clear that ~.(~가 분명하다.)'를 쓰기도 한다. 'bet'은 '내기를 걸다, 틀림없다'의 뜻으로 'I bet that ~.'이라고 하면 '틀림없이 ~이다.'라는 뜻이 된다. 앞으로 할 일이나 일어날 일에 대하여 상대방에게 확신을 주거나, 원하는 것이나 좋은 일이 일어날 것이 확실함을 나타낼 때는 'I have no doubt that ~.(~할 거라고 믿는다., ~을 믿어 의심치 않는다., ~할 거라고 확신한다.)'이라는 표현을 사용한다.

다짐 말하기

- I promise to ~. 나는 ~하겠다고 약속해.
- I promise you that I'll ~. 나는 ~하겠다고 약속드릴게요.
- She will make sure that ~. 그녀는 반드시 ~하도록 할 거다.
- He swears he will ~. 그는 ~하겠다고 약속한다.
- I'm sure that ~. 나는 반드시 ~할 것이다.
- I'm certain that ~. 나는 확실히 ~할 것이다.

핵심 Check

2. 다음 대화의 밑줄 친 (A)의 우리말에 해당하는 적절한 표현을 쓰시오.

B: Mom, I want to take cooking classes.

W: What? I thought you were interested in sports.

B: I was but not anymore. I want to become a chef.

W: Are you sure? Cooking is hard work.

M: Don't worry. (A)최선을 다하겠다고 약속할게요. (do, promise)

W: O.K., then.

➡ _____

Listen & Speak 1 A-1

B: Wow! Did you draw this?

G: I did. Do you like it?

B: Yes, the bread and the milk ❶look so real. ❷I feel like having a bite of the bread.

G: Thanks, but ❸I'm not satisfied with it. It's not ❹unique.

B: I don't think ❺so. I think it's a fantastic drawing.

B: 우와! 이거 네가 그린 거야?

G: 내가 그렸어. 마음에 들어?

B: 응, 빵이랑 우유가 정말 진짜 같아. 빵을 한 입 먹고 싶어지는데.

G: 고마워, 하지만 이건 만족스럽진 않아. 독창적이지 않아.

B: 난 그렇게 생각 안 해. 정말 멋진 그림인 것 같아.

❶ look+형용사: ~하게 보이다
❷ feel like ~ing: ~하고 싶다
❸ 'be not satisfied with'는 불만족을 표현하는 말이다.
❹ unique: 독창적인
❺ so는 'It's not unique.'를 대신하고 있다.

Check(√) True or False

(1) The girl is satisfied with what she drew.　　　　　　　　　　T ☐　F ☐

(2) The boy thinks the bread and the milk look so real.　　　　　T ☐　F ☐

Listen & Speak 1 A-2

M: Hello, ma'am. How can I help you?

W: I bought this phone only a week ago, but it sometimes turns off ❶ by itself.

M: Oh, I see. May I ❷have a look at it? (*Pause*) We're sorry for the ❸ inconvenience. ❹It'll take a few hours to fix it.

W: ❺I'm not satisfied with the phone. I'd like a new ❻one.

M: Of course. I just need to ❼fill out this form.

M: 안녕하세요, 고객님. 무엇을 도와드릴까요?

W: 이 휴대전화를 겨우 일주일 전에 샀는데, 가끔 저절로 꺼져요.

M: 오, 그렇군요. 제가 좀 봐도 될까요? 불편을 드려 죄송합니다. 고치는 데 몇 시간 정도 걸릴 거예요.

W: 이 휴대전화가 만족스럽지 않아요. 새것을 원해요.

M: 물론이죠. 이 서류만 작성하면 됩니다.

❶ by itself: 스스로, 저절로 = naturally, automatically(자동으로)
❷ have a look at: ~을 한 번 보다, it은 this phone을 가리킨다.
❸ inconvenience: 불편
❹ take: (시간이) 걸리다, fix: 고치다, 수리하다
❺ 'be not satisfied with'는 불만족을 표현하는 말이다.
❻ one은 phone을 대신해서 쓰인 부정대명사이다.
❼ fill out a form: 서식을 작성하다

Check(√) True or False

(3) The woman bought the phone a few weeks ago.　　　　　　　T ☐　F ☐

(4) The man needs to fill out a form.　　　　　　　　　　　　　T ☐　F ☐

Listen & Speak 2 A-1

G: Wow, I like this blueberry jam. Where did you buy it?

B: I made it ❶myself.

G: Really? ❷This is better than any other jam I've ever had. You should sell it.

B: Do you think people would want to buy this?

G: Of course. ❸I promise I'll be your first customer.

❶ 강조 용법으로 쓰인 재귀대명사이다.
❷ '비교급+than any other+단수 명사'로 최상급의 의미이다. jam 뒤에는 관계대명사 that이 생략되어 있는 형태로 관계사절이 선행사인 jam을 수식하고 있다.
❸ 다짐을 말할 때 쓰는 표현이다. promise 뒤에는 구체적인 내용을 명사절로 써서 나타내며, "I promise to be your first customer."로 바꿔 쓸 수 있다.

Listen & Speak 2 A-2

B: Mom, I want to go to an arts high school. I want to become an actor.

W: What? I thought you were interested in science.

B: I was but ❶not anymore. I want to become a movie star.

W: Are you sure you want to be an actor?

B: Yes, I'll learn ❷how to act. ❸I promise I'll do my best.

❶ 'not anymore'는 'I'm not interested in science anymore.'에서 중복되는 것을 생략하고 쓴 표현이다.
❷ 'how to act'는 '의문사+to부정사'로 learn의 목적어 역할을 하고 있다.
❸ 다짐을 말할 때 쓰는 표현으로 'I promise to do my best.'로 바꿔 쓸 수 있다.

Communicate A

Man: Are you enjoying your meal?

Woman: Well, the bread was good, and the salad was fresh.

Man: How about your steak?

Woman: Honestly, ❶I'm not satisfied with the steak. It's too ❷rare for me.

Man: I'm sorry. Would you like me to bring you another one?

Woman: ❸That's O.K. I need to be going. Let me just have the check, please.

Man: I'm really sorry. You won't have to pay for the steak.

Woman: O.K. Thanks.

Man: ❹I promise we'll provide you with a better experience next time you visit.

❶ 'be not satisfied with'는 불만족을 표현하는 말이다.
❷ rare: 설익은, 덜 익은
❸ That은 다른 것으로 가져다 주겠다는 앞 문장의 내용을 받고 있다.
❹ 다짐을 말할 때 쓰는 표현이다.

Progress Check 1

M: Hello, ma'am. How can I help you?

W: I got this hat as a gift yesterday, ❶but I'm not satisfied with the color.

M: Oh, I see. We have this hat in different colors.

W: Do you have ❷one in blue?

M: Yes, we ❸do. I'll get ❷one for you.

W: Thanks.

❶ 'be not satisfied with'는 불만족을 표현하는 말이다.
❷ one은 hat을 대신해서 쓰인 부정대명사이다.
❸ do는 'have the hat in blue'를 대신하는 대동사이다.

Progress Check 2

B: Mom, I want to ❶take cooking classes.

W: What? I thought you were interested in sports.

B: I was but ❷not anymore. I want to become a chef.

W: Are you sure? Cooking is hard work.

B: Don't worry. ❸I promise I'll do my best.

W: O.K., ❹then.

❶ take classes: 수업을 듣다
❷ 'not anymore'는 'I'm not interested in sports anymore.'에서 중복되는 것을 생략하고 쓴 표현이다.
❸ 다짐을 말할 때 쓰는 표현으로 'I promise to do my best.'로 바꿔 쓸 수 있다.
❹ then은 'If you promise you'll do your best'를 대신한다고 볼 수 있다.

Progress Check 3

G: Dad, I want to watch a movie on TV now.

M: ❶Have you finished your homework?

G: No, but ❷I promise I'll finish it after I watch TV.

❶ 현재완료의 완료 용법이다.
❷ 다짐을 말할 때 쓰는 표현으로 'I promise to finish it after I watch TV.'로 바꿔 쓸 수 있다.

● 다음 우리말과 일치하도록 빈칸에 알맞은 말을 쓰시오.

Listen & Speak 1 A-1

B: Wow! Did you draw this?

G: I _____. Do you like _____?

B: Yes, the bread and the milk _____ _____. I _____ _____ _____ the bread.

G: Thanks, but _____ _____ _____ _____ it. It's not _____.

B: I don't think _____. I think it's a _____ _____.

Listen & Speak 1 A-2

M: Hello, ma'am. _____ _____ I _____ you?

W: I bought this phone _____ _____ _____ _____, but it _____ _____ _____ _____.

M: Oh, I see. May I _____ _____ _____ _____ it? (Pause) We're sorry for the _____. It'll _____ a _____ _____ _____ fix it.

W: _____ _____ _____ _____ the phone. I'd like a new _____.

M: Of course. I just need to _____ _____ this _____.

Listen & Speak 2 A-1

G: Wow, I like this blueberry jam. Where did you buy it?

B: I made it _____.

G: Really? This is _____ _____ _____ _____ _____ I've ever had. You should sell _____.

B: Do you think people _____ want to buy this?

G: Of course. _____ _____ _____ _____ your first customer.

Listen & Speak 2 A-2

B: Mom, I want to go to an arts high school. I want to become an actor.

W: What? I thought you _____ _____ science.

B: I was but _____ _____. I _____ _____ become a movie star.

W: _____ you _____ you want to be an actor?

B: Yes, I'll learn _____ _____. _____ _____ _____ my best.

해석

B: 우와! 이거 네가 그린 거야?
G: 내가 그렸어. 마음에 들어?
B: 응, 빵이랑 우유가 정말 진짜 같아. 빵을 한 입 먹고 싶어지는데.
G: 고마워, 하지만 이건 만족스럽진 않아. 독창적이지 않아.
B: 난 그렇게 생각 안 해. 정말 멋진 그림인 것 같아.

M: 안녕하세요, 고객님. 무엇을 도와드릴까요?
W: 이 휴대전화를 겨우 일주일 전에 샀는데, 가끔 저절로 꺼져요.
M: 오, 그렇군요. 제가 좀 봐도 될까요? 불편을 드려 죄송합니다. 고치는 데 몇 시간 정도 걸릴 거예요.
W: 그 휴대전화가 만족스럽지 않아요. 새것을 원해요.
M: 물론이죠. 이 서류만 작성하면 됩니다.

G: 우와, 이 블루베리 잼 마음에 든다. 어디서 샀어?
B: 직접 만든 거야.
G: 정말? 내가 지금껏 먹어본 잼 중에 제일 좋아. 팔아도 되겠어.
B: 사람들이 이걸 사길 원할 거라고 생각해?
G: 물론이지. 내가 너의 첫 손님이 되겠다고 약속할게.

B: 엄마, 저 예술 고등학교에 가고 싶어요. 배우가 되고 싶어요.
W: 뭐라고? 네가 과학에 관심이 있다고 생각했는데.
B: 그랬었는데 더는 아니에요. 저는 영화배우가 되고 싶어요.
W: 배우가 되고 싶은 게 확실하니?
B: 네, 연기하는 방법을 배울 거예요. 최선을 다하겠다고 약속할게요.

Communicate A

Man: Are you enjoying _____ _____?

Woman: Well, the bread was _____, and the salad was _____.

Man: How _____ your steak?

Woman: Honestly, _____ _____ _____ _____ the steak. It's too _____ for me.

Man: I'm sorry. Would you like me _____ _____ you _____ _____?

Woman: That's O.K. I need to _____ _____. Let me just _____ the _____, please.

Man: I'm really sorry. You _____ _____ _____ pay for the steak.

Woman: O.K. Thanks.

Man: _____ _____ _____ _____ you _____ a better experience next time you visit.

Progress Check 1

M: Hello, ma'am. _____ _____ _____ help you?

W: I _____ this hat _____ a gift yesterday, but _____ _____ _____ _____ the color.

M: Oh, I see. We have this hat _____ different colors.

W: Do you have _____ _____ _____?

M: Yes, we _____. I'll _____ _____ for you.

W: Thanks.

Progress Check 2

B: Mom, I want to _____ cooking _____.

W: What? I thought you were _____ _____ sports.

B: I was but _____ _____. I want to become a chef.

W: Are you sure? Cooking is hard work.

B: Don't _____. _____ _____ _____ _____ my best.

W: O.K., _____.

Progress Check 3

G: Dad, I want to watch a movie _____ TV now.

M: _____ you _____ your homework?

G: No, but _____ _____ _____ _____ it after I watch TV.

해석

남자: 식사가 마음에 드십니까?
여자: 음, 빵은 괜찮았고, 샐러드도 신선했어요.
남자: 스테이크는 어떠세요?
여자: 솔직히, 스테이크는 만족스럽지 않아요. 제겐 너무 덜 익었어요.
남자: 죄송합니다. 다른 것으로 가져다 드릴까요?
여자: 괜찮아요. 가봐야 해서요. 그냥 계산서 좀 갖다주세요.
남자: 정말 죄송합니다. 스테이크 값은 지불하지 않으셔도 됩니다.
여자: 알겠습니다. 감사해요.
남자: 다음에 방문하실 때는 더 좋은 경험을 드릴 것을 약속드릴게요.

M: 안녕하세요, 고객님. 무엇을 도와드릴까요?
W: 어제 이 모자를 선물 받았는데, 색상이 마음에 들지 않아요.
M: 오, 그렇군요. 이 모자로 다른 색상도 있습니다.
W: 파란 것도 있나요?
M: 네, 있습니다. 하나 가져다 드릴게요.
W: 고맙습니다.

B: 엄마, 저 요리 수업을 듣고 싶어요.
W: 뭐? 네가 스포츠에 관심이 있다고 생각했는데.
B: 그랬는데 더는 아니에요. 저는 요리사가 되고 싶어요.
W: 정말이니? 요리는 힘든 일이란다.
B: 걱정하지 마세요. 최선을 다하겠다고 약속할게요.
W: 그래, 그럼.

G: 아빠, 저 지금 TV에서 영화를 보고 싶어요.
M: 숙제는 끝냈니?
G: 아니요, 하지만 TV를 보고 나서 끝낼 것을 약속드릴게요.

01 다음 빈칸 (A)에 알맞은 문장을 고르시오.

> B: Wow! Did you draw this?
>
> G: I did. Do you like it?
>
> B: Yes, the bread and the milk look so real. I feel like having a bite of the bread.
>
> G: Thanks, but _____(A)_____ . It's not unique.
>
> B: I don't think so. I think it's a fantastic drawing.

① I'm pleased with it

② I'm not satisfied with it

③ I think I can make it more real

④ I think it's rather natural

⑤ I think it looks like real bread and milk

02 밑줄 친 우리말을 주어진 어구를 이용해 영작하시오.

> G: Wow, I like this blueberry jam. Where did you buy it?
>
> B: I made it myself.
>
> G: Really? This is better than any other jam I've ever had. You should sell it.
>
> B: Do you think people would want to buy this?
>
> G: Of course. 내가 너의 첫 손님이 되겠다고 약속할게. (promise, be first customer, 7 단어)

➡ _____

03 다음 대화가 자연스럽게 연결되도록 (A)~(D)를 적절하게 배열하시오.

> M: Hello, ma'am. How can I help you?
>
> (A) I'm not satisfied with the phone. I'd like a new one.
>
> (B) Oh, I see. May I have a look at it? (*Pause*) We're sorry for the inconvenience. It'll take a few hours to fix it.
>
> (C) I bought this phone only a week ago, but it sometimes turns off by itself.
>
> (D) Of course. I just need to fill out this form.

➡ _____

중요

01 다음 중 짝지어진 대화가 <u>어색한</u> 것은?

① A: Wow! Did you draw this?
   B: Yes, I did. Do you like it?

② A: I'm not satisfied with the phone. I'd like a new one.
   B: Of course. I just need to fill out this form.

③ A: Are you sure you want to be an actor?
   B: Yes, I'll learn how to act. I promise I'll do my best.

④ A: I was but not anymore. I want to become a chef.
   B: I thought you were interested in sports.

⑤ A: Are you enjoying your meal?
   B: Well, the bread was good, and the salad was fresh.

[02~05] 다음 대화를 읽고 물음에 답하시오.

M: Hello, ma'am. How can I help you?
W: I got this hat as a gift yesterday, but I'm not satisfied with _____(A)_____.
M: Oh, I see. We have this hat in different colors.
W: (a)파란 것도 있나요? (one, have, in)
M: _____(B)_____ I'll get one for you.
W: Thanks.

02 빈칸 (A)에 알맞은 말을 고르시오.

① the color   ② the shape
③ its convenience ④ its size
⑤ its price

서답형

03 위 대화의 빈칸 (B)에 들어갈 말로 알맞은 말을 we를 포함한 3 단어로 쓰시오.

➡ _____

서답형

04 밑줄 친 (a)의 우리말에 맞게 괄호 안에 주어진 어휘를 이용하여 영작하시오.

➡ _____

중요

05 위 대화의 내용과 일치하는 것은?

① The man is a customer.
② The woman bought a hat yesterday.
③ The woman is satisfied with the gift.
④ The woman has a blue hat.
⑤ The man will get a hat for the woman.

[06~07] 다음 대화를 읽고 물음에 답하시오.

B: Mom, I want to go to an arts high school. I want to become an actor.
W: What? I thought you were interested in science.
B: I was but (a)더는 아니에요. I want to become a movie star.
W: Are you sure you want to be an actor?
B: Yes, I'll learn how to act. _____(A)_____

06 위 대화의 빈칸 (A)에 들어갈 말로 알맞은 것은?

① Do you want me to do my best?
② I don't want to try my best.
③ Let me wish good luck.
④ I hope I'll do my best.
⑤ I promise I'll do my best.

서답형

07 밑줄 친 (a)의 우리말에 맞게 두 단어로 영작하시오.

➡ _____

서답형

08 주어진 글 사이에 대화가 자연스럽게 연결되도록 (A)~(D)를 적절하게 배열하시오.

> M: Hello, ma'am. How can I help you?

> (A) Do you have one in blue?
> (B) Oh, I see. We have this hat in different colors.
> (C) I got this hat as a gift yesterday, but I'm not satisfied with the color.
> (D) Yes, we do. I'll get one for you.

> W: Thanks.

➡ _____

[09~12] 다음 대화를 읽고 물음에 답하시오.

Man: Are you enjoying your meal?
Woman: Well, the bread was good, and the salad was fresh.
Man: How about your steak?
Woman: Honestly, _____(A)_____. It's too rare for me.
Man: I'm sorry. Would you like me to bring you another __(B)__ ?
Woman: That's O.K. I need to be going. Let me just have the check, please.
Man: I'm really sorry. You won't have to pay for the steak.
Woman: O.K. Thanks.
Man: I promise we'll provide you with a better experience (a)다음에 방문하실 때는.

09 위 대화의 빈칸 (A)에 알맞은 말은?

① I enjoyed a lot
② I think this restaurant is very good
③ I think the service is not so good
④ I'm not satisfied with the steak
⑤ it's very good and delicious

서답형

10 위 대화의 빈칸 (B)에 알맞은 말을 부정대명사를 이용하여 쓰시오.

➡ _____

11 위 대화를 읽고 대답할 수 <u>없는</u> 것은?

① What does the woman think about the salad?
② Does the man always serve the steak rare?
③ Did the woman enjoy the steak?
④ Will the woman pay for the steak?
⑤ Will the man serve the woman better next time she visits?

서답형

12 위 대화의 밑줄 친 (a)의 우리말을 'time'을 이용하여 영작하시오.

➡ _____

13 다음 대화의 밑줄 친 부분의 의도로 알맞은 것은?

> G: Dad, I want to watch a movie on TV now.
> M: Have you finished your homework?
> G: No, but I promise I'll finish it after I watch TV.

① 불만족 표현하기　② 희망 표현하기
③ 설명하기　④ 경험 말하기
⑤ 다짐 말하기

[01~03] 다음 대화를 읽고 물음에 답하시오.

Man: Are you enjoying your meal?

Woman: Well, the bread was good, and the salad was fresh.

(A) That's O.K. I need to be going. Let me just have the check, please.

(B) Honestly, I'm not satisfied with the steak. It's too rare for me.

(C) I'm sorry. Would you like me to bring you another one?

(D) How about your steak?

Man: I'm really sorry. (a)<u>스테이크 값은 지불하지 않으셔도 됩니다.</u> (won't, the steak)

Woman: O.K. Thanks.

Man: I promise we'll provide you with a better experience next time you visit.

01 위 대화의 (A)~(D)를 알맞은 순서로 배열하시오.

➡ _____

02 괄호 안에 주어진 어휘를 이용하여 밑줄 친 우리말 (a)에 맞게 8 단어로 쓰시오.

➡ _____

03 Why isn't the woman satisfied with the steak? Use the word 'because'.

➡ _____
_____
_____

[04~05] 다음 대화를 읽고 물음에 답하시오.

M: Hello, ma'am. How can I help you?

W: I bought this phone only a week ago, but it sometimes turns off (a)<u>저절로</u>.

M: Oh, I see. May I have a look at it? (*Pause*) We're sorry for the inconvenience. It'll take a few hours to fix it.

W: _____(A)_____ I'd like a new one.

M: Of course. I just need to fill out this form.

04 위 대화의 빈칸 (A)에 '전화기가 만족스럽지 않음'을 표현하는 말을 6 단어로 쓰시오.

➡ _____

05 밑줄 친 (a)의 우리말을 2 단어로 쓰시오.

➡ _____

06 다음 대화에서 어법상 어색한 것을 찾아 바르게 고치시오. (2개)

B: Wow! Did you draw this?

G: I was. Do you like it?

B: Yes, the bread and the milk look so real. I feel like to have a bite of the bread.

G: Thanks, but I'm not satisfied with it. It's not unique.

B: I don't think so. I think it's a fantastic drawing.

(1) _____ ➡ _____

(2) _____ ➡ _____

Grammar

① 관계부사

> • He wanted to create a place **where** people could try his innovative food.
> 그는 사람들이 그의 획기적인 음식을 먹어볼 수 있는 장소를 만들기를 원했다.
>
> • That's the reason **why** he hasn't finished the painting yet.
> 그것이 그가 아직 그림을 끝내지 못한 이유이다.

■ 관계부사는 접속사와 부사의 역할을 동시에 하는 것으로 선행사를 수식한다.

- I remember **the day**. We first met **on the day**.
  = I remember the day **when** we first met. 나는 우리가 처음 만난 날을 기억한다.
- That is **the building**. My uncle works **in the building**.
  = That is the building **where** my uncle works. 저기가 나의 삼촌이 일하는 건물이다.

■ 선행사가 장소, 시간, 이유, 방법 등의 명사일 때 전치사와 관계대명사로 표현 가능하며, 생략 등 각각의 용례도 조금씩 다르다.

(1) 장소(where): This is **the house**. Da Vinci lived **in the house**.
  → This is the house **which[that]** da Vinci lived **in**.
  → This is the house **in which** da Vinci lived. (in that (X))
  → This is the house **where** da Vinci lived. 이곳이 다빈치가 살았던 집이다.

(2) 시간(when): This is **the day**. Da Vinci was born **on the day**.
  → This is the day **which[that]** da Vinci was born **on**.
  → This is the day **on which** da Vinci was born. (on that (X))
  → This is the day **where** da Vinci was born. 이 날이 다빈치가 태어난 날이다.

(3) 이유(why): This is **the reason**. Da Vinci is a genius **for the reason**.
  → This is the reason **which[that]** da Vinci is a genius **for**.
  → This is the reason **for which** da Vinci is a genius. (for that (X))
  → This is the reason **why** da Vinci is a genius. 이것이 다빈치가 천재인 이유이다.
  → This is **why** da Vinci is a genius. (the reason 또는 why 둘 중의 하나 생략 가능)

(4) 방법(how): This is **the way**. Da Vinci escaped **in the way**.
  → This is the way **which[that]** da Vinci escaped **in**.
  → This is the way **in which** da Vinci escaped. (in that (X))
  → This is **the way how** da Vinci escaped.(X) (the way와 how를 같이 쓸 수 없다.)
  → This is **the way** da Vinci escaped. 이것이 다빈치가 탈출한 방법이다.
  → This is **how** da Vinci escaped. (the way 또는 how 둘 중의 하나만 써야 한다.)

핵심 Check

1. 괄호 안에서 알맞은 말을 고르시오.

(1) Sumi doesn't tell me the reason (why / which) she cried yesterday.

(2) This is the year (how / when) the teacher decided to start a business.

❷ 접속부사

> • Some dishes were even decorated with flowers. Customers, **however**, were unhappy. 몇몇 음식들은 심지어 꽃으로 장식되었다. 하지만, 손님들은 불만족스러워했다.
>
> • He wanted to cook much more quickly and easily. **Thus**, he invented new machines for his kitchen. 그는 훨씬 더 빠르고 더 쉽게 요리하고 싶어 했다. 따라서 그는 그의 부엌을 위해 새로운 기계들을 발명하였다.

■ 접속부사는 앞에 제시된 문장의 내용을 부가적으로 연결하는 역할을 하며, 앞 문장과 대조되는 상황일 때는 'however'(그러나)와 같은 역접을, 자연스러운 인과 관계일 때는 'thus'(그러므로)와 같은 순접을 쓴다. 또한, 접속부사는 접속사가 아니라 부사이므로 문장들을 직접 연결할 수는 없다. 문장의 접속사 역할을 하는 세미콜론 뒤 또는 문장 맨 앞이나 뒤에서 쉼표와 함께 쓰이며, 문장 중간에 올 때는 앞뒤에 쉼표가 오게 된다.
  • David is active, **however**, his son is quiet and shy. David은 활동적이지만, 그의 아들은 조용하고 부끄럼을 탄다.
  • The road was blocked. **Thus**, we had to go back. 길이 막혀서, 우리는 되돌아가야 했다.

■ 같은 의미의 문장을 접속사, 접속부사 등으로 표현할 수 있다.
  • **Because** it rained yesterday, the ground is wet. 어제 비가 와서, 땅이 젖었다.
    = **Because of** the rain yesterday, the ground is wet. 어제 비 때문에, 땅이 젖었다.
    = It rained yesterday. **Thus**, the ground is wet. 어제 비가 왔다. 그래서 땅이 젖었다.
  • **Though** he was small, he jumped the hurdle. 비록 그는 작았지만, 장애물을 뛰어넘었다.
    = He was small. **However**, he jumped the hurdle. 그는 작았다. 하지만 그는 장애물을 뛰어넘었다.

■ 그 밖의 다양한 접속부사나 연결어들의 종류와 의미
  (1) 역접: 대조, 양보 (however, still, on the contrary, nevertheless 등)
  (2) 인과, 결과 (thus, therefore, so, hence, consequently, as a result)
  (3) 예시 (for example, for instance)
  (4) 부가, 추가 (in addition, furthermore, moreover 등)
  (5) 유사 (likewise, similarly, in the same way 등)
  • She didn't like to eat it. **Nevertheless**, she did it.
    그녀는 그것을 먹고 싶지 않았다. 그럼에도 불구하고 결국은 그것을 먹었다.
  • **For example**, a virus that causes severe symptoms may be less likely to be transmitted.
    예를 들어, 심각한 증상을 초래하는 바이러스는 전염이 덜 될지도 모른다.

핵심 Check

2. 다음 빈칸에 however 또는 thus를 사용하여 두 문장을 연결하시오.

(1) Mary wanted to buy a new pen. _____, she doesn't have enough money.

(2) The soldiers threatened the citizens. _____, the public was very upset.

01 다음 빈칸에 들어갈 말로 알맞은 것은?

> The concert was cancelled due to the virus. _____, the singer and her fans were very disappointed.

① However   ② For example   ③ Thus
④ Similarly   ⑤ Instead

02 다음 두 문장을 한 문장으로 연결할 때, 각각의 빈칸에 들어갈 알맞은 말을 써 넣으시오.

(1) Tom bought the house. A famous musician lived in the house.
→ Tom bought the house _____ _____ a famous musician lived.
→ Tom bought the house _____ a famous musician lived.

(2) I want to know the reason. Mina was angry for the reason.
→ I want to know the reason _____ _____ Mina was angry.
→ I want to know the reason _____ Mina was angry.

03 다음 밑줄 친 부분 중 어법상 옳지 <u>않은</u> 것을 고르시오.

① That is the restaurant <u>where</u> I found my credit card.
② Venice is the city <u>where</u> Marco Polo was born in.
③ I'm interested in the house <u>where</u> the singer lived.
④ They don't know the reason <u>why</u> their mother left them.
⑤ Eric developed the way in <u>which</u> he could make much money.

04 다음 빈칸에 however 또는 thus 중 알맞은 단어를 써 넣으시오.

(1) Megan wanted to buy me coffee. _____, I don't like caffeine.

(2) It is proved that sleep helps with your memory. _____, it is important to get enough sleep to get good grades.

(3) Fred has been sick since last night. He looks more lively than anybody else, _____.

(4) Sharon is a small and weak child. _____, she has the courage enough to fight against injustice.

(5) The film is based on real events. _____, it gives the audience a more realistic feeling.

01 다음 중 어법상 어색한 것은?

① Do you remember the day when we first met?

② This is the library where you can enjoy reading 3D books.

③ Sujin will show Peter the way how she could solve the problem.

④ This is the kindergarten where my mom is working.

⑤ Judy is wondering about the reason why her brother is so happy.

[02~03] 다음 중 밑줄 친 부분이 문맥상 어색한 것을 고르시오.

02 ① Clara bought her son a bag that he wanted. However, he didn't seem to be happy with it.

② Ben learned about the importance of the environment. Thus, he decided to save electricity every day.

③ Watson was very hungry; however, he handed out his food to the poor.

④ William has lived next to the park for 3 years. Thus, he has never been there.

⑤ I have never been to Japan. I know and speak Japanese very well, however.

03 ① Jane can speak Chinese. In addition, she can speak German.

② The movie was very disappointing. Therefore, the actors' performances were excellent.

③ Monkeys do not plan for the future. On the other hand, we human beings live by planning.

④ Anna often feels tired. So, she's going to take vitamins.

⑤ Liz has been learning to swim for 5 years. Nevertheless, she is really bad at swimming.

[04~05] 다음 우리말을 어법상 알맞게 영작한 것을 고르시오.

04 그 회의가 끝나게 될 시간을 아십니까?

① Do you know when will the meeting be over?

② When do you know the time the meeting will be over?

③ Do you know the time at when the meeting will be over?

④ Do you know the time which the meeting will be over?

⑤ Do you know the time when the meeting will be over?

05 이것이 내가 성공한 이유이다.

① This is why I succeeded.

② This is the reason which I succeeded.

③ This is the reason why I succeeded for.

④ This is which I succeeded for.

⑤ This is the reason on which I succeeded.

서답형

06 다음 〈보기〉에 주어진 단어들을 한 번씩만 사용해서 글의 흐름에 알맞게 빈칸을 채워 넣으시오.

┌─ 보기 ├┐

Therefore, For example, However,
Moreover, Similarly

①Shakespeare invented many words in his works. _____, he took the noun 'elbow' and turned it into the verb.

(2) It was very cold. _____, the wind blew hard.

(3) A son is likely to follow his father. _____, a daughter tends to go after her mother.

(4) Lily has a passive personality. _____, she actively works and raises her voice for the poor.

(5) The world economy became even worse than before. _____, lots of people lost their jobs.

[07~08] 다음 중 글의 흐름상 However 또는 Thus가 바르게 쓰인 문장은?

07 ① Judy lost David's phone number. However, she couldn't contact him.

② All the passengers saw the accident. Thus, most of them could stay calm.

③ My boyfriend prepared our dinner. However, my family were happy about it.

④ Clara likes only the pen. Thus, she was pleased to get it stolen.

⑤ The teacher explained the solution of the question. However, Lisa felt that the answer was wrong.

08 ① Both of us watched the movie. Thus, we couldn't understand the story of it.

② The doctor explained that Sarah would be fine. However, I felt relieved.

③ Jerome studied hard not to lose the opportunity. Thus, he finally got the job.

④ Robert fixed the car himself. However, he knew of the car better than anyone.

⑤ Andrew found out the answer. Thus, he couldn't solve the hard problem.

[09~10] 다음 중 어법상 옳지 <u>않은</u> 문장은?

09 ① She told me the reason for which her son became a world famous pianist.

② She told me the reason why her son became a world famous pianist.

③ She told me the reason which her son became a world famous pianist for.

④ She told me why her son became a world famous pianist.

⑤ She told me the reason in which her son became a world famous pianist.

10 ① Michael showed me the way which he escaped from the prison in.

② Michael showed me the way he escaped from the prison.

③ Michael showed me the way in how he escaped from the prison.

④ Michael showed me how he escaped from the prison.

⑤ Michael showed me the way in which he escaped from the prison.

[11~12] 다음 두 문장을 한 문장으로 표현할 때, 빈칸에 들어갈 알맞은 말을 쓰시오.

서답형

11

• Jason often goes to the local market.
• He can find fresh vegetables there.

➡ Jason often goes to the local market _____ he can find fresh vegetables.

서답형

12

• Now is the time.
• The babies go to sleep at the time.

➡ Now is the time _____ the babies go to sleep.

[13~14] 우리말과 일치하도록 괄호 안에 주어진 어구들을 바르게 배열하시오.

서답형

13

나의 어머니는 2차 세계대전이 발생했던 해에 태어나셨다.
→ My (World War Ⅱ, the year, broke, born, was, when, out, in, mother).

➡ My _____
_____.

서답형

14

많은 사람들이 지하철이 30분이나 도착하지 않은 이유를 알고 싶어 한다.
Many people want to know (has, for, the subway, why, 30 minutes, arrived, not).

➡ Many people want to know _____
_____.

15 다음 〈보기〉의 문장과 가장 가까운 뜻을 가진 문장을 고르시오.

┌─ 보기 ┐
Dahyun had five pieces of pizza and two burgers. She was still hungry, however.
└──────┘

① Since Dahyun had five pieces of pizza and two burgers, she was still hungry.
② As Dahyun had five pieces of pizza and two burgers, she was still hungry.
③ Though Dahyun had five pieces of pizza and two burgers, she was still hungry.
④ Unless Dahyun had five pieces of pizza and two burgers, she was still hungry.
⑤ Once Dahyun had five pieces of pizza and two burgers, she was still hungry.

서답형

16 다음 그림을 보고 자연스러운 문장이 되도록 괄호 안에 주어진 어구를 바르게 배열하여 빈칸을 완성하시오.

(1)

➡ Seokbong _____
_____, looking at his poor handwriting. (his mother, couldn't understand, them, about, the way, straight, cut)

(2)

➡ My friends were surprised _____
_____. (rich, how, hear, be, I, could, to)

01 다음 괄호 안에서 어법상 알맞은 것을 고르시오.

> Da Vinci believed that people would soon appreciate his creative cooking. (However / Thus), that never happened.

02 다음 우리말과 일치하도록 괄호 안에 주어진 단어들을 바르게 배열하여 문장을 완성하되, 빈칸에 해당하는 Thus와 However 중에서 문맥상 알맞은 접속부사를 선택하여 문두에 쓰시오.

(1) 다빈치는 몇몇 음식들을 심지어 꽃으로 장식했다. _____, 손님들은 고기 요리에 익숙했기 때문에 불만족스러워했다. (unhappy, customers, because, used, were, were, to, they)
➡ Da Vinci even decorated some foods with flowers. _____

_____ meat dishes.

(2) 그는 훨씬 더 빠르고 더 쉽게 요리하고 싶어 했다. _____, 그는 그의 부엌을 위해 새로운 기계들을 발명했다. (new machines, kitchen, he, for, his, invented)
➡ He wanted to cook much more quickly and easily. _____
_____.

(3) 당신의 몸이 당신의 마음을 바꿀 수 있다. _____, 당신의 마음도 당신의 행동을 바꿀 수 있다. (can, as, your mind, your behavior, change, well)
➡ Your body can change your mind. _____
_____.

(4) Mina는 마음을 정리하고 싶었다. _____, 그녀는 혼자 하루 여행을 떠나기로 결심했다. (by herself, to take, she, a day trip, decided)
➡ Mina wanted to clear her mind. _____
_____.

03 다음 (A)와 (B) 두 문장을 한 문장으로 연결할 때, 주어진 〈조건〉에 맞게 영작하시오.

┌─ 조건 ─┐
1. (A)의 위에서부터 순서대로 영작할 것.
2. (A)가 앞에 오는 문장일 것.
3. 가급적 '선행사+관계부사'로 영작할 것.
4. 관계부사는 생략하지 말 것. (that은 사용할 수 없음.)

(A)	(B)
They found a special cave.	She could be world famous in the way.
The singer told me the way.	I can see the life coming back in the season.
My favorite season is spring.	The Korean national football team beat Brazil at the stadium.
Please tell your mom the reason.	My first daughter was born on the day.
That is the soccer stadium.	You hid the letter from Grace for the reason.
I remember the day.	Their ancestors spent the winter in the cave.

(1) _____
_____
(2) _____
(3) _____
_____
(4) _____
_____
(5) _____
_____
(6) _____

04 다음은 어느 백화점 내부의 모습이다. 그림을 참고하여, 관계부사와 각각의 번호에 주어진 표현들을 모두 사용하여 문장을 완성하시오.

(1) restaurant, she, make a hamburger
➡ A receipt was handed over to a man at _____.

(2) charity box, a girl, put some money
➡ There was _____.

(3) the cafe, we, talk over tea and coffee
➡ This was _____.

(4) laptop, she, write a marketing report
➡ Brenda brought _____.

05 다음 글의 빈칸 (A)~(D)에 들어갈 알맞은 접속부사를 However 또는 Thus만을 사용하여 써 넣으시오.

Da Vinci believed that people would soon appreciate his creative cooking. (A)_____, that never happened. He created machines that could crush vegetables and pull spaghetti. Surely, they were all very innovative. (B)_____, most of them were too big or too difficult to use. Da Vinci never became a successful cook. (C)_____, he showed great interest in cooking throughout his life. Now you know all about his secret passion for cooking. (D)_____, you will never look at *The Last Supper* the same way.

06 다음 밑줄 친 ①~⑥에서 어색한 곳을 모두 찾아 고치시오. (단, 본문에 있는 단어만을 사용하여 수정할 것)

When he graduates from high school next year, Taeho wants to become a professional farmer. ①However, he has never told anyone about it. He is worried that his parents or his friends will not understand. ②As he wanted to clear his mind, Taeho decided to take a day trip on a train by himself. On the train, he told a complete stranger sitting beside him about his problem. He didn't know the reason ③why he did it. ④Thus, he felt much better when he got off the train. Strangely enough, we often tell strangers about our problems just like Taeho. That is ⑤because we do not have to worry about being judged or seeing them again. ⑥However, if you have a problem that you cannot share with your family or friends, try talking to a stranger. You will feel much better.

➡ _____

07 다음 그림을 보고 괄호 안의 단어를 배열하여 빈칸을 알맞게 채우시오.

(in, with, she, the pool, when, played, the summer vacation)
➡ Minju could never forget _____ her cousins.

Reading

Da Vinci the Cook

Leonardo da Vinci is known as one of the greatest painters of all
time. He was also a great inventor, scientist, and musician. Very few
people, however, know that da Vinci was also a creative cook.

In 1473, twenty-year-old da Vinci worked as a cook at a restaurant in
Florence, Italy. When he took charge of the kitchen, da Vinci changed
the menu completely. He made simple but artistic dishes like fish with
a few carrot slices. Some dishes were even decorated with flowers.
Customers, however, were unhappy because they were used to dishes
with big servings of meat. As a result, da Vinci lost his job.

A few years later, da Vinci opened a restaurant with his friend
Sandro Botticelli. He wanted to create a place where people could try
his innovative food. They put up a beautifully painted sign and made
a uniquely written menu. Da Vinci believed that people would soon
appreciate his creative cooking. Unfortunately, that never happened.

---

of all time 역대, 지금껏

few 소수의, 거의 없는

creative 창의적인, 창조적인

take charge of ~의 책임을 지다, ~을 떠맡다

dish 음식, 요리

slice 한 조각, 일부

decorate 장식하다, 꾸미다

customer 손님, 고객

be used to ~에 익숙하다

innovative 획기적인

put up 내붙이다, 게시하다

uniquely 독특하게

appreciate 진가를 알아보다, 고마워하다

unfortunately 불행하게도

📎 **확인문제**

● 다음 문장이 본문의 내용과 일치하면 T, 일치하지 <u>않으면</u> F를 쓰시오.

1 Leonardo da Vinci is known as one of the greatest painters of all time. ☐

2 Customers liked da Vinci's dishes decorated with flowers. ☐

3 Leonardo da Vinci once ran a restaurant with his friend. ☐

4 People appreciated da Vinci's creative cooking. ☐

In the early 1480s, da Vinci began to work for Ludovico Sforza in Milan. He was given many different roles, such as a musician, a painter, and an engineer. He was also put in charge of the kitchen. He was happy to be given another chance to pursue his passion for cooking. Da Vinci did not stop at cooking creative dishes. He wanted to cook much more quickly and easily. Thus, he invented new machines for his kitchen. He created machines that could crush vegetables and pull spaghetti. He even made a device that could scare frogs away from the water tank. Surely, they were all very innovative, but most of them were too big or too difficult to use.

In 1495, Sforza asked da Vinci to make a grand painting, which was based on the last supper of Jesus, on the wall of a church in Milan. Da Vinci gladly took on the project because he had always been interested in food. He spent a lot of time cooking all kinds of food to decide what to put on the table in his picture. "Da Vinci has wasted his time in the kitchen for over a year. That's the reason why he hasn't finished the painting yet," complained the people from the church to Sforza.

Although da Vinci never became a successful cook, he showed great interest in cooking throughout his life. He was not only a great painter but also a creative cook. Now that you know all about his secret passion for cooking, you will never look at *The Last Supper* the same way.

put ... in charge of …에게 ~의 책임을 맡기다

pursue 추구하다, 추진하다

passion 열정, 흥미

tank (물·기름 등의) 탱크

surely 확실히, 분명히

grand 웅장한, 위대한

supper 만찬, 저녁 식사

take on 떠맡다

reason 이유

complain 불평하다

throughout ~ 동안 내내

now that ~이기 때문에, ~이므로

 확인문제

● 다음 문장이 본문의 내용과 일치하면 T, 일치하지 <u>않으면</u> F를 쓰시오.

1 Da Vinci was happy to be given another chance to pursue his passion for cooking.

2 Da Vinci stopped at cooking creative dishes.

3 Da Vinci never became a successful cook.

4 Da Vinci was not a great painter but a creative cook.

● 우리말을 참고하여 빈칸에 알맞은 말을 쓰시오.

1 Da Vinci _____ _____

2 Leonardo da Vinci _____ _____ _____ one of the greatest _____ _____ _____ _____.

3 He was _____ a great inventor, scientist, and musician.

4 Very _____ people, _____, know that da Vinci was also a _____ cook.

5 In 1473, _____ da Vinci worked _____ a cook at a restaurant in Florence, Italy.

6 When he _____ _____ _____ the kitchen, da Vinci changed the menu _____.

7 He made simple _____ artistic dishes _____ fish with _____ _____ carrot slices.

8 Some dishes _____ _____ _____ _____ flowers.

9 Customers, _____, were unhappy because they _____ _____ _____ dishes with big _____ of meat.

10 _____ _____ _____, da Vinci lost his job.

11 _____ _____ years later, da Vinci opened a restaurant with his friend Sandro Botticelli.

12 He wanted to create a place _____ people could try his _____ food.

13 They put up a _____ _____ sign and made a _____ _____ menu.

14 Da Vinci believed that people _____ soon _____ his cooking.

15 Unfortunately, that never _____.

16 In the early 1480s, da Vinci began _____ _____ for Ludovico Sforza in Milan.

17 He _____ _____ many different roles, _____ _____ a musician, a painter, and an engineer.

18 He _____ also _____ _____ _____ _____ the kitchen.

19 He was happy _____ _____ _____ _____ chance _____ _____ his passion for cooking.

20 Da Vinci did not _____ _____ cooking creative dishes.

21 He wanted to cook _____ _____ quickly and easily.

22 _____, he invented new machines for his kitchen.

23 He created machines _____ could crush vegetables and pull spaghetti.

24 He even made a device _____ could _____ frogs _____ _____ the water tank.

25 Surely, they were all very innovative, but most of them _____ _____ big or _____ difficult _____ use.

26 In 1495, Sforza asked da Vinci _____ _____ a grand painting, _____ _____ _____ _____ the last supper of Jesus, on the wall of a church in Milan.

27 Da Vinci gladly _____ _____ the project because he _____ always _____ interested in food.

28 He spent _____ _____ _____ time _____ all kinds of food to decide _____ _____ _____ on the table in his picture.

29 "Da Vinci has wasted his time in the kitchen _____ _____ a year. That's the reason _____ he hasn't finished the painting yet," complained the people from the church _____ Sforza.

30 _____ da Vinci never became a successful cook, he showed great interest in cooking _____ his life.

31 He was _____ _____ a great painter _____ _____ a creative cook.

32 _____ _____ you know all about his secret passion for cooking, you will never look at *The Last Supper* _____ _____ _____.

16 1480년대 초반에, 다빈치는 밀라노에서 루도비코 스포르차를 위해 일하기 시작했다.

17 그는 음악가, 화가, 그리고 공학자와 같은 많은 역할들을 부여받았다.

18 그는 또한 주방을 책임지게 되었다.

19 그는 요리를 향한 그의 열정을 추구할 또 다른 기회를 얻게 되어 행복했다.

20 다빈치는 창의적인 요리를 만드는 것에 멈추지 않았다.

21 그는 훨씬 더 빠르고 쉽게 요리하고 싶어했다.

22 따라서, 그는 그의 주방에서 사용할 새로운 기계들을 발명하였다.

23 그는 채소를 으깨고 스파게티를 뽑는 기계들을 만들었다.

24 그는 심지어 개구리를 겁주어 물탱크에서 쫓아낼 수 있는 기구도 만들었다.

25 확실히 그것들은 모두 매우 획기적이었지만, 그것들 중 대부분은 사용하기에 너무 크거나 너무 어려웠다.

26 1495년, 스포르차는 다빈치에게 웅장한 그림을 밀라노에 있는 교회의 벽에 그려 달라고 부탁했는데, 그것은 예수의 최후의 만찬을 바탕으로 한 것이었다.

27 다빈치는 기꺼이 그 작업을 맡았는데, 그가 항상 음식에 흥미를 가졌기 때문이었다.

28 그는 그림 속 식탁 위에 어떤 음식을 올릴지 결정하기 위해 모든 종류의 음식을 요리하느라 많은 시간을 썼다.

29 "다빈치는 1년 넘게 부엌에서 시간을 낭비해 오고 있습니다. 그것이 그가 아직도 그림을 끝내지 못한 이유입니다."라고 교회 사람들이 스포르차에게 불평을 했다.

30 다빈치는 결코 성공적인 요리사는 되지 못했지만 그는 그의 생애 내내 요리에 대한 큰 흥미를 보여 주었다.

31 그는 훌륭한 화가일 뿐만 아니라 창의적인 요리사였다.

32 이제 여러분은 요리에 대한 그의 비밀스런 열정을 모두 알게 되었기 때문에 〈최후의 만찬〉을 절대 같은 식으로는 보지 않을 것이다.

● 우리말을 참고하여 본문을 영작하시오.

1 요리사 다빈치
➡ _____

2 레오나르도 다빈치는 역대 가장 위대한 화가들 중의 한 명으로 알려져 있다.
➡ _____

3 그는 또한 위대한 발명가, 과학자, 그리고 음악가였다.
➡ _____

4 하지만, 극히 소수의 사람들만이 또한 그가 창의적인 요리사였다는 것을 안다.
➡ _____

5 1473년, 스무 살의 레오나르도 다빈치는 이탈리아 플로렌스에 있는 음식점에서 요리사로 일했다.
➡ _____

6 그가 부엌을 책임지게 되었을 때, 다빈치는 메뉴를 완전히 바꿔 버렸다.
➡ _____

7 그는 약간의 당근 조각을 곁들인 생선과 같이 간단하지만 예술적인 음식을 만들었다.
➡ _____

8 몇몇 음식들은 심지어 꽃으로 장식되었다.
➡ _____

9 하지만, 손님들은 많은 양의 고기 요리에 익숙했었기 때문에 불만족스러워했다.
➡ _____

10 그 결과, 다빈치는 그의 직업을 잃었다.
➡ _____

11 몇 년 후, 다빈치는 그의 친구인 산드로 보티첼리와 함께 음식점을 열었다.
➡ _____

12 그는 사람들이 그의 획기적인 음식을 먹어 볼 수 있는 장소로 만들기를 원했다.
➡ _____

13 그들은 아름답게 그려진 간판을 내걸었고 독특하게 써진 메뉴를 만들었다.
➡ _____

14 다빈치는 사람들이 곧 그의 창의적인 요리의 진가를 알아볼 것이라고 믿었다.
➡ _____

15 불행히도, 그런 일은 결코 일어나지 않았다.
➡ _____

16 1480년대 초반에, 다빈치는 밀라노에서 루도비코 스포르차를 위해 일하기 시작했다.
➡ _____

17 그는 음악가, 화가, 그리고 공학자와 같은 많은 역할들을 부여받았다.
➡ _____

18 그는 또한 주방을 책임지게 되었다.

➡ _____

19 그는 요리를 향한 그의 열정을 추구할 또 다른 기회를 얻게 되어 행복했다.

➡ _____

20 다빈치는 창의적인 요리를 만드는 것에 멈추지 않았다.

➡ _____

21 그는 훨씬 더 빠르고 쉽게 요리하고 싶어했다.

➡ _____

22 따라서, 그는 그의 주방에서 사용할 새로운 기계들을 발명하였다.

➡ _____

23 그는 채소를 으깨고 스파게티를 뽑는 기계들을 만들었다.

➡ _____

24 그는 심지어 개구리를 겁주어 물탱크에서 쫓아낼 수 있는 기구도 만들었다.

➡ _____

25 확실히 그것들은 모두 매우 획기적이었지만, 그것들 중 대부분은 사용하기에 너무 크거나 너무 어려웠다.

➡ _____

26 1495년, 스포르차는 다빈치에게 웅장한 그림을 밀라노에 있는 교회의 벽에 그려 달라고 부탁했는데, 그것은 예수의 최후의 만찬을 바탕으로 한 것이었다.

➡ _____

_____

27 다빈치는 기꺼이 그 작업을 맡았는데, 그가 항상 음식에 흥미를 가졌기 때문이었다.

➡ _____

28 그는 그림 속 식탁 위에 어떤 음식을 올릴지 결정하기 위해 모든 종류의 음식을 요리하느라 많은 시간을 썼다.

➡ _____

29 "다빈치는 1년 넘게 부엌에서 시간을 낭비해 오고 있습니다. 그것이 그가 아직도 그림을 끝내지 못한 이유입니다."라고 교회 사람들이 스포르차에게 불평을 했다.

➡ _____

_____

30 다빈치는 결코 성공적인 요리사는 되지 못했지만 그는 그의 생애 내내 요리에 대한 큰 흥미를 보여 주었다.

➡ _____

_____

31 그는 훌륭한 화가일 뿐만 아니라 창의적인 요리사였다.

➡ _____

32 이제 여러분은 요리에 대한 그의 비밀스런 열정을 모두 알게 되었기 때문에 〈최후의 만찬〉을 절대 같은 식으로는 보지 않을 것이다.

➡ _____

_____

[01~03] 다음 글을 읽고 물음에 답하시오.

Leonardo da Vinci is known as one of the greatest painters of all time. He was also a great inventor, scientist, and musician. Very few people, however, know that da Vinci was also _____(A)_____.

In 1473, twenty-year-old da Vinci worked as a cook at a restaurant in Florence, Italy. When he took charge of the kitchen, da Vinci changed the menu completely. He made simple but artistic dishes like fish with a few carrot slices. Some dishes were even decorated with flowers. Customers, however, were unhappy because they were used to dishes with big servings of meat. As a result, da Vinci lost his job.

A few years later, da Vinci opened a restaurant with his friend Sandro Botticelli. He wanted to create a place where people could try his innovative food. They put up a beautifully painted sign and made a uniquely written menu. Da Vinci believed that people would soon ___(B)___ his creative cooking. Unfortunately, that never happened.

01 위 글의 빈칸 (A)에 들어갈 알맞은 말을 고르시오.

① a good barista
② a creative cook
③ a great psychologist
④ an innovative physician
⑤ a natural philosopher

서답형

02 주어진 영영풀이를 참고하여 빈칸 (B)에 들어갈 단어를 철자 a로 시작하여 쓰시오.

> to like something because you recognize its good qualities

➡ _____

03 According to the passage, which is NOT true?

① Da Vinci is known as one of the greatest painters.
② Da Vinci was also a great inventor and musician.
③ Da Vinci made simple but artistic dishes like fish with a few carrot slices.
④ Da Vinci lost his job because customers liked dishes decorated with flowers.
⑤ Da Vinci opened a restaurant with Sandro Botticelli.

[04~06] 다음 글을 읽고 물음에 답하시오.

In the early 1480s, da Vinci began to work for Ludovico Sforza in Milan. He was given many different roles, such as a musician, a painter, and an engineer. He was also put in charge of the kitchen. He was happy to be given another chance to pursue his passion ___ⓐ___ cooking. Da Vinci did not stop at cooking creative dishes. He wanted to cook much more quickly and easily. ___ⓑ___, he invented new machines for his kitchen. He created machines that could crush vegetables and pull spaghetti. He even made a device that could scare frogs away ___ⓒ___ the water tank. Surely, they were all very innovative, but most of them were too big or too difficult ___ⓓ___.

04 위 글의 빈칸 ⓐ와 ⓒ에 들어갈 전치사가 바르게 짝지어진 것은?

① on – for   ② on – to
③ for – from   ④ for – for
⑤ in – from

05 위 글의 빈칸 ⓑ에 들어갈 알맞은 말을 고르시오.

① Thus
② As a result
③ Surely
④ However
⑤ Unfortunately

06 위 글의 빈칸 ⓓ에 use를 알맞은 형태로 쓰시오.

➡ _____

[07~09] 다음 글을 읽고 물음에 답하시오.

In 1495, Sforza asked da Vinci to make a ① <u>grand</u> painting, which was based on the last supper of Jesus, on the wall of a church in Milan.

(A) "Da Vinci has ②<u>wasted</u> his time in the kitchen for over a year. That's the reason why he hasn't finished the painting yet," ③<u>commended</u> the people from the church to Sforza.

(B) He spent a lot of time cooking all kinds of food to decide what to put on the table in his picture.

(C) Da Vinci ④<u>gladly</u> took on the project because he had always been interested in food.

Although da Vinci never became a ⑤ <u>successful</u> cook, he showed great interest in cooking throughout his life. He was not only a great painter but also a creative cook. ____ⓐ____ you know all about his secret passion for cooking, you will never look at *The Last Supper* the same way.

07 위 글의 (A)~(C)의 순서로 가장 적절한 것은?

① (A)-(C)-(B)
② (B)-(A)-(C)
③ (B)-(C)-(A)
④ (C)-(A)-(B)
⑤ (C)-(B)-(A)

08 위 글의 빈칸 ⓐ에 'As' 대신 쓸 수 있는 말을 두 단어로 쓰시오.

➡ _____

09 위 글의 밑줄 친 ①~⑤에서 문맥상 어색한 것을 고르시오.

① ② ③ ④ ⑤

[10~12] 다음 글을 읽고 물음에 답하시오.

Leonardo da Vinci is known as one of the greatest (A)[painter / painters] of all time. He was also a great inventor, scientist, and musician. Very few people, however, know that da Vinci was also a creative cook.

In 1473, twenty-year-old da Vinci worked as a cook at a restaurant in Florence, Italy. When he took charge of the kitchen, da Vinci changed the menu completely. He made simple but artistic dishes like fish with (B)[a few / a little] carrot slices. Some dishes were even decorated with flowers. Customers, however, were unhappy because they were used to dishes with big servings of meat. As a result, da Vinci (C)[got / lost] his job.

A few years later, da Vinci opened a restaurant with his friend Sandro Botticelli. He wanted to create a place where people could try his innovative food. They put up a beautifully painted ⓐ<u>sign</u> and made a uniquely written menu. Da Vinci believed that people would soon appreciate his creative cooking. Unfortunately, that never happened.

10 위 글의 괄호 (A)~(C)에서 문맥이나 어법상 알맞은 낱말을 골라 쓰시오.

➡ (A) _____ (B) _____ (C) _____

11 Which question CANNOT be answered after reading the passage?

① Do many people know that da Vinci was a creative cook?

② What was da Vinci's job in 1473?

③ What did da Vinci do when he took charge of the kitchen?

④ How long did da Vinci work as a cook?

⑤ Why did da Vinci lose his job?

12 위 글의 밑줄 친 ⓐsign과 같은 의미로 쓰인 것을 고르시오.

① Headaches may be a sign of stress.

② Many building signs are written in English.

③ He gave a thumbs-up sign.

④ He signed to me to enter the garden.

⑤ There is no sign of habitation.

[13~15] 다음 글을 읽고 물음에 답하시오.

In the early 1480s, da Vinci began to work for Ludovico Sforza in Milan. He was given many different roles, such as a musician, a painter, and an engineer. He was also put in charge of the kitchen. He was happy to be given another chance to pursue his passion for cooking. ⓐDa Vinci did not stop at cooking creative dishes. ⓑHe wanted to cook much more quickly and easily.(only, also) Thus, he invented new machines for his kitchen. He created machines that could crush vegetables and pull spaghetti. He even made a device ⓒ개구리를 겁주어 물탱크에서 쫓아낼 수 있는.(frogs, that, away, could, the water tank, scare, from) Surely, they were all very ___(A)___ , but most of them were too big or too difficult to use.

13 위 글의 빈칸 (A)에 들어갈 말로 적절한 것은?

① common   ② routine   ③ plain

④ traditional   ⑤ innovative

서답형

14 위 글의 밑줄 친 문장 ⓐ와 ⓑ를 괄호 안에 주어진 어휘를 이용하여 한 문장으로 쓰시오.

➡ _____

_____

15 위 글의 밑줄 친 ⓒ의 우리말에 맞게 괄호 안에 주어진 어휘를 배열하시오.

➡ _____

[16~19] 다음 글을 읽고 물음에 답하시오.

In 1495, Sforza asked da Vinci to make a grand painting, which was based on the last supper of Jesus, on the wall of a church in Milan. Da Vinci gladly took on the project because he had always been interested in food. ⓐ그는 그림 속 식탁 위에 어떤 음식을 올릴지 결정하기 위해 모든 종류의 음식을 요리하느라 많은 시간을 썼다. "Da Vinci has ___(A)___ his time in the kitchen for over a year. That's the reason why he hasn't finished the painting yet," complained the people from the church to Sforza.

___(B)___ da Vinci never became a successful cook, he showed great interest in cooking throughout his life. He was not only a great painter but also a creative cook. Now that you know all about his secret passion for cooking, you will never look at *The Last Supper* the same way.

16 위 글의 빈칸 (A)에 들어갈 말로 알맞은 것은?

① saved   ② wasted   ③ kept
④ prevented   ⑤ recovered

17 빈칸 (B)에 들어갈 알맞은 말을 고르시오.

① When   ② Since   ③ If
④ Although   ⑤ Unless

서답형

18 위 글의 밑줄 친 ⓐ의 우리말에 맞게 주어진 어휘를 배열하시오.

> he, all kinds, on the table, what, time, spent, in his picture, a lot of, cooking, food, decide, put, of, to, to

➡ _____

_____

중요

19 Which question CANNOT be answered after reading the passage?

① What did da Vinci ask Sforza to do to make a grand painting?
② What was the grand painting based on?
③ Why did da Vinci gladly take on the project?
④ Why did da Vinci spend a lot of time cooking all kinds of food?
⑤ Why will we never look at *The Last Supper* the same way?

[20~22] 다음 글을 읽고 물음에 답하시오.

In the early 1480s, da Vinci began to work for Ludovico Sforza in Milan. He was given many different roles, such as a musician, a painter, and an engineer.

(A) Surely, they were all very innovative, but most of them were too big or too difficult to use.

(B) He was also put in charge of the kitchen. He was happy to be given another chance to ___ⓐ___ his passion for cooking. Da Vinci did not stop at cooking creative dishes. He wanted to cook much more quickly and easily.

(C) Thus, he invented new machines for his kitchen. He created machines that could crush vegetables and pull spaghetti. He even made a device that could scare frogs away from the water tank.

서답형

20 주어진 영영풀이에 해당하는 말을 빈칸 ⓐ에 철자 p로 시작하여 쓰시오.

> to make efforts to achieve a particular aim or result, often over a long period of time

➡ _____

중요

21 위 글의 (A)~(C)의 순서로 가장 적절한 것은?

① (A)-(C)-(B)   ② (B)-(A)-(C)
③ (B)-(C)-(A)   ④ (C)-(A)-(B)
⑤ (C)-(B)-(A)

22 위 글에서 다빈치가 루도비코 스포르차를 위해 한 일에 해당하지 않는 것을 고르시오.

① 과학자   ② 주방장   ③ 화가
④ 기술자   ⑤ 음악가

[01~03] 다음 글을 읽고 물음에 답하시오.

Leonardo da Vinci is known as one of the greatest painters of all time. He was also a great inventor, scientist, and musician. Very few people, however, know that da Vinci was also a creative cook.

In 1473, twenty-year-old da Vinci worked as a cook at a restaurant in Florence, Italy. When he took charge of the kitchen, da Vinci changed the menu completely. He made simple but artistic dishes like fish with a few carrot slices. Some dishes were even decorated with flowers. Customers, however, were unhappy because they were used to dishes with big servings of meat. As a result, da Vinci lost his job.

A few years later, da Vinci opened a restaurant with his friend Sandro Botticelli. ⓐ그는 사람들이 그의 획기적인 음식을 먹어 볼 수 있는 장소로 만들기를 원했다. They put up a beautifully painted sign and made a uniquely written menu. Da Vinci believed that people would soon appreciate his creative cooking. Unfortunately, ⓑthat never happened.

01 Why did da Vinci lose his job? Answer in English using the words, 'It's because, creative and satisfied.'

➡ _____

_____

02 밑줄 친 ⓐ의 우리말에 맞게 'a place, try, innovative'를 이용하여 13 단어로 영작하시오.

➡ _____

_____

03 위 글의 밑줄 친 ⓑthat이 가리키는 것을 본문에서 찾아 쓰시오.

➡ _____

[04~06] 다음 글을 읽고 물음에 답하시오.

In the early 1480s, da Vinci began to work for Ludovico Sforza in Milan. He was given many different roles, such as a musician, a painter, and an engineer. He was also put in charge of the kitchen. ⓐHe was happy to be given the other chance to pursue his passion for cooking. Da Vinci did not stop at cooking creative dishes. He wanted to cook much more quickly and easily. Thus, he invented new machines for his kitchen. He created machines that could crush vegetables and pull spaghetti. He even made a device that could scare frogs away from the water tank. Surely, ⓑthey were all very innovative, but most of them were too big or too difficult to use.

04 What did da Vinci do to cook much more quickly and easily?

➡ _____

05 밑줄 친 ⓐ에서 어색한 것을 찾아 바르게 고치시오.

_____ ➡ _____

06 위 글의 밑줄 친 ⓑthey가 가리키는 것을 본문에서 찾아 쓰시오.

➡ _____

[07~09] 다음 글을 읽고 물음에 답하시오.

In 1495, Sforza asked da Vinci to make a grand painting, ⓐwhich was based on the last supper of Jesus, on the wall of a church in Milan. Da Vinci gladly took on the project because he had always been interested in food. He spent a lot of time cooking all kinds of food to decide what to put on the table in his picture. "Da Vinci has wasted his time in the kitchen for over a year. That's the reason why he hasn't finished the painting yet," complained the people from the church to Sforza.

Although da Vinci never became a successful cook, he showed great interest in cooking throughout his life. ⓑHe was not only a great painter but also a creative cook. Now that you know all about his secret passion for cooking, you will never look at *The Last Supper* the same way.

07 위 글의 밑줄 친 ⓐ를 접속사를 사용하여 바꿔 쓰시오.

➡ _____

08 위 글의 밑줄 친 ⓑ를 'as well as'를 이용하여 바꿔 쓰시오.

➡ _____

09 Why did da Vinci spend a lot of time cooking all kinds of food? Fill in the blank with suitable words.

➡ It was to _____

_____ .

[10~12] 다음 글을 읽고 물음에 답하시오.

In 1473, twenty-year-old da Vinci worked as a cook at a restaurant in Florence, Italy. When he took charge of the kitchen, da Vinci changed the menu (A)[complete / completely]. He made simple but artistic dishes like fish with a few carrot slices. Some dishes were even decorated with flowers. Customers, ⓐ , were (B)[happy / unhappy] because they were used to dishes with big servings of meat. As a result, da Vinci lost his job.

A few years later, da Vinci opened a restaurant with his friend Sandro Botticelli. He wanted to create a place where people could try his innovative food. ⓑThey put up a beautifully painted sign and made a uniquely written menu. Da Vinci believed that people would soon (C)[appreciate / depreciate] his creative cooking. Unfortunately, that never happened.

10 위 글의 빈칸 ⓐ에 알맞은 말을 쓰시오.

➡ _____

11 위 글의 괄호 (A)~(C)에서 문맥이나 어법상 알맞은 낱말을 고르시오.

➡ (A) _____ (B) _____ (C) _____

12 위 글의 밑줄 친 ⓑThey가 가리키는 것을 본문에서 찾아 쓰시오.

➡ _____

구석구석

Write

My name is Kim Jieun. I am an artist who uses technology. There was a
주격 관계대명사   선행사(시간)
special moment when I decided what I wanted to be. Back in 2030, I made
관계부사   관계대명사
a small statue using technology. It was a great chance to learn about using
분사구문   형용사적 용법   전치사+동명사
technology for arts. Thus, I decided to go to a technical high school. After I
graduated from high school, I entered Korea Art College and learned more
자동사+전치사   타동사(전치사 불필요)
about arts and technology. This year, I held my first exhibition. I am very
satisfied with my life.
감정을 나타내는 과거분사

구문해설 · statue: 동상 · hold: 개최하다 · exhibition: 전시회 · satisfied with: ~에 만족하는

해석

내 이름은 김지은이다. 나는 기술을 사용하는 예술가다. 내가 예술가가 되기로 결심했을 때 특별한 순간이 있었다. 2030년에, 나는 기술을 사용해 작은 동상을 만들었다. 그것은 예술을 위한 기술을 배우는 데에 아주 좋은 기회였다. 따라서, 나는 기술 고등학교에 진학하기로 결심했다. 고등학교를 졸업한 뒤, 나는 한국 예술 대학에 입학해서 예술과 기술에 대해 더 배웠다. 올해, 나는 내 첫 전시회를 열었다. 나는 내 인생에 매우 만족한다.

Link

Some people think creativity is the most important thing to consider when
최상급   형용사적 용법
they choose their career. They like to come up with new ideas and design new
명사적 용법(like의 목적어)   to come과 병렬 관계
things. Thus, they want to work at a place where they can use their creativity.
결과를 이끄는 접속부사   관계부사(= in which)

구문해설 · creativity: 창의력 · come up with: ~을 생각해 내다

어떤 사람들은 직업을 선택할 때 고려해야 할 가장 중요한 것은 창의력이라고 생각한다. 그들은 새로운 아이디어를 떠올리고 새로운 것들을 구상하기를 좋아한다. 따라서, 그들은 그들의 창의력을 발휘할 수 있는 곳에서 일하기를 원한다.

Watch and Think Share

Winston Churchill is known for being the Prime Minister of the United
~로 알려지다
Kingdom during World War II. Very few people, however, know that he
during: 특정 기간 (for 다음에는 보통 숫자로 나타내는 기간이 나옴)   역접의 접속부사
was also a historian, a painter, and a writer. He even won the Nobel Prize in
심지어
Literature in 1953.

구문해설 · Prime Minister: 수상 · historian: 사학자 · the Nobel Prize in Literature: 노벨 문학상

Winston Churchill은 제2차 세계대전 중 영국의 수상이었던 것으로 알려져 있다. 하지만, 극소수의 사람들은 그가 또한 사학자이며, 화가이자, 작가임을 알고 있다. 심지어 그는 1953년에 노벨 문학상을 수상하기도 했다.

01 〈보기〉의 밑줄 친 어휘와 같은 의미로 쓰인 것을 고르시오.

┌─ 보기 ─┐
Let me have the check, please.

① Can I have the check, please?
② They carried out security checks at the airport.
③ Would you please check if I filled out this card right?
④ I need to cash this check.
⑤ Cars are checked as they come off the production line.

02 다음 대화의 빈칸에 〈영영풀이〉에 해당하는 어휘를 쓰시오.

A: What are you going to do tomorrow?
B: I'm going to _____ the Christmas tree.

<영영 풀이> to make something look more attractive by putting something pretty on it

➡ _____

03 괄호 안에 주어진 어휘를 이용하여 빈칸에 알맞게 쓰시오.

• It is _____ for a large asteroid to come so close to Earth. (usual)
• _____, I won't be able to attend the meeting. (fortunate)

*asteroid: 소행성

04 다음 영영풀이에 해당하는 단어를 주어진 철자로 시작하여 빈칸에 쓰고, 알맞은 것을 골라 문장을 완성하시오.

• r_____ : why someone decides to do something, or the cause or explanation for something that happens
• r_____ : cooked a short time; still red inside

(1) Do you have a _____ for being so late?
(2) My father likes _____ meat that is still a little pink inside.

05 다음 짝지어진 단어의 관계가 같도록 빈칸에 알맞은 말을 쓰시오. (철자 p로 시작할 것)

rare : well-done = sell : _____

06 다음 문장의 빈칸에 공통으로 들어갈 알맞은 말을 쓰시오.

• They _____ him in charge of the park.
• He _____ up a sign saying, "No pets."
• Fire engines arrived to _____ out a fire.
• I have a sweater you can _____ on.

Conversation

07 다음 중 짝지어진 대화가 어색한 것은?

① A: I'm not satisfied with this bag.
   B: Why not?
   A: I don't like the color.

② A: These plants are dying.
   B: I'm sorry. I promise I'll water them more often.

③ A: I want to become a movie star.
   B: I promise I'll do my best.

④ A: Have you finished your homework?
   B: No, but I promise I'll finish it after I watch TV.

⑤ A: Do you have this in a smaller size?
   B: No, I'm sorry, but the smaller ones are all sold out. I promise I'll have one for you by next week.

[08~10] 다음 대화를 읽고 물음에 답하시오.

G: Wow, I like this blueberry jam. Where did you buy it?
(A) Do you think people would want to buy this?
(B) Really? This is better than any other jam I've ever had. You should sell it.
(C) I made it myself.
(D) Of course. _____ (a)

08 위 대화의 빈칸 (a)에 첫 손님이 되겠다는 다짐을 말하는 표현을 7 단어로 쓰시오.

➡ _____

09 주어진 글 다음의 대화가 자연스럽게 연결되도록 (A)~(D)를 순서대로 가장 적절하게 배열한 것은?

① (B) – (A) – (C) – (D)
② (B) – (C) – (A) – (D)
③ (C) – (B) – (A) – (D)
④ (C) – (B) – (D) – (A)
⑤ (C) – (D) – (B) – (A)

10 위 대화의 내용과 일치하지 않는 것은?

① 소녀는 블루베리 잼이 마음에 든다.
② 블루베리 잼은 사 온 것이다.
③ 블루베리 잼은 소녀가 먹어본 잼 중에 제일 좋았다.
④ 소녀는 사람들이 블루베리 잼을 사기를 원할 거라고 생각한다.
⑤ 소녀는 첫 손님이 되겠다고 약속한다.

Grammar

11 다음 주어진 문장을 둘로 나눌 때, 원래 문장과 의미가 가장 가까운 것은?

> Although Tracy lived alone in that big apartment, she rarely felt lonely.
> → Tracy lived alone in that big apartment. _____, _____.

① Fortunately, she felt lonely.
② Consequently, she rarely felt lonely.
③ Instead, she felt lonely.
④ Nevertheless, she rarely felt lonely.
⑤ Therefore, she rarely felt lonely.

[12~13] 다음 중 어법상 <u>어색한</u> 문장을 고르시오.

12 ① This is the hotel where the singer stayed last week.
② This is the hotel that the singer stayed in last week.
③ This is the hotel which the singer stayed last week.
④ This is the hotel in which the singer stayed last week.
⑤ This is the hotel which the singer stayed in last week.

13 ① Would you tell us the reason why Sandra hasn't come yet?
② The house where the photographer lived had a beautiful studio.
③ Timothy can't forget the day when Anne left Paris for New York.
④ An auditorium is a large space or building in which is used for events such as meetings or concerts.
⑤ Now is the time when they should start to produce the cure for the disease.

14 다음 괄호 안에서 어법상 알맞은 것을 고르시오.

(1) Da Vinci did not feel well. (However / Thus), he still kept painting.

(2) Dr. Kim required that everyone present at the lecture wear a mask. (However / Thus), most of them didn't take it seriously.

(3) Everything she said turned out to be untrue. (However / Thus), many people were disappointed with her.

(4) My grandmother has rarely brushed her teeth after meals. (However / Thus), despite her age of 90, she has healthy teeth.

(5) James was in deep sleep after working all night. (However / Thus), he didn't answer the phone.

(6) Da Vinci had always been interested in food. (However / Thus), when he was asked to make a painting of the last supper of Jesus, he gladly took on the project.

15 다음 그림을 보고 괄호 안의 단어를 배열하여 빈칸을 알맞게 채우시오.

(1)

➡ People were not interested in _____ _____. (da Vinci, his, cooking, made, creative, how)

(2)

➡ At school, I like lunchtime best _____ _____.

(have, with, can, when, a, my friends, meal, I, delicious)

[16~17] 다음 밑줄 친 부분 중 어법상 어색한 것을 고르시오.

16 ① Let her know <u>how</u> the machines work in such a hot and humid environment.
② That evening was the moment <u>when</u> I fell in love with the princess.
③ I will show you the way <u>how</u> the magician escaped from the steel box.
④ Tom can't forget the day <u>when</u> he first ate cold bean soup noodles.
⑤ Does Sarah know the reason <u>why</u> her husband came here?

17 ① Venice is the city <u>where</u> Marco used to live in.
② That is the square <u>where</u> I picked up her credit cards.
③ This is the building <u>in which</u> my parents met for the first time.
④ I remember the shop <u>which</u> I bought some souvenirs at.
⑤ The town <u>where</u> she's going to move is not far from here.

18 다음 밑줄 친 부분의 쓰임이 〈보기〉와 같은 것은?

> Friday is the day <u>when</u> my daughter goes to the pool to learn swimming.

① Mina was taking a shower <u>when</u> someone visited her.
② I wonder <u>when</u> you will leave here for Africa to volunteer.
③ No one knows <u>when</u> the virus disease could be treated properly.
④ I like the Christmas season <u>when</u> I can meet all my family.
⑤ <u>When</u> does she think she can call me?

19 다음 접속부사가 쓰인 두 문장을 한 문장으로 적절하게 바꾼 것을 고르시오.

> His explanation was unclear. Thus, I didn't understand it.

① Although his explanation was unclear, I didn't understand it.
② Whereas his explanation was unclear, I didn't understand it.
③ As soon as his explanation was unclear, I didn't understand it.
④ Since his explanation was unclear, I didn't understand it.
⑤ Unless his explanation was unclear, I didn't understand it.

Reading

[20~22] 다음 글을 읽고 물음에 답하시오.

Leonardo da Vinci is known as one of the greatest painters of all time. He was also a great inventor, scientist, and musician. Very ____ⓐ____ people, however, know that da Vinci was also a creative cook.

In 1473, twenty-year-old da Vinci worked as a cook at a restaurant in Florence, Italy. When he took charge of the kitchen, da Vinci changed the menu completely. (①) He made simple but artistic dishes like fish with a few carrot slices. (②) Some dishes were even decorated with flowers. (③) As a result, da Vinci lost his job.

A few years later, da Vinci opened a restaurant with his friend Sandro Botticelli. (④) He wanted to create a place where people could try his innovative food. (⑤) They put up a beautifully painted sign and made a uniquely written menu. Da Vinci believed that people would soon appreciate his creative cooking. Unfortunately, that never happened.

20 위 글의 빈칸 ⓐ에 들어갈 알맞은 말을 고르시오.

① many   ② few   ③ a few

④ little   ⑤ a little

21 위 글의 흐름으로 보아, 주어진 문장이 들어가기에 가장 적절한 곳은?

> Customers, however, were unhappy because they were used to dishes with big servings of meat.

①   ②   ③   ④   ⑤

22 What did da Vinci do when he took charge of the kitchen?

➡ _____

[23~25] 다음 글을 읽고 물음에 답하시오.

In the early 1480s, da Vinci began to work for Ludovico Sforza in Milan. He was given many different roles, ____ⓐ____ a musician, a painter, and an engineer. He was also put in charge of the kitchen. He was happy to be given another chance to pursue his passion for cooking. Da Vinci did not stop at cooking creative dishes. He wanted to cook much more quickly and easily. Thus, he invented new machines for his kitchen. He created machines ____ⓑ____ could crush vegetables and pull spaghetti. He even made a device ____ⓑ____ could scare frogs away from the water tank. Surely, they were all very innovative, but ⓒ그것들 중 대부분은 사용하기에 너무 크거나 너무 어려웠다.

23 위 글의 빈칸 ⓐ에 들어갈 말로 like 대신 쓸 수 있는 말을 쓰시오. (two words)

➡ _____

24 위 글의 빈칸 ⓑ에 공통으로 들어갈 알맞은 말을 쓰시오.

➡ _____

25 위 글의 밑줄 친 ⓒ의 우리말에 맞게 주어진 어휘를 이용하여 11 단어로 영작하시오.

> them, too, most, difficult, use, or

➡ _____

[26~28] 다음 글을 읽고 물음에 답하시오.

In 1495, Sforza asked da Vinci to make a grand painting, which was based on the last supper of Jesus, on the wall of a church in Milan. (①) He spent a lot of time cooking all kinds of food to decide what to put on the table in his picture. (②) "Da Vinci has wasted his time in the kitchen for over a year. That's the reason ___ⓐ___ he hasn't finished the painting yet," complained the people from the church to Sforza.

(③) Although da Vinci never became a successful cook, he showed great interest in cooking throughout his life. (④) He was not only a great painter but also a creative cook. Now that you know all about his secret passion for cooking, you will never look at *The Last Supper* the same way. (⑤)

26 위 글의 빈칸 ⓐ에 들어갈 말로 알맞은 것을 고르시오.

① when   ② where   ③ how
④ why   ⑤ what

27 위 글의 흐름으로 보아, 주어진 문장이 들어가기에 가장 적절한 곳은?

> Da Vinci gladly took on the project because he had always been interested in food.

①   ②   ③   ④   ⑤

28 What was the grand painting based on? Answer in English with 9 words.

➡ _____

[29~30] 다음 글을 읽고 물음에 답하시오.

Some people think creativity is the most important thing ⓐto consider when they choose their career. They like to come up with new ideas and design new things. Thus, they want to work at a place ⓑ그들의 창의력을 발휘할 수 있는 곳에서(use, creativity).

29 위 글의 밑줄 친 ⓐ와 문법적 쓰임이 같은 것을 고르시오.

① I'd like some time to consider.
② They sat down to consider the problem.
③ It is important to consider the cost of repairs.
④ I decided to consider the money he borrowed lost.
⑤ Everyone in the office is meeting to consider forming a union.

30 위 글의 밑줄 친 ⓑ의 우리말에 맞게 주어진 어휘를 이용하여 6 단어로 영작하시오.

➡ _____

01 다음 중 짝지어진 단어의 관계가 나머지와 <u>다른</u> 것은?

① inconvenience – convenience
② sell – purchase
③ check – bill
④ satisfied – dissatisfied
⑤ creative – uncreative

02 다음 밑줄 친 부분의 의미로 알맞지 <u>않은</u> 것은?

① We would <u>appreciate</u> you letting us know of any problems. (고마워하다)
② I really don't <u>feel like</u> working anymore. (~할 마음이 나다)
③ It's <u>not</u> a quiet island <u>anymore</u>. (더 이상 ~ 아니다)
④ Don't you want to <u>have a bite of</u> this burger? (한 입 베어 물다)
⑤ <u>Now that</u> I finally know I'll take care of you. (이제)

03 다음 빈칸에 공통으로 들어갈 알맞은 말을 쓰시오.

> • I was put in _____ of the office.
> • He took _____ of the farm after his father's death.

04 다음 주어진 우리말에 맞게 빈칸을 채우시오. (철자가 주어진 경우 주어진 철자로 시작할 것)

(1) 그는 역대 최고의 선수라고 불려요.
➡ He is called the greatest player _____ _____ t_____.

(2) Frank는 거리에서 사람들이 자기를 알아보는 것에 익숙해 있다.
➡ Frank is u_____ _____ being recognized in the street.

(3) 코알라는 호주 고유의 동물이다.
➡ The koala is u_____ to Australia.

[05~07] 다음 대화를 읽고 물음에 답하시오.

B: Wow! Did you draw this?
G: I ⓐdid. Do you like it?
B: Yes, the bread and the milk look so ⓑreally. (A)빵을 한 입 먹고 싶어지는데.
G: Thanks, but I'm not satisfied ⓒwith it. It's not ⓓunique.
B: I don't think ⓔso. I think it's a fantastic drawing.

05 위 대화의 밑줄 친 ⓐ~ⓔ 중 어법상 어색한 것을 고르시오.

① ⓐ   ② ⓑ   ③ ⓒ   ④ ⓓ   ⑤ ⓔ

06 위 대화를 읽고 대답할 수 없는 질문을 고르시오.

① Who did draw it?

② Does the girl like the drawing?

③ Does the boy think the bread and the milk look so real?

④ Does the boy think the drawing is fantastic?

⑤ What is unique in the drawing?

07 위 대화의 밑줄 친 (A)의 우리말에 맞게 영작하시오. (9 단어)

➡ _____

[08~10] 다음 대화를 읽고 물음에 답하시오.

Man: Are you enjoying your meal?

Woman: Well, the bread was good, and the salad was fresh.

Man: How about your steak?

Woman: Honestly, _____ (A) _____. It's too rare for me.

Man: I'm sorry. Would you like me to bring you another one? __(B)__ __(C)__

Woman: That's O.K. I need to be going. Let me just have the check, please.

Man: I'm really sorry. You won't have to pay for the steak.

Woman: O.K. Thanks.

Man: I promise we'll provide you with a better experience next time you visit.

08 위 글의 빈칸 (A)에 들어갈 말로 어울리지 않는 것을 고르시오.

① I'm not pitiful with the steak

② I'm not satisfied with the steak

③ I'm dissatisfied with the steak

④ I'm not happy with the steak

⑤ I don't like the steak

09 What does the woman ask the man to do?

➡ _____

10 위 대화의 내용과 일치하지 않는 것은?

① 여자는 빵에는 만족했고, 샐러드에는 실망했다.

② 여자는 스테이크에 만족하지 않았다.

③ 남자는 다른 스테이크로 가져다 주겠다고 제안한다.

④ 여자는 스테이크 값을 지불하지 않아도 된다.

⑤ 남자는 다음 방문 때는 더 좋은 경험을 드리겠다고 약속한다.

11 다음 빈칸에 접속부사 however 또는 thus 중에서 알맞은 것을 선택하여 써 넣으시오.

(1) Leonardo da Vinci is known as one of the greatest painters and also a great inventor, scientist, and musician. Very few people, _____, know that da Vinci was a creative cook.

(2) Customers who saw da Vinci's creative food were unhappy because they were used to dishes with big servings of meat. _____, da Vinci lost his job.

(3) Da Vinci wanted to make creative food much more quickly and easily. _____, he invented new machines that could crush vegetables and pull spaghetti.

(4) Da Vinci never became a successful cook when he lived. _____, he showed great interest in cooking throughout his life.

(5) I have learned all about the secret passion for cooking of da Vinci. _____, I think I will never look at *The Last Supper* the same way as before.

12 다음 글의 빈칸 ①∼⑤에 들어갈 단어가 **잘못된** 것은?

In 1495, Sforza asked da Vinci to make a grand painting, ①_____ was based on the last supper of Jesus, on the wall of a church in Milan. Da Vinci gladly took on the project ②_____ he had always been interested in food. He spent a lot of time cooking all kinds of food to decide ③_____ to put on the table in his picture. "Da Vinci has wasted his time in the kitchen for over a year. That's the ④_____ why he hasn't finished the painting ⑤_____," complained the people from the church to Sforza.

① which　　② because　　③ that
④ reason　　⑤ yet

13 다음 그림을 보고 괄호 안의 단어를 배열하여 빈칸을 알맞게 채우시오.

People complained that da Vinci wasted too much time on food and that was

_____.

(the painting, why, finished, he, earlier, the reason, hadn't)

14 다음 두 문장을 가능하다면 선행사와 관계부사를 모두 써서 한 문장으로 쓰시오. (단, 관계부사는 반드시 사용해야 함)

(1) • Jamaica is the country.
　　• International reggae festivals take place every summer in Jamaica.
　➡ _____
　　_____

(2) • Show your brother the way.
　　• You solved the puzzle in such a short time in that way.
　➡ _____
　　_____

(3) • Everyone but me knows the day.
　　• I will be transferred to Jeju island on the day.
　➡ _____
　　_____

(4) • Katherine won't tell her teacher the reason.
　　• She ran out of the classroom for that reason.
　➡ _____
　　_____

15 다음 그림을 보고 괄호 안의 단어를 배열하여 빈칸을 알맞게 채우시오.

(pizza, people, line up, to eat, have to, all night, where)

➡ That is the famous restaurant _____

_____ .

[16~18] 다음 글을 읽고 물음에 답하시오.

Leonardo da Vinci is known as one of the greatest painters of all time. He was also a great inventor, scientist, and musician. Very few people, however, know that da Vinci was also a creative cook.

In 1473, twenty-year-old da Vinci worked as a cook at a restaurant in Florence, Italy. When he took charge of the kitchen, da Vinci changed the menu completely. He made simple but artistic dishes like fish with a few carrot slices. Some dishes were even decorated with flowers. Customers, however, were unhappy because they were ⓐused to dishes with big servings of meat. As a result, da Vinci lost his job.

A few years later, da Vinci opened a restaurant with his friend Sandro Botticelli. _____(A)_____ . They put up a beautifully painted sign and made a uniquely written menu. Da Vinci believed that people would soon appreciate his creative cooking. Unfortunately, that never happened.

16 위 글의 빈칸 (A)에 주어진 두 문장을 한 문장으로 바꾸어 쓰시오.

• He wanted to create a place.
• People could try his innovative food at the place.

➡ _____

_____

17 위 글의 밑줄 친 ⓐ와 바꿔 쓸 수 있는 것을 고르시오.

① utilized   ② accustomed
③ served   ④ applied
⑤ spent

18 위 글의 제목으로 알맞은 것을 고르시오.

① Why Is da Vinci Famous?
② How to Become a Cook
③ What to do as a Cook
④ Jack of All Trades: Leonardo da Vinci
⑤ Unachieved Dream of da Vinci

[19~22] 다음 글을 읽고 물음에 답하시오.

In the early 1480s, da Vinci began to work for Ludovico Sforza in Milan. He was given many different roles, such as a musician, a painter, and an engineer. He was also put in charge of the kitchen. He was happy to be given another chance to pursue his passion for cooking. Da Vinci did not stop ___ⓐ___ cooking creative dishes. He wanted to cook much more quickly and easily. Thus, he invented new machines for his kitchen. He created machines that could crush vegetables and pull spaghetti. He even made a device that could scare frogs away from the water tank. Surely, they were all very innovative, but (A)most of them were too big or too difficult to use.

출제율 90%

19 위 글의 빈칸 ⓐ에 알맞은 말을 쓰시오.

➡ _____

출제율 100%

20 Which question can be answered after reading the passage?

① Who was Ludovico Sforza in Milan?

② What did da Vinci ask Ludovico Sforza to work for?

③ Why did da Vinci want to cook more differently?

④ Why did da Vinci invent new machines for his kitchen?

⑤ How could the device scare frogs away from the water tank?

출제율 95%

21 다음 문장에서 위 글의 내용과 다른 부분을 찾아서 고치시오.

Da Vinci was happy to have another chance to pursue his passion for painting.

_____ ➡ _____

출제율 90%

22 밑줄 친 (A)를 that을 이용하여 바꿔 쓰시오.

➡ _____

_____

단원별 예상문제 **51**

[01~03] 다음 대화를 읽고 물음에 답하시오.

> M: Hello, ma'am. How can I help you?
> W: I bought this phone only a week ago, but it sometimes _____(A)_____.
> M: Oh, I see. May I have a look at it? (Pause) We're sorry for the ___(B)___. It'll take a few hours to fix it.
> W: (C)I don't like the phone. I'd like a new one.
> M: Of course. I just need to fill out this form.

01 다음 customer service report를 참고하여 빈칸 (A)를 알맞게 채우시오.

CUSTOMER SERVICE REPORT	
(1) Product	☐ TV ✓ Phone ☐ Refrigerator
(2) Problem	☐ It doesn't turn on. ✓ It turns off by itself.
(3) Service needed	☐ Fix broken parts. ✓ Provide a new one.

➡ _____

02 다음 영영풀이에 해당하는 말을 빈칸 (B)에 쓰시오.

> problems caused by something which annoy or affect you

➡ _____

03 위 대화의 밑줄 친 (C)와 같은 뜻의 말을 'satisfied'를 이용하여 쓰시오.

➡ _____

04 다음 주어진 문장의 밑줄 친 부분을 다시 쓰고자 한다. 빈칸에 알맞은 관계부사를 써 넣으시오.

(1) The exhausted employee needs a place to rest in which she can refresh her mind.
> ➡ The exhausted employee needs a place to rest _____ she can refresh her mind.

(2) Lunar New Year's Day is the day on which people gather and eat together.
> ➡ Lunar New Year's Day is the day _____ people gather and eat together.

(3) The police are trying to find out the way in which he escaped from the heavily guarded prison.
> ➡ The police are trying to find out _____ he escaped from the heavily guarded prison.

(4) No one knew the reason for which Brian cried while performing on his concert stage.
> ➡ No one knew the reason _____ Brian cried while performing on his concert stage.

(5) His funeral will be held next Friday on which all of his children will gather together.
> ➡ His funeral will be held next Friday _____ all of his children will gather together.

05 다음 〈보기〉에 주어진 단어들을 한 번씩만 사용해서 글의 흐름에 알맞게 빈칸을 채우시오.

> ┤ 보기 ├
> Thus, However, For example, In addition, In other words

(1) Da Vinci constantly made unique and creative dishes. _____, he was an experimental cook.

(2) Da Vinci wanted to be a successful cook. _____, people did not think of him as a cook.

(3) Da Vinci designed a device to crush vegetables. _____, he invented a machine to pull pasta out.

(4) Da Vinci was interested in cooking. _____, he thought long about what food to put on "*the Last Supper*" table.

(5) Da Vinci is known for his talents in various areas. _____, he is a painter, architect, mathematician and musician.

[06~08] 다음 글을 읽고 물음에 답하시오.

Leonardo da Vinci is known as one of the greatest painters of all time. He was also a great inventor, scientist, and musician. Very few people, however, know that da Vinci was also a creative cook.

ⓐIn 1473, twenty-years-old da Vinci worked as a cook at a restaurant in Florence, Italy. When he took charge of the kitchen, da Vinci changed the menu completely. He made simple but artistic dishes like fish with a few carrot slices. Some dishes were even decorated with flowers. Customers, however, were unhappy because they were used to dishes with big servings of meat. (A) , da Vinci lost his job.

A few years later, da Vinci opened a restaurant with his friend Sandro Botticelli. He wanted to create a place where people could try his innovative food. They put up a beautifully painted sign and made a uniquely written menu. Da Vinci believed that people would soon appreciate his creative cooking. Unfortunately, that never happened.

06 위 글의 빈칸 (A)에 들어갈 알맞은 말을 3 단어의 영어로 쓰시오.

➡ _____

07 위 글의 밑줄 친 ⓐ에서 어법상 <u>어색한</u> 것을 찾아 바르게 고치시오.

_____ ➡ _____

08 Why did da Vinci lose his job?

➡ _____

창의사고력 서술형 문제

01 다음 그림을 보고 〈보기〉의 표현을 이용하여 다음 대화의 빈칸에 알맞은 말을 쓰시오.

┌─ 보기 ─┐
(1) drawing / color
(2) steak / rare

A: I'm not satisfied with this _____.
B: Why not?
A: _____.

02 다음 그림을 보고 〈보기〉의 단어들을 활용하여, 자유롭게 관계부사가 들어간 문장을 2개 만드시오. (단, 꼭 써야 할 단어는 포함해야 한다.)

(1)　　　　　(2)　　　　　(3)

┌─ 보기 ─┐
선행사: the place, the day, how / 꼭 써야 할 단어: eat(또는 not eat), the apple

(1) _____
(2) _____
(3) _____

03 다음 내용을 바탕으로 20년 뒤 자신의 꿈이 이루어졌다고 가정하고 쓴 자서전의 빈칸을 채우시오.

2030 made a small statue using technology, 2031 entered Korea Technical High School, 2034 entered Korea Art College, 2040 held my first exhibition, an artist who uses technology

My name is Kim Jieun. I am (A)_____ who uses technology. There was a special moment when I decided what I wanted to be. Back in 2030, I made a small statue (B)_____. It was a great chance to learn about (B)_____ for arts. Thus, I decided to go to a (C)_____ high school. After I graduated from high school, I entered Korea Art College and learned more about arts and technology. This year, I held (D)_____. I am very satisfied with my life.

단원별 모의고사

01 다음 짝지어진 단어의 관계가 같도록 빈칸에 알맞은 말을 쓰시오. (철자 p로 시작하여 쓸 것.)

> surely – certainly : supply – _____

02 주어진 영어 설명에 맞게 문장의 빈칸에 알맞은 말을 쓰시오.

> The car was completely _____ed under the truck.

> <영어설명> to press something so hard that it breaks or is damaged

➡ _____

03 다음 빈칸에 알맞은 말로 짝지어진 것을 고르시오.

> • We _____ our happiness for the rest of our lives.
> • I've never heard him _____ about anything.

① determine – provide
② decorate – appreciate
③ decorate – complain
④ pursue – complain
⑤ pursue – provide

04 다음 문장에 공통으로 들어갈 말은?

> • She was put in charge _____ the matter.
> • He is the greatest speaker _____ all time.

① by　　　② with　　　③ from
④ to　　　⑤ of

05 우리말에 맞게 빈칸에 알맞은 말을 철자 t로 시작하여 쓰시오.

> 그 박물관은 연중 내내 매일 문을 연다.
> ➡ The museum is open daily _____ the year.

➡ _____

06 다음 영영풀이를 참고하여 빈칸에 알맞은 말을 쓰시오.

> to repair something that is broken or not working properly

> Can you organize someone to come over and _____ it?

➡ _____

[07~09] 다음 대화를 읽고 물음에 답하시오.

B: Mom, I want to go to an arts high school. I want to become an actor.
W: What? I thought you were interested in science.
B: I was but not anymore. I want to become a movie star.
W: Are you sure you want to be an actor?
B: Yes, ⓐI'll learn how to act. ⓑI promise I'll do my best.

07 위 대화의 밑줄 친 ⓐ를 'should'를 이용하여 바꿔 쓰시오.

➡ _____

08 위 대화의 밑줄 친 ⓑ를 'sure'를 이용하여 바꿔 쓰시오.

➡ _____

09 Why does the boy want to go to an arts high school? Answer with the words "It's because."

➡ _____

[10~12] 다음 대화를 읽고 물음에 답하시오.

M: Hello, ma'am. How can I help you?
W: I bought this phone only a week ago, but it sometimes turns off by itself. (①)
M: Oh, I see. (②) (*Pause*) We're sorry for the inconvenience. It'll take a few hours to fix it.
W: I'm not satisfied with the phone. (③) I'd like a new one. (④)
M: Of course. I just need to fill out this form. (⑤)

10 위 대화의 (①)~(⑤) 중에서 주어진 문장이 들어가기에 가장 적절한 곳은?

| May I have a look at it? |

①   ②   ③   ④   ⑤

11 What is the problem of the phone the woman bought?

➡ _____

12 If the woman had her phone repaired, how long would it take to repair it?

➡ _____

[13~14] 다음 주어진 두 개의 문장을 같은 내용의 하나의 문장으로 바르게 옮긴 것은?

13

| Sam didn't have breakfast. However, he didn't feel hungry. |

① If he had breakfast, Sam wouldn't feel hungry.
② Since he didn't have breakfast, Sam felt hungry.
③ Though he didn't have breakfast, Sam didn't feel hungry.
④ As he didn't have breakfast, Sam didn't feel hungry.
⑤ Before he didn't have breakfast, Sam didn't feel hungry.

14

| The students had close contact with a patient in the PC cafe. Thus, they were infected with the virus. |

① Although the students had close contact with a patient in the PC cafe, they were infected with the virus.
② Since the students didn't have close contact with a patient in the PC cafe, they were infected with the virus.
③ As the students had close contact with a patient in the PC cafe, they were not infected with the virus.
④ Because the students had close contact with a patient in the PC cafe, they were infected with the virus.
⑤ Whereas the students had close contact with a patient in the PC cafe, they were infected with the virus.

15 다음 각 문장의 밑줄 친 '전치사+관계대명사'를 관계부사로 바꿀 때 어법상 어색한 것은?

① Paris is the city in which many artists come to live.
→ Paris is the city where many artists come to live.

② Donald will never forget the moment at which he saw the killer.
→ Donald will never forget the moment when he saw the killer.

③ She will tell you the reason for which you failed the test.
→ She will tell you the reason why you failed the test.

④ That's the way in which Paul persuaded the customer companies.
→ That's the way how Paul persuaded the customer companies.

⑤ This is the restaurant in which we had Bulgogi last month.
→ This is the restaurant where we had Bulgogi last month.

16 다음 각 문장의 밑줄 친 관계부사를 관계대명사를 이용해서 전환한 문장으로 옳지 않은 것은?

① Hongkong is the city where Henry was born.
→ Hongkong is the city which Henry was born in.

② Do you know the reason why Jerome didn't come?
→ Do you know the reason for which Jerome didn't come?

③ Teach me how the machine works.
→ Teach me the way in which the machine works.

④ The accident happened on the day when the president came back.
→ The accident happened on the day which the president came back in.

⑤ All of us saw the building where your mother works.
→ All of us saw the building which your mother works in.

17 다음 각 그림을 보고, 주어진 어구를 알맞게 배열하되, 반드시 However나 Thus 중 하나로 시작하는 문장을 만드시오.

(1)

➡ The hedgehog just wanted to get along with the dog. _____
_____. (painful, so, that, the dog, it, ran away, was)

(2)

➡ Today is the day when Sumi's parents are on duty for lunch. _____
_____.

(side dishes, Sumi, a lot of, asked for)

[18~19] 다음 글을 읽고 물음에 답하시오.

Leonardo da Vinci is known as one of the greatest painters of all time. He was also a great inventor, scientist, and musician. Very few people, however, know that da Vinci was also a creative cook.

In 1473, twenty-year-old da Vinci worked as a cook at a restaurant in Florence, Italy. When he took charge of the kitchen, da Vinci changed the menu completely. He made simple but artistic dishes like fish with a few carrot slices. Some dishes were even decorated with flowers. Customers, however, were unhappy because they were used to dishes with big servings of meat. As a result, da Vinci lost his job.

18 위 글에 언급된 다빈치의 직업이 <u>아닌</u> 것은?

① 화가   ② 발명가   ③ 조각가
④ 음악가   ⑤ 요리사

19 When he took charge of the kitchen, what did da Vinci do with his dishes? Answer with 6 words.

➡ _____

[20~22] 다음 글을 읽고 물음에 답하시오.

My name is Kim Jieun. I am an artist who uses technology. There was a special moment _____ⓐ_____ I decided what I wanted to be. (①) Back in 2030, I made a small statue using technology. (②) It was a great chance to learn about using technology for arts. (③) After I graduated from high school, I entered Korea Art College and learned more about arts and technology. (④) This year, I held my first exhibition. (⑤) I am very satisfied with my life.

20 위 글의 빈칸 ⓐ에 알맞은 것을 고르시오.

① what   ② why   ③ how
④ where   ⑤ when

21 위 글의 흐름으로 보아, 주어진 문장이 들어가기에 가장 적절한 곳은?

> Thus, I decided to go to a technical high school.

①   ②   ③   ④   ⑤

22 According to the passage, which is NOT true?

① Jieun is an artist who uses technology.
② Jieun's special moment was in 2030.
③ Jieun had a great chance to learn about using technology for arts.
④ Jieun decided to leave Korea Art College.
⑤ Jieun is very satisfied with her life.

Lesson 7

Wit and Wisdom

🎤 의사소통 기능

- 이해 확인하기
  Do you mean we should not judge others by their looks?
- 바람 · 소원 표현하기
  I wish I could sing like Jiho.

🎤 언어 형식

- 소유격 관계대명사 whose
  Among them was a man **whose** name was Raja Birbal.
- 가정법 과거
  If I **were** you, I **would give** him sweets.

Words & Expressions

Key Words

- **among** [əmʌ́ŋ] 전 ~ 중에, ~의 사이에
- **break** [breik] 동 깨지다, 부러뜨리다
- **certainly** [sə́:rtnli] 부 틀림없이, 분명히
- **correct** [kərékt] 형 맞는, 정확한
- **court** [kɔ:rt] 명 대궐, 궁궐
- **emperor** [émpərər] 명 황제
- **exactly** [igzǽktli] 부 정확하게
- **exam** [igzǽm] 명 시험
- **expression** [ikspréʃən] 명 표현
- **favor** [féivər] 명 청, 부탁
- **gift** [gift] 명 선물
- **honesty** [ánisti] 명 정직
- **indeed** [indíːd] 부 정말, 확실히
- **journey** [dʒə́:rni] 명 여행, 여정
- **leave** [liːv] 동 떠나다
- **match** [mætʃ] 명 경기, 시합, 성냥
- **must** [məst] 조 (틀림없이) ~일 것이다
- **mystery** [místəri] 명 수수께끼, 미스터리
- **narrow** [nǽrou] 형 좁은
- **offer** [ɔ́:fər] 동 내놓다, 제공하다
- **official** [əfíʃəl] 명 고위 공무원, 관리

- **over** [óuvər] 전 (다른 사람·사물이 덮이도록) ~ 위에
- **past** [pæst] 명 과거
- **policy** [páləsi] 명 정책
- **potful** [pátful] 명 한 항아리[냄비]의 양
- **precious** [préʃəs] 형 귀중한, 값비싼
- **present** [préznt] 명 현재, 지금
- **pull** [pul] 동 끌다, 당기다, 끌어당기다
- **pumpkin** [pʌ́mpkin] 명 호박
- **punish** [pʌ́niʃ] 동 처벌하다, 벌주다
- **quick** [kwik] 형 빠른
- **really** [ríːəli] 부 정말로
- **return** [ritə́:rn] 동 되돌려주다
- **speechless** [spíːtʃlis] 형 (화나거나 놀라서) 말을 못 하는
- **strange** [streindʒ] 형 이상한
- **sweet** [swiːt] 명 사탕, 단것 형 단, 달콤한
- **thus** [ðʌs] 부 그러므로
- **wisdom** [wízdəm] 명 지혜, 슬기, 현명함
- **wise** [waiz] 형 지혜로운, 현명한, 슬기로운
- **wit** [wit] 명 기지, 재치
- **worm** [wə:rm] 명 (땅속에 사는) 벌레

Key Expressions

- **a number of** 많은
- **a potful of** 한 냄비의, 한 항아리의
- **be careful not to** ~하지 않도록 조심하다
- **be famous for** ~로 유명하다
- **be good at** ~을 잘하다
- **Break a leg!** 행운을 빌어!
- **come up with** ~을 찾아내다, ~을 떠올리다
- **focus on** ~에 주력하다, 집중하다
- **for oneself** 혼자서, 스스로
- **get up** 일어나다

- **hand in** ~을 제출하다
- **in one's place** ~의 처지에서, ~의 상황에서
- **It's better late than never.** 안 하는 것보다는 늦어도 하는 것이 낫다.
- **make sense** 타당하다, 말이 되다
- **over again** 다시 한 번
- **thanks to** ~ 덕분에
- **That's why ~.** 그것이 ~하는 이유이다.
- **the other** (둘 중) 다른 하나의
- **Time flies.** 시간이 쏜살같다.
- **without+동사-ing** ~하지 않고

Word Power

※ 서로 비슷한 뜻을 가진 어휘

- □ **certainly** 틀림없이 – **surely** 확실히
- □ **correct** 맞는, 정확한 – **accurate** 정확한
- □ **court** 대궐, 궁궐 – **palace** 궁전
- □ **emperor** 황제 – **monarch** 군주
- □ **exactly** 정확하게 – **correctly** 정확하게
- □ **gift** 선물 – **present** 선물

- □ **indeed** 정말, 확실히 – **truly** 정말로
- □ **journey** 여행, 여정 – **travel** 여행
- □ **offer** 내놓다, 제공하다 – **provide** 제공하다
- □ **precious** 귀중한 – **valuable** 귀중한
- □ **quick** 빠른 – **swift** 신속한

※ 서로 반대되는 뜻을 가진 어휘

- □ **correct** 맞는, 정확한 ↔ **incorrect** 정확하지 않은
- □ **exactly** 정확하게 ↔ **inexactly** 부정확하게
- □ **honesty** 정직 ↔ **dishonesty** 불성실
- □ **leave** 떠나다 ↔ **arrive** 도착하다
- □ **narrow** 좁은 ↔ **wide** 넓은

- □ **over** ~ 위에 ↔ **under** ~ 아래에
- □ **precious** 귀중한 ↔ **worthless** 가치 없는
- □ **pull** 끌다 ↔ **push** 밀다
- □ **punish** 처벌하다 ↔ **praise** 칭찬하다
- □ **quick** 빠른 ↔ **slow** 느린

※ 접미사 -less

- □ **care** + **less** – **careless** 부주의한
- □ **hope** + **less** – **hopeless** 절망적인
- □ **use** + **less** – **useless** 쓸모없는
- □ **speech** + **less** – **speechless** 말문이 막히는
- □ **worth** + **less** – **worthless** 가치 없는
- □ **power** + **less** – **powerless** 힘없는

- □ **meaning** + **less** – **meaningless** 무의미한
- □ **value** + **less** – **valueless** 가치 없는
- □ **end** + **less** – **endless** 끝없는
- □ **penny** + **less** – **penniless** 돈이 없는
- *cf.* **price** + **less** – **priceless** 매우 소중한

※ Word Partner: out과 함께 쓰는 동사

- □ **take out** 가지고 나가다
- □ **check out** 확인하다
- □ **find out** 찾아내다
- □ **turn out** 판명되다, 밝혀지다

- □ **work out** 운동하다, 잘 풀리다
- □ **hang out** 많은 시간을 보내다
- □ **figure out** 알아내다

English Dictionary

- □ **court** 대궐, 궁궐
  → the place where a king or queen lives and works
  왕이나 여왕이 살며 일하는 장소

- □ **emperor** 황제
  → the man who is the ruler of an empire
  제국의 통치자인 남자

- □ **journey** 여행, 여정
  → an occasion when you travel from one place to another
  한 장소에서 다른 장소로 여행하는 일

- □ **leave** 떠나다
  → to go away from a place or a person
  한 장소나 사람에게서 멀어져 가다

- □ **match** 경기, 시합
  → an organized sport event between two teams or people
  두 팀이나 사람 사이에 조직되어 있는 스포츠 행사

- □ **narrow** 좁은
  → measuring only a small distance from one side to the other; not wide
  한 쪽에서 다른 쪽까지 작은 거리만 측정되는; 넓지 않은

- □ **official** 고위 공무원, 관리
  → someone who is in a position of authority in an organization
  어떤 조직에서 권력 있는 직책에 있는 사람

- □ **pumpkin** 호박
  → a lagre round vegetable with thick orange skin
  주황색 껍질이 두껍고 둥글고 큰 채소

01 다음 짝지어진 단어의 관계가 같도록 빈칸에 알맞은 말은?

> wit – humor : palace – _____

① emperor ② course ③ pot
④ official ⑤ court

02 주어진 영어 설명에 맞게 문장의 빈칸에 알맞은 말을 쓰시오.

> He was a White House _____ during the Bush presidency.

> <영어 설명> someone who is in a position of authority in an organization

➡ _____

03 밑줄 친 부분의 의미로 알맞지 않은 것을 고르시오.

① Try to put yourself in my place and think how you would feel. (나의 입장에)
② It doesn't make sense for the government to tax certain foods. (타당하다, 말이 되다)
③ What can you come up with from his poem? (떠올리다)
④ There were quite a number of people in the park. (~의 수)
⑤ If you don't focus on the money but on doing a good job, the money will come. (~에 집중하다)

04 다음 빈칸에 들어갈 알맞은 말을 고르시오.

> In this job you need to exhibit the _____ of Solomon.

① wisdom ② punish ③ favor
④ expression ⑤ pumpkin

05 다음 <보기>의 단어를 사용하여 자연스러운 문장을 만들 수 없는 것은?

> ┤ 보기 ├
> punish speechless correct certainly

① I will _____ go there again.
② Laura was _____ with surprise.
③ You have to wait a day or two to get your _____ balance.
④ My parents used to _____ me by not letting me watch TV.
⑤ A cold spring will _____ a natural check on the number of insects.

06 다음 빈칸에 알맞은 말로 바르게 짝지어진 것을 고르시오.

> • This novel is full of the author's _____.
> • The early bird catches the _____.

① wit – warm ② wit – worm
③ clever – warm ④ clever – worm
⑤ intelligence – fever

01 다음 영영풀이에 알맞은 어휘를 〈보기〉에서 찾아 쓰시오.

┌─ 보기 ─┐
court match pumpkin journey
└─────┘

(1) the place where a king or queen lives and works

➡ _____

(2) an occasion when you travel from one place to another

➡ _____

(3) an organized sport event between two teams or people

➡ _____

(4) a large round vegetable with thick orange skin

➡ _____

02 다음 짝지어진 두 단어의 관계가 같도록 빈칸에 알맞은 말을 쓰시오.

(1) care : careless = value : _____

(2) punish : punishment = wise : _____

03 다음 우리말에 맞도록 빈칸에 알맞은 한 단어를 쓰시오.

(1) 오늘 상영시간표 확인했어?

➡ Did you _____ out today's movie schedule?

(2) 그 소식을 듣고 나는 잠시 말을 못 했다.

➡ The news struck me _____ for a while.

(3) 쓰기를 멈추고 시험지를 제출하세요.

➡ Stop writing and _____ in your papers.

(4) 누군가를 이해할 수 없을 때에는 그의 입장에 처했다고 생각해 보라.

➡ When you can't understand someone, just try to put yourself in his _____.

04 우리말에 맞게 한 단어를 추가하여 주어진 단어를 알맞게 배열하시오.

(1) 난 쌍둥이 한 명을 다른 한 명과 구분할 수가 없다. (I, twin, one, can't, tell, the, from)

➡ _____

(2) 시민들은 길거리로 지갑을 가지고 나가도 안전함을 느낀다. (citizens, streets, wallets, secure, the, feel, their, out, on)

➡ _____

(3) 나는 내 인격의 완전한 표현을 위해 자유를 원한다. (I, personality, freedom, the, want, full, my, of, for)

➡ _____
_____

(4) 각 연습 문제는 각기 다른 문법 사항에 집중한다. (exercise, point, grammar, focuses, different, a, each)

➡ _____
_____

Conversation

Do you mean we should not judge others by their looks?
사람을 겉모습으로 판단해선 안 된다는 뜻이야?

■ 'Do you mean ~?'은 '~라는 말이니?'라는 뜻으로 자신이 이해한 의미가 상대가 의도한 것인지를 확인하는 말이다. 'You're saying ~?(~라고 말하는 거니?)', 'I think you mean ~(나는 네가 ~을 의미한다고 생각해.)'와 같은 표현도 자신이 이해한 의미를 상대에게 확인하는 표현이다.

■ 'Do you know what I mean?(내가 무슨 말 하는지 알겠어?)'는 자신이 한 말을 상대가 이해했는지를 확인하기 위하여 묻는 말이다. 'Do you understand what I am saying?(내가 무슨 말 하는지 이해하겠어?)', 'Do you follow me?(내 말 이해해?)', 'Do you get it?(이해해?)', 'Are you with me?(내 말 알겠니?)'도 마찬가지로 상대의 이해를 확인하는 말이다.

■ 'Can you explain that?(그걸 설명해 줄 수 있니?)'는 상대의 말을 알아듣지 못했을 때 설명을 요청하는 말이다. 'Could you give me more information?', 'Can you explain more in detail?', 'Could you be more specific?', 'Can you explain it to me?' 등도 마찬가지로 상대의 설명을 요청하는 말이다.

이해 확인하기

• Do you mean ~? ~라는 말이니?

• You're saying ~? ~라고 말하는 거니?

• I think you mean ~. 나는 네가 ~을 의미한다고 생각해.

이해 점검하기

• Do you know/see what I mean? 내가 무슨 말 하는지 알겠어?

• Do you understand what I am saying? 내가 무슨 말 하는지 이해하겠어?

• Do you follow me? 내 말 이해해?

• Are you with me? 내 말 알겠니?

핵심 Check

1. 괄호 안에 주어진 어휘를 이용하여 밑줄 친 우리말을 영작하시오.

G: You look worried. Is something wrong?

B: I had to hand in my science report by yesterday, but I didn't.

G: It's better late than never.

B: 늦었더라도 내는 게 낫다는 뜻이야? (mean, hand, even though)

G: Yes, exactly. You should always finish what you've started.

➡ _____

② 바람·소원 표현하기

I wish I could sing like Jiho. 지호처럼 노래할 수 있으면 좋겠어.

- 'I wish I could ~.'는 '~라면 좋겠어.'의 뜻으로 바람이나 소원을 표현하는 말이다. '~라면 …할 텐데.'의 의미로 소원을 나타내는 말은 'If I were ~, I would/could ~.'이고 '나는 ~하기를 원한다.'는 'I want to ~.'이다. '~하기를 기대한다.'라고 할 때는 'I look forward to -ing.'라고 하고 'I expect to ~.'도 역시 기대를 나타내는 말이다.

- 소망이나 바람을 나타낼 때 사용하는 표현 'I wish I could ~'는 'I wish+가정법 과거'의 형태를 사용하여 '내가 ~할 수 있다면 좋을 텐데.'라는 뜻이다. 뒤에 나오는 가정법 과거는 동사의 과거형으로 나타내고, be동사는 주로 were를 쓴다. 이 표현은 어떤 일을 할 수 있으면 좋겠지만, 실제로 지금은 그렇게 할 수 없는 현재의 일에 대하여 말하는 사람의 소원을 나타내는 문장이다.

- 앞으로 일어날 일이나 하고 싶은 일에 대한 기대를 표현할 때는 '~을 기대한다.'라는 의미로 'I look forward to ~.'의 표현을 사용한다. 여기서 to는 전치사이므로 뒤에 명사나 동명사가 와야 한다. '~을 너무 하고 싶다.'의 뜻으로 'I can't wait for ~.', 'I can't wait to ~.'라고 하기도 한다.

- 강한 소원, 기대를 나타낼 때는 '열망하다'라는 의미의 동사 long을 써서 'I'm longing to+동사원형', 'I'm longing for+명사'라고 하거나 형용사 eager(열망하는)를 써서 'I'm eager to+동사원형', 'I'm eager for+명사'의 형태로 나타내기도 한다.

바람·소원 표현하기

- I wish 주어+과거 동사 ~. ~할 수 있으면 좋을 텐데.
- If I were ~, I would … 내가 ~라면 …할 텐데.
- I want to ~. 나는 ~하기를 원한다.
- I look forward to -ing…. ~하기를 기대한다.
- I hope to ~. ~하기를 희망한다.
- I'd like to ~. ~하고 싶다.
- I expect to 동사원형 ~. ~하기를 기대한다.

핵심 Check

2. 괄호 안에 주어진 어휘를 이용하여 밑줄 친 우리말을 영작하시오.

B: Wow, you really dance well.

G: Thanks. I love dancing. Everyone in my family is good at dancing.

B: Really? Your parents dance well, too?

G: Yes. They're also good singers.

B: What a family! <u>나도 너처럼 춤을 출 수 있으면 좋겠어.</u> (wish, like)

➡ _____

Listen & Speak 1 A-1

G: You ❶look tired this morning.

B: I got up very early ❷to study for the exam.

G: ❸Good for you. The early bird catches the worm.

B: No. The early bird ❹gets tired quickly.

G: ❺Do you mean you don't like to get up early?

B: Yes, that's exactly ❻what I mean.

G: 오늘 아침 너 피곤해 보인다.
B: 시험 공부 하려고 아주 일찍 일어났거든.
G: 잘했어. 일찍 일어나는 벌레를 잡는 법이지.
B: 아니. 일찍 일어나는 새가 빨리 지쳐.
G: 일찍 일어나는 게 싫다는 말이야?
B: 응, 정확히 그런 뜻이야.

❶ look+형용사: ~하게 보이다
❷ 부사적 용법 중에서 '목적(~하기 위해서)'으로 쓰였다.
❸ Good for you.: 잘했다, cf. be good for: ~에 좋다
❹ get+형용사: ~하게 되다
❺ 'Do you mean ~?'은 이해를 확인하기 위해 쓰는 표현이다.
❻ what은 선행사를 포함하는 관계대명사이다.

Check(√) True or False

(1) The girl looks tired this morning.　　　T ☐ F ☐

(2) The boy doesn't like to get up early.　　　T ☐ F ☐

Listen & Speak 1 A-2

G: I have to sing at the school's English pop song contest.

B: Wow. ❶Break a leg!

G: What? ❷Do you mean I have to break ❸one of my legs?

B: No, ❹it's an expression ❺meaning ❻I hope you do well.

G: 나는 학교의 영어 팝송 부르기 대회에서 노래를 해야 해.
B: 우와. 행운을 빌어!
G: 뭐? 내가 내 다리 한 쪽을 부러뜨려야 한다는 말이야?
B: 아니. 네가 잘하길 빈다는 뜻의 표현이야.

❶ Break a leg!: 행운을 빌어!
❷ 'Do you mean ~?'은 이해를 확인하기 위해 쓰는 표현이다.
❸ one of+복수 명사: ~ 중의 하나
❹ it은 'Break a leg!'을 가리키는 말이다.
❺ meaning은 현재분사로 an expression을 뒤에서 수식하고 있다.
❻ hope 다음에 목적절을 이끄는 접속사 that이 생략되어 있다.

Check(√) True or False

(3) The boy knows the expression, 'Break a leg!'　　　T ☐ F ☐

(4) The girl has to break one of her legs.　　　T ☐ F ☐

Listen & Speak 2 A-1

B: Wow, you really dance well.

G: Thanks. I love dancing. Everyone in my family ❶is good at dancing.

B: Really? Your parents dance well, too?

G: Yes. They're also good singers.

B: ❷What a family! ❸I wish I could dance like you.

❶ Everyone은 단수로 받는다. be good at: ~을 잘하다
❷ 감탄문으로 '굉장한 가족이다!' 정도의 뜻이다.
❸ 'I wish ~' 가정법 과거로 현재 사실과 반대되는 바람이나 소원을 말할 때 쓰는 표현이며 '~라면 좋을 텐데' 정도의 뜻이다. 'I'm sorry I can't dance like you.'로 바꿔 쓸 수 있다.

Listen & Speak 2 A-2

B: Hello, everyone! Time flies. I can't believe it's time ❶to say goodbye. ❷Thanks to my teachers and friends, I was really happy here. ❸I wish I could go back to my first year and live these years over again, but it's time ❹to start a new journey to high school. I hope I can see you again. Thank you.

❶ time을 수식하는 형용사적 용법의 부정사이다.
❷ thanks to: ~ 덕분에
❸ 'I wish ~' 가정법 과거로 'I'm sorry I can't go back to ~.'로 바꿔 쓸 수 있다.
❹ time을 수식하는 형용사적 용법의 부정사이다.

Communicate A

Anna: What's wrong? You don't ❶look so good.

Suho: I'm still thinking about our soccer match last week.

Anna: ❷Do you mean the game you lost last week?

Suho: Yes. ❸I wish I could forget about it, but I can't.

Anna: Well, you should always live for today.

Suho: Do you mean I should forget the past and ❹focus on the present?

Anna: Yes, exactly. People say, "Yesterday is history, tomorrow is a mystery, and today is a gift. ❺That's why it's called the present."

Suho: Now I see. You know so many great expressions. You're ❻as wise as my grandma.

❶ look+형용사: ~하게 보이다
❷ 'Do you mean ~?'은 이해를 확인하기 위해 쓰는 표현이다.
❸ 'I wish ~' 가정법 과거로 'I'm sorry I can't forget about it.'으로 바꿔 쓸 수 있다.
❹ focus on: ~에 집중하다
❺ That's why ~: 그것이 ~한 이유이다.
❻ 'as ~ as'는 동등 비교를 나타내는 표현이다.

Progress Check 1

G: You look worried. ❶Is something wrong?

B: I had to hand in my science report by yesterday, but I didn't.

G: It's better late than never.

B: ❷Do you mean it's better to ❸hand it in even though it's late?

G: Yes, exactly. You should always finish ❹what you've started.

❶ 'thing'으로 끝나는 부정대명사는 형용사가 뒤에서 수식한다.
❷ 'Do you mean ~?'은 이해를 확인하기 위해 쓰는 표현이다.
❸ '타동사+부사'로 이루어진 구동사의 경우 목적어가 인칭대명사이면 반드시 '타동사+대명사 목적어+부사'의 순서로 쓴다.
❹ what은 선행사를 포함하는 관계대명사이다.

Progress Check 2

B: Wow, you play the guitar so well.

G: Thanks. I love playing the guitar. I learned ❶it from my dad.

B: Really? Does your father play the guitar, too?

G: Yes. He was in a famous band.

B: ❷What a family! I wish I could play the guitar like you.

❶ it은 'playing the guitar'를 가리킨다.
❷ 감탄문으로 '굉장한 가족이다!' 정도의 뜻이다.

Progress Check 3

M: You broke your friend's phone, and you don't know ❶what to do. Another friend says to you, "Honesty is the best policy." You don't know ❷what that means exactly.

❶ 'what to do'는 '의문사+to부정사'로 know의 목적어 역할을 하고 있다.
❷ 'what that means exactly'는 간접의문문으로 know의 목적어로 쓰이고 있다.

● 다음 우리말과 일치하도록 빈칸에 알맞은 말을 쓰시오.

Listen & Speak 1 A-1

G: You _____ _____ this morning.

B: I got up very early _____ _____ for the exam.

G: _____ _____ you. The early bird catches the worm.

B: No. The early bird _____ _____ quickly.

G: _____ _____ _____ you don't like to get up early?

B: Yes, that's exactly _____ _____ _____.

Listen & Speak 1 A-2

G: I _____ _____ sing at the school's English pop song contest.

B: Wow. Break _____ _____!

G: What? _____ _____ _____ I have to break _____ of my _____?

B: No, it's an expression _____ I hope _____ _____ _____.

Listen & Speak 2 A-1

B: Wow, you really dance well.

G: Thanks. I love dancing. Everyone in my family _____ _____ _____ dancing.

B: Really? Your parents dance well, _____?

G: Yes. They're also _____ _____.

B: _____ _____ family! _____ _____ _____ _____ _____ dance like you.

Listen & Speak 2 A-2

B: Hello, everyone! Time flies. I _____ _____ it's time _____ _____ goodbye. _____ _____ my teachers and friends, I was really happy here. _____ _____ _____ _____ go back to my first year and live these years over again, but it's time _____ _____ a new journey to high school. I hope I can see you again. Thank you.

해석

G: 오늘 아침 너 피곤해 보인다.
B: 시험 공부를 하려고 아주 일찍 일어났거든.
G: 잘했어. 일찍 일어나는 새가 벌레를 잡는 법이지.
B: 아니. 일찍 일어나는 새가 빨리 지쳐.
G: 일찍 일어나는 게 싫다는 말이야?
B: 응, 정확히 그런 뜻이야.

G: 나는 학교의 영어 팝송 부르기 대회에서 노래를 해야 해.
B: 우와. 행운을 빌어!
G: 뭐? 내가 내 다리 한 쪽을 부러뜨려야 한다는 말이야?
B: 아니, 네가 잘하길 빈다는 뜻의 표현이야.

B: 우와, 너 춤 정말 잘 춘다.
G: 고마워. 나 춤추는 거 정말 좋아해. 우리 가족 모두가 춤을 잘 춰.
B: 정말? 너희 부모님도 춤을 잘 추시니?
G: 맞아. 노래도 잘하셔.
B: 굉장한 가족이다! 나도 너처럼 춤을 출 수 있으면 좋겠어.

B: 안녕, 모두들! 시간이 참 빠르네요. 이제 작별 인사를 해야 할 시간이라는 게 믿어지지 않아요. 선생님들과 친구들 덕분에, 이곳에서 정말 행복했어요. 첫 해로 돌아가서 이 해들을 다시 지낼 수 있다면 좋겠지만, 이제는 고등학교로 새로운 여행을 떠나야 할 시간이에요. 여러분을 다시 볼 수 있다면 좋겠어요. 고맙습니다.

Communicate A

Anna: What's wrong? You don't _____ so _____.

Suho: I'm still thinking about our soccer match last week.

Anna: _____ _____ _____ the game you lost last week?

Suho: Yes. _____ _____ _____ _____ forget about it, but I can't.

Anna: Well, you should always _____ _____ _____.

Suho: _____ _____ _____ I should forget the past and _____ _____ the present?

Anna: Yes, exactly. People say, "Yesterday is history, tomorrow is a mystery, and today is a gift. That's _____ it's _____ the present."

Suho: Now I see. You know so many great expressions. You're _____ _____ _____ my grandma.

Progress Check 1

G: You _____ _____. Is something _____?

B: I had to _____ _____ my science report by yesterday, but I didn't.

G: It's _____ _____ _____ _____.

B: _____ _____ _____ it's better to _____ _____ _____ even though it's late?

G: Yes, exactly. You should always finish _____ you've started.

Progress Check 2

B: Wow, you _____ _____ _____ so well.

G: Thanks. I love playing the guitar. I learned _____ from my dad.

B: Really? Does your father play the guitar, _____?

G: Yes. He was _____ a famous band.

B: _____ _____ family! _____ _____ _____ I _____ play the guitar like you.

Progress Check 3

M: You broke your friend's phone, and you don't know _____ _____ _____. _____ friend says to you, "Honesty is the best policy." You don't know _____ _____ _____ exactly.

해석

Anna: 무슨 일 있니? 별로 좋아 보이질 않네.

수호: 지난주 우리의 축구 시합을 여전히 생각하고 있어.

Anna: 지난주에 진 게임 말이니?

수호: 응. 그걸 잊을 수 있음 좋겠는데, 못하겠네.

Anna: 음, 넌 항상 오늘을 살아야 해.

수호: 과거는 잊고 현재에 집중해야 한다는 뜻이니?

Anna: 그래, 바로 그거야. 사람들이 "어제는 역사, 내일은 미스터리, 그리고 오늘은 선물이다. 그게 바로 오늘을 선물이라 부르는 이유."라고 하잖아.

수호: 그렇구나. 넌 정말 좋은 표현들을 많이 알고 있구나. 넌 우리 할머니만큼 현명해.

G: 걱정이 있는 것 같아 보인다. 무슨 문제 있니?

B: 어제까지 과학 보고서를 냈어야 했는데, 내지 않았어.

G: 늦더라도 안 하는 것보다는 낫지.

B: 늦었더라도 내는 게 낫다는 뜻이야?

G: 맞아, 정확해. 언제나 시작을 했으면 끝을 봐야지.

B: 우와, 너 기타 정말 잘 친다.

G: 고마워. 나 기타 치는 거 정말 좋아해. 아버지께 배웠어.

B: 정말? 너희 아버지도 기타를 치시니?

G: 응. 유명한 밴드에 계셨어.

B: 굉장한 가족이다! 나도 너처럼 기타를 칠 수 있다면 좋겠어.

M: 여러분은 친구의 휴대전화를 부수었고, 어떻게 해야 할지 모릅니다. 다른 친구가 여러분에게, "정직이 최선의 방책이야."라고 말합니다. 여러분은 그것이 정확히 무슨 뜻인지 모릅니다.

Conversation 시험대비 기본평가

01 다음 빈칸 (A)에 알맞은 문장을 고르시오.

> G: You look tired this morning.
> B: I got up very early to study for the exam.
> G: Good for you. The early bird catches the worm.
> B: No. The early bird gets tired quickly.
> G: Do you mean you don't like to get up early?
> B: _____ (A) _____

① Yes, I wish I could get up early.
② Yes, that's exactly what I mean.
③ No, I think I'm not satisfied with getting up early.
④ No, I think it's a little boring.
⑤ No, I mean I'm lazy.

02 밑줄 친 우리말을 주어진 단어를 이용하여 영작하시오.

> G: I have to sing at the school's English pop song contest.
> B: Wow. Break a leg!
> G: What? 내가 내 다리 한 쪽을 부러뜨려야 한다는 말이야?
>   (mean, break, one, leg, 11 단어)
> B: No, it's an expression meaning I hope you do well.

➡ _____

03 주어진 문장 다음의 대화가 자연스럽게 연결되도록 (A)~(D)를 순서대로 적절하게 배열하시오.

> G: You look worried. Is something wrong?
> (A) Yes, exactly. You should always finish what you've started.
> (B) It's better late than never.
> (C) I had to hand in my science report by yesterday, but I didn't.
> (D) Do you mean it's better to hand it in even though it's late?

➡ _____

01 다음 중 짝지어진 대화가 <u>어색한</u> 것은?

① A: Wow, you really dance well.

B: Thanks. I love dancing. Everyone in my family is good at dancing.

② A: I'm still thinking about our soccer match last week.

B: Do you mean the game you lost last week?

③ A: Do you mean I have to break one of my legs?

B: Break a leg!

④ A: I love playing the guitar. I learned it from my dad.

B: Really? Does your father play the guitar, too?

⑤ A: Your parents dance well, too?

B: Yes. They're also good singers.

A: What a family! I wish I could dance like you.

[02~04] 다음 대화를 읽고 물음에 답하시오.

G: I have to sing at the school's English pop song contest.

B: Wow. ____(A)____

G: What? (a)You're saying I have to break one of my legs?

B: No, it's an expression ____(B)____ I hope you do well.

02 빈칸 (A)에 알맞은 말을 고르시오.

① Break a leg!

② Great English pop song contest.

③ What a nice school!

④ Good job.

⑤ Congratulations!

03 위 대화의 빈칸 (B)에 들어갈 말로 알맞은 것을 고르시오.

① mean ② means ③ meant

④ to mean ⑤ meaning

서답형

04 위 대화의 밑줄 친 (a)와 같은 의미가 되도록 'mean'을 이용하여 다시 쓰시오.

➡ _____

[05~07] 다음 글을 읽고 물음에 답하시오.

B: Hello, everyone! (a)시간이 참 빠르네요. (①) Thanks to my teachers and friends, I was really happy here. (②) I wish ____(A)____ my first year and live these years over again, but it's time to start a new journey to high school. (③) I hope I can see you again. (④) Thank you. (⑤)

05 위 글의 빈칸 (A)에 들어갈 말로 알맞은 것은?

① I hope to go back to

② I can go back to

③ I can't go back to

④ I couldn't go back to

⑤ I could go back to

06 위 글의 (①)~(⑤) 중에서 주어진 문장이 들어가기에 적절한 곳은?

I can't believe it's time to say goodbye.

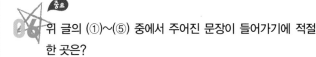

① ② ③ ④ ⑤

서답형

07 밑줄 친 (a)의 우리말에 맞게 두 단어로 영작하시오.

➡ _____

중요

08 다음 대화의 밑줄 친 부분의 의도로 알맞은 것은?

> G: You look worried. Is something wrong?
> B: I had to hand in my science report by yesterday, but I didn't.
> G: It's better late than never.
> B: <u>Do you mean it's better to hand it in even though it's late?</u>
> G: Yes, exactly. You should always finish what you've started.

① 불만 묻기　　② 희망 묻기
③ 이해 확인하기　　④ 경험 묻기
⑤ 바람·소원 표현하기

서답형

09 주어진 문장 사이의 대화가 자연스럽게 연결되도록 (A)~(D)를 순서대로 적절하게 배열하시오.

> G: You look tired this morning.

> (A) No. The early bird gets tired quickly.
> (B) I got up very early to study for the exam.
> (C) Good for you. The early bird catches the worm.
> (D) Do you mean you don't like to get up early?

> B: Yes, that's exactly what I mean.

➡ _____

[10~12] 다음 대화를 읽고 물음에 답하시오.

> Anna: What's wrong? You don't look so good.
> Suho: I'm still thinking about our soccer match last week.
> Anna: Do you mean the game you lost last week?
> Suho: Yes. I wish I could forget about it, but I can't.
> Anna: Well, you should always live for today.
> Suho: _____(A)_____ the past and focus on the present?
> Anna: Yes, exactly. People say, "Yesterday is history, tomorrow is a mystery, and today is a gift. That's ___(B)___ it's called the present."
> Suho: Now I see. You know so many great expressions. You're as wise as my grandma.

10 위 대화의 빈칸 (A)에 알맞은 말은?

① Do you think I already forgot
② Do you want me to remember
③ Do you mean I should forget
④ Do you know why I should forget
⑤ Do you think I'd better remember

서답형

11 위 대화의 빈칸 (B)에 알맞은 말을 한 단어로 쓰시오.

➡ _____

중요

12 위 대화를 읽고 대답할 수 <u>없는</u> 것은?

① Why doesn't Suho look so good?
② Is Suho still thinking about his soccer match last week?
③ What does Suho wish?
④ Why does Anna live for today?
⑤ Does Anna know so many great expressions?

[01~03] 다음 대화를 읽고 물음에 답하시오.

Anna: What's wrong? You don't look so good.

Suho: I'm still thinking about our soccer match last week.

Anna: Do you mean the game you lost last week?

Suho: Yes. _____(A)_____ but I can't.

Anna: Well, you should always live for today.

Suho: Do you mean I should forget the past and focus on the present?

Anna: Yes, exactly. People say, "Yesterday is history, tomorrow is a mystery, and today is a gift. That's why it's called the present."

Suho: Now I see. You know so many great expressions. (a)넌 우리 할머니만큼 현명해. (wise, my grandma.)

01 위 대화의 빈칸 (A)에 'I'm sorry I can't forget about it.'의 뜻을 갖는 문장을 wish를 포함하는 가정법으로 쓰시오.

➡ _____

02 괄호 안에 주어진 어휘를 이용하여 밑줄 친 우리말 (a)에 맞게 6 단어로 쓰시오.

➡ _____

03 Why is today called the present? Use the word 'because'.

➡ _____
_____

[04~05] 다음 대화를 읽고 물음에 답하시오.

B: Wow, you play the guitar so well.

G: Thanks. I love playing the guitar. I learned it from my dad.

B: Really? Does your father play the guitar, too? _____(A)_____

G: Yes. He was in a famous band.

B: What a family!

04 위 대화의 빈칸 (A)에 '기타를 칠 수 있기를 바라는' 말을 7 단어로 쓰시오.

➡ _____

05 From whom did the girl learn how to play the guitar?

➡ _____

06 다음 대화에서 어법상 어색한 것을 찾아 바르게 고치시오. (2개)

G: You look worried. Is something wrong?

B: I had to hand in my science report by yesterday, but I didn't.

G: It's better late than never.

B: Do you mean it's better to hand in it even though it's late?

G: Yes, exactly. You should always finish that you've started.

(1) _____ ➡ _____

(2) _____ ➡ _____

Grammar

1 소유격 관계대명사 whose

- Among them was a man **whose** name was Raja Birbal.
  그들 중에는 Raja Birbal이라는 이름의 한 남자가 있었다.

- Birbal came back with two pots **whose** necks were really narrow.
  Birbal은 목이 매우 좁은 항아리 두 개를 가지고 돌아왔다.

■ 관계대명사의 소유격은 선행사가 그 뒤에 나오는 문장에서 소유격 형태로 등장할 때, 두 문장을 하나로 이어 주어 '접속사'와 '대명사의 소유격'의 역할을 한다.

- I know a man. **His** daughter is an artist.
  = I know a man **and his** daughter is an artist.
  = I know a man **whose** daughter is an artist. 나는 딸이 화가인 한 남자를 안다.
- This is the house. **Its** roof is painted sky blue.
  = This is the house **whose** roof is painted sky blue. 이게 지붕 색이 스카이블루인 집이다.

■ 소유격을 대신하기 때문에 whose 뒤에 명사가 오고, 구조는 완전한 문장처럼 보인다. 그렇지만, whose 뒤에 오는 명사가 관사가 없다는 사실을 생각하면 완전한 문장은 아니다.

- The lawyer met a lady. **Her** son stole a car.
  = The lawyer met a lady **whose** <u>son</u> <u>stole</u> <u>a car</u>. 그 변호사는 아들이 차를 훔친 숙녀를 만났다.
                                     주어 동사 목적어

■ 관계대명사의 소유격은 선행사에 상관없이 whose를 쓸 수 있으나, 선행사가 사물일 경우에는 of which 로 바꿔 쓸 수 있다. (of which가 받는 명사 앞에는 정관사 the를 써야 하고, 선행사가 사람일 경우에는 of which를 쓸 수 없다.)

- They want to buy <u>the cars</u>. **Their** <u>engines</u> are in good condition.
  = They want to buy <u>the cars</u> **and their** <u>engines</u> are in good condition.
  = They want to buy <u>the cars</u> **whose** <u>engines</u> are in good condition.
  = They want to buy <u>the cars</u> **of which** <u>the engines</u> are in good condition.
  = They want to buy <u>the cars</u> <u>the engines</u> **of which** are in good condition.

핵심 Check

1. 괄호 안에서 알맞은 말을 고르시오.

   (1) Minju has a friend (whose / whom) mom is Vietnamese.

   (2) This is the house (which / of which) the door is painted black.

② **가정법 과거: 'If+주어+동사의 과거형 ~, 주어+would/could+동사원형 …'**

> • If I **were** you, I **would give** him sweets. 내가 당신이라면 그에게 사탕을 줄 텐데.
>
> • It **would be** great if there **were** a man as wise as Birbal in our country.
>   우리나라에도 비르발처럼 현명한 자가 있다면 정말 좋을 텐데.

■ 가정법 과거: '만약 ~라면 …할 텐데'의 뜻으로, 현재 사실을 반대로 가정하거나 실현 가능성이 없는 일에 대해서 가정할 때 쓰며, 'If+주어+동사 과거형 ~, 주어+would/could+동사원형 …'의 형태로 나타낸다.

   • If I **have** money, I **will buy** a new shirt. 내게 돈이 있다면, 새로운 셔츠를 살 것이다. (조건문, 사실)
   • If I **had** money, I **would buy** a new shirt. 내게 돈이 있다면, 새로운 셔츠를 살 텐데.(가정법 과거, 현재 사실의 반대 가정)
     = As I don't have money, I won't buy a new shirt. 내게 돈이 없기 때문에, 나는 새로운 셔츠를 사지 않을 것이다.
   • If she **were** my teacher, I **would follow** her. 그녀가 나의 선생님이라면, 그녀를 따라갈 텐데.

■ 'I wish' 가정법은 현재 사실에 반대되는 소망을 나타낸다.
   • I wish I **were** as wise as Birbal. 나도 Birbal만큼 지혜롭다면 좋을 텐데
     = In fact, I'm not as wise as Birbal.

■ 가정법 과거완료는 이미 일어난 과거 사실을 반대로 가정하는데 사용하며, 'If+주어+had+과거분사 ~, 주어+would/could+have+과거분사 …'의 형태로 나타낸다.
   • If the companies **had accepted** my suggestion, they **would** not **have failed**.
     그 기업들이 내 제안을 받아들였더라면, 그들은 망하지 않았을 텐데.

■ 가정법의 다양한 표현들로 직설법의 의미를 나타낼 수 있다.
   • As he is short, he cannot touch the ceiling. 그는 작기 때문에, 천장에 손이 닿을 수 없다. (직설법)
     → If he **were** not short, he **could touch** the ceiling. 그가 작지 않으면, 천장에 손이 닿을 수 있을 텐데. (가정법)
     → **Were** he not short, he **could touch** the ceiling. (If를 생략, 도치)

■ 다음은 주의할 가정법의 표현들이다.
   • If it **were not for** the sun, we **could** not **live** at all. 태양이 없다면 우리는 전혀 살 수 없을 텐데.
     → **Without** the sun, we **could** not **live** at all. (without 표현)
     → **Were it not for** the sun, we **could** not **live** at all. (If 생략, 도치)

핵심 Check

2. 다음 우리말에 맞게 괄호 안의 단어를 바르게 배열하시오.

   (1) 내가 개라면, 하루 종일 잘 텐데. (a dog, sleep, long, if, would, all day, I, I, were)

   ➡ _____

   (2) 그녀가 뉴욕에 산다면, 햄버거만 먹을 텐데. (lived, would, hamburgers, only, eat, in, if, she, she, New York)

   ➡ _____

Grammar 시험대비 기본평가

01 다음 밑줄 친 부분 중 어법상 바르지 <u>않은</u> 것은?

① I have a friend <u>whose</u> puppy is all black.

② We saw the house <u>whose</u> roof was covered with grass.

③ Sarah went to the cinema <u>whose</u> the movie was playing.

④ Thomas met a girl <u>whose</u> father was a police officer.

⑤ We needed a table <u>whose</u> legs are a bit long.

02 다음 각 가정법 문장에서 어법상 <u>어색한</u> 단어를 한 개씩만 찾아 고치시오.

(1) If it is not raining, Susan would walk her dog.

_____ ➡ _____

(2) If I finished homework, I will go to the playground.

_____ ➡ _____

(3) If Andy has much money, he would buy a new car.

_____ ➡ _____

(4) I will go to the future if I had a time machine.

_____ ➡ _____

03 다음 두 문장을 관계대명사를 이용하여 하나의 문장으로 만드시오.

Cathy heard of a man. His wife wrote novels.

➡ _____

04 다음 빈칸에 들어갈 말로 알맞은 것은?

If Minju _____ his number, she would make a phone call to him.

① know   ② knows   ③ has known

④ knew   ⑤ had known

01 다음 문장의 밑줄 친 단어들 중 어법상 어색한 단어는?

> A lady ①of which hair ②was blond ③ was waiting for you at the cafe ④whose view ⑤was good.

①   ②   ③   ④   ⑤

02 다음 중 어법상 어색한 문장은?

① If he were a good pitcher, we would win this game.

② If I knew the correct answer, I would tell him immediately.

③ If it were not for your help, we would not be able to fix our bikes.

④ If I were in Tokyo, I wouldn't be sure I would be OK from the disease.

⑤ If my father were super rich, he'll buy me any car I wanted.

서답형

[03~06] 다음 우리말과 일치하도록 괄호 안에 주어진 단어들을 바르게 배열하시오.

03

> Oliver는 색이 빨간 자전거를 갖고 있다.
> (a bike, is, Oliver, red, whose, has, color)

➡ _____

04

> 내가 그녀라면, 포기하지 않을 텐데.
> (give up, she, I, I, not, if, would, were)

➡ _____

05

> 나는 Bob처럼 그림을 잘 그리고 싶다.
> (wish, could, Bob, like, draw, I, I, well)

➡ _____

06

> 그들은 풍경이 아름다운 집을 구입할 것이다.
> (the scenery, buy, a house, are, they, of which, beautiful, going, is, to)

➡ _____
_____

07 다음 중 빈칸 ⓐ~ⓕ에 같은 단어가 들어가는 것끼리 바르게 짝지어진 것은?

> • The team rescued a boy ⓐ_____ boat was hit by a big wave.
> • Birbal brought two pots ⓑ_____ the necks were really narrow.
> • They gave the prize to the singer ⓒ_____ performance was very excellent.
> • They were looking for the house ⓓ_____ the rooms were wide enough to raise cats.
> • My mother worked at a company ⓔ_____ goal was to contribute to the society.
> • This was the park ⓕ_____ the girl lost her watch.

① ⓐ, ⓒ, ⓓ   ② ⓐ, ⓒ, ⓔ

③ ⓒ, ⓔ, ⓕ   ④ ⓒ, ⓓ, ⓕ

⑤ ⓑ, ⓓ, ⓔ

[08~09] 다음 중 밑줄 친 부분의 쓰임이 나머지와 다른 것은?

08 ① I wish I <u>could</u> speak Chinese.

② If she got good grades, she <u>could</u> go to the amusement park.

③ If he were rich, he <u>could</u> buy me the luxury car.

④ I <u>could</u> not help laughing at him yesterday evening.

⑤ If I had a passport, I <u>could</u> go to L.A. to watch the game.

09 ① Do you like the cat <u>whose</u> hair is short?

② Shanon is the girl <u>whose</u> singing skill is at the highest level.

③ Do you remember the politician <u>whose</u> speech was so impressive?

④ We wondered <u>whose</u> book the thief stole.

⑤ I can't eat the pizza <u>whose</u> taste changed.

10 다음 중 같은 뜻을 가진 문장끼리 짝지어진 것은?

① My mom can't write a letter to my brother as she doesn't know his address.

= My mom couldn't write a letter to my brother if she didn't know his address.

② It rained, so we stayed home.

= If it rained, we wouldn't stay home.

③ Bobby doesn't work hard, so he can't make enough money he wants.

= If Bobby worked hard, he could make enough money he wants.

④ Tom didn't have a car, so he wouldn't drive.

= If Tom had a car, he would drive.

⑤ My uncle doesn't have a smartphone, so he wants to get one.

= My uncle would get a smartphone if he wanted to have one.

11 다음 중 어법상 옳은 문장은?

① Amy has a book of which cover is torn away.

② Mr. Parker invited me to the event whose organizer is unknown.

③ Laura is a good mom whose the kids respect her.

④ The young man of which the name is Peter came to see you.

⑤ The fish swam to the pond water of which is very dirty.

12 다음 중 어법상 어색한 것은?

① If I could be awarded the prize, my kids would be proud of me.

② If Mike had put on the glasses, he would have noticed her.

③ If Sujin got up earlier this morning, she wouldn't be late for school.

④ If Angelina missed the bus, she would not have been late for school.

⑤ If the girls told the truth to her, she would be surprised at what he did for her.

다음 짝지어진 두 문장의 의미가 같지 <u>않은</u> 것은?

① If Paul didn't run fast, he couldn't catch the first train.

= As Paul runs fast, he can catch the first train.

② If David told lies more often, I would not believe him.

= As David doesn't tell lies more often, I believe him.

③ I wish Kelly were a great singer.

= I'm sorry that she was not a great singer.

④ If my friends studied harder, they could get good grades.

= As my friends don't study harder, they can't get good grades.

⑤ I wish I could play the drums.

= I am sorry that I can't play the drums.

[14~15] 다음 주어진 두 문장을 관계대명사를 사용해서 하나의 문장으로 바르게 고친 것을 고르시오.

14

• The boy seemed to be embarrassed.
• His guitar was broken.

① The boy the guitar of which was broken seemed to be embarrassed.

② The boy whose the guitar was broken seemed to be embarrassed.

③ The boy who the guitar of his was broken seemed to be embarrassed.

④ The boy whose guitar was broken seemed to be embarrassed.

⑤ The boy whom the guitar was broken seemed to be embarrassed.

15

• More help is needed for small businesses.
• Their sales were damaged most during the crisis of Corona virus.

① More help is needed for small businesses the sales of whom were damaged most during the crisis of Corona virus.

② Small businesses whose help is needed were damaged most during the crisis of Corona virus.

③ More help is needed for small businesses of which sales were damaged most during the crisis of Corona virus.

④ Small businesses' sales were damaged most who are needed more help during the crisis of Corona virus.

⑤ More help is needed for small businesses whose sales were damaged most during the crisis of Corona virus.

 다음 우리말을 영작할 때, 어법상 옳지 <u>않은</u> 문장을 고르시오.

물이 없다면, 지구에 생명체가 살 수 없을 것이다.

① If there were no water, life on Earth would not be able to live.

② If it were not for water, life on Earth would not be able to live.

③ Were it not for water, life on Earth would not be able to live.

④ If there is no water, life on Earth would not be able to live.

⑤ Without water, life on Earth would not be able to live.

01 다음 우리말과 일치하도록 괄호 안에 주어진 단어들을 빈칸에 알맞게 배열하시오.

(1) 내가 당신이라면, 당신의 머리카락을 잡아 당긴 사람에게 사탕을 줄 것이다. (would, pulled, to, sweets, who, were, I, you, the person, give)

➡ If I _____

_____ your hair.

(2) 우리나라에도 Birbal처럼 현명한 자가 있다면 정말 좋을 텐데. (if, as, would, were, great, wise, a man, be, there)

➡ It _____

as Birbal in our country.

(3) 그는 목이 매우 좁은 항아리 두 개를 들고 돌아왔다. (necks, narrow, whose, pots, were, two, really)

➡ He came back with _____

_____.

(4) 그들 중에는 Raja Birbal이라는 이름의 한 남자가 있었다. (was, whose, was, name, them, a man)

➡ Among _____

Raja Birbal.

02 다음 〈보기〉의 문장과 같은 뜻이 되도록 괄호 안에 주어진 조건에 맞게 빈칸을 채우시오.

┌─ 보기 ├─
Without his wisdom, we could be in trouble with Persia.
└──────────

(1) _____ his wisdom, we could be in trouble with Persia. (it, be동사 활용, 5 단어)

(2) _____ his wisdom, we could be in trouble with Persia. (it, be동사 활용, 4 단어)

(3) _____ his wisdom, we could be in trouble with Persia. (2 단어)

(4) _____ not be in trouble with Persia. (직설법, there, 접속사 as 활용, 7 단어)

03 다음 주어진 문장과 뜻이 같도록 빈칸을 알맞게 채우시오. (총 5 단어)

As the lady doesn't exercise regularly, she can't stay healthy.
➡ If the lady _____

_____ healthy.

04 다음 각 문장에서 어법상 어색한 단어를 한 개씩만 찾아 모두 고치시오.

(1) Amy has a book whose the pages are missing.
(2) My uncle ordered a table legs of which are very long.
(3) I played badminton after school with a friend who name is Tom.
(4) I would give sweets to the person whose pulled your hair.
(5) There is an officer who job is to check all the baggage at the airport.
(6) Grace bought a house which the roof was covered with grass.

➡ _____

_____

_____

[05~06] 다음 그림을 보고, 우리말에 맞게 괄호 안의 단어를 배열하여 빈칸을 채우시오.

05

다리가 네 개인 귀여운 몬스터가 나를 향해 손을 흔들었다.

➡ A cute monster the _____

_____ me.

(wave, four, legs, which, at, of, are, 총 7 단어, 어형 변화 가능)

그녀의 눈이 피로해진 한 소녀가 따뜻한 천으로 마사지를 하는 중이다.

➡ A girl _____

_____ cloth.

(massage, is, with, whose, tired, warm, eyes, are, a / 총 9 단어, 어형 변화 가능)

07 다음 우리말을 괄호 안에 주어진 단어들을 사용하여 영작하시오. (필요시 단어를 추가할 수 있으나, 변형은 하지 말 것.)

(1) 나는 어머니가 매우 유명한 마술사인 친구가 있다. (magician, very, a friend, have, whose)

➡ _____

(2) 이것은 표지가 흑백인 잡지이다. (which, black and white, magazine, cover of)

➡ _____

(3) 내 남동생은 그의 영화를 당신이 본 배우이다. (an actor, film, watched, whose, little brother)

➡ _____

_____

08 다음 각 가정법 문장에서 어법상 어색한 부분을 모두 찾아 바르게 고치시오.

(1) If I am the boss of the company, I would give every employee one month holidays.
(2) I wish I am as wise as Birbal.
(3) If you are in my situation, you would understand the decision.
(4) If I had a car, I can visit my aunt in Incheon more often.
(5) If it were not for the effort of the medical staff, we will not survive the disease.
(6) If there were no tests at school, I will be happy.
(7) Mary wouldn't be late for the meeting yesterday if she had not missed the bus.

➡ _____

_____

_____

Reading

교과서

Tales of Birbal

Akbar, the third Mogul emperor, had a number of wise officials at his
court. Among them was a man whose name was Raja Birbal. He was
= many. a lot of. lots of
Among them이 문두로 도치된 구문   소유격 관계대명사
famous for his quick wit and was very wise with his words. Thus, the
접속부사(앞 문장과 인과 관계를 나타냄.)
emperor always liked to have Birbal near him.

Sweet Punishment

To test his officials' wisdom, Akbar often asked them strange
부사적 용법(목적)   간접목적어 직접목적어
questions. One day, he came up with an interesting question.

Akbar: Someone pulled a hair from my head today. What should I do to him?

Official 1: He should be punished, of course.
'조동사+be+p.p.' 형태의 수동태
Official 2: Yes, punish him!

Akbar turned to Birbal.

Akbar: What would you do if you were in my place, Birbal?
가정법 과거(If+주어+동사의 과거형, 주어+조동사의 과거형+동사원형): 현재 사실과 반대되는 말을 가정
Birbal: If I were you, I would give him sweets.

Official 3: What's he talking about?

Official 4: Birbal's crazy!

Akbar: What made you say so?
= Why did you say so?
Birbal: The person who pulled your hair must be your grandson. No one
주격 관계대명사   강한 추측: ~임에 틀림없다. 틀림없이 ~일 것이다
else could do such a thing.

Akbar: You are indeed correct, Birbal. I'm so glad to have someone as
부사적 용법(감정의 원인)
wise as you near me.
동등 비교(as+형용사·부사의 원형+as): ~만큼 …한

emperor 황제	
a number of 많은	
wise 지혜로운, 현명한, 슬기로운	
official 고위 공무원, 관리	
court 대궐, 궁궐	
among ~ 중에, ~의 사이에	
wit 기지, 재치	
wisdom 지혜, 슬기, 현명함	
strange 이상한	
come up with 찾아내다, 떠올리다	
pull 끌다, 당기다, 끌어당기다	
punish 처벌하다, 벌주다	

확인문제

● 다음 문장이 본문의 내용과 일치하면 T, 일치하지 <u>않으면</u> F를 쓰시오.

1 Birbal was the third Mogul emperor. ☐

2 Akbar often asked his officials strange questions. ☐

3 Birbal thought that the officials were crazy. ☐

4 Akbar was glad to have Birbal near him. ☐

A Potful of Wisdom

One day, the king of Persia sent an official with a strange favor.

Persian Official: I hear you have a lot of wise men in your country. I've been asked by my king to bring him a potful of wisdom. _{현재완료 수동태}

Official 5: That makes no sense! How can we put wisdom in a pot?

Akbar: Can you bring him a potful of wisdom, Birbal?

Birbal: It won't be a problem.

Birbal: Could you please wait a few weeks?

Persian Official: Of course! Take as much time as you need. _{동등 비교}

A few weeks later, Birbal came back with two pots whose necks were really narrow. He offered one to the Persian official. _{a few+복수 명사} _{소유격 관계대명사}

Birbal: You can take this pot of wisdom to your king. Please ask him to return the pot to us after he takes the wisdom out of it.

Birbal: The pot is very precious, so please be careful not to break it. We only have two pots of wisdom.

The Persian official looked inside the pot and became speechless.

He thanked Birbal and left for his country.

Persian Official: It would be great if there were a man as wise as Birbal in our country. _{가정법 과거} _{동등 비교}

After the Persian official left, Akbar asked Birbal what was inside the pot. _{간접의문문(의문사+주어+동사)}

Birbal: Here is the other pot. You can see for yourself. _{두 개 중에서 나머지 하나를 지칭} _{직접 보다}

Akbar looked inside the other pot and found a pumpkin just as big as the pot.

Akbar: I see! The pumpkin can't be taken out without breaking the pot. How did you do it?

Birbal: I put the pots over pumpkin flowers and waited until the pumpkins grew as big as the pots. _{꼭 항아리만큼 큰 호박을 항아리 안에 넣은 것을 말함}

Akbar: Hahaha! This certainly is a potful of wisdom! _{동등 비교}

a potful of 한 냄비만큼의, 한 항아리만큼의
favor 청, 부탁
make sense 타당하다, 말이 되다
narrow 좁은
offer 내놓다, 제공하다
precious 귀중한, 값비싼
speechless (화나거나 놀라서) 말을 못하는
the other (둘 중) 다른 하나의
pumpkin 호박
without+동사-ing ~하지 않고
over (다른 사람·사물이 덮이도록) ~ 위에
certainly 틀림없이, 분명히

 확인문제

● 다음 문장이 본문의 내용과 일치하면 T, 일치하지 않으면 F를 쓰시오.

1 A Persian Official was asked to bring his king a potful of wisdom. ☐

2 The Persian official looked at Birbal and became speechless. ☐

3 The pumpkin could be taken out without breaking the pot. ☐

● 우리말을 참고하여 빈칸에 알맞은 말을 쓰시오.

1 _____ of Birbal

2 Akbar, the third Mogul emperor, had _____ _____ _____ wise officials at his _____.

3 Among them _____ a man _____ _____ was Raja Birbal.

4 He was famous _____ his quick wit and was very wise _____ his words.

5 _____, the emperor always liked _____ _____ Birbal _____ him.

6 Sweet _____

7 _____ _____ his officials' wisdom, Akbar often _____ _____ _____ _____.

8 One day, he _____ _____ _____ an interesting question.

9 Akbar: Someone pulled _____ _____ from my head today. What _____ _____ _____ _____ him?

10 Official 1: He should _____ _____, of course.

11 Official 2: Yes, _____ him!

12 Akbar _____ _____ Birbal.

13 Akbar: What _____ you _____ _____ you _____ _____ _____, Birbal?

14 Birbal: _____ I _____ _____, I _____ _____ him sweets.

15 Official 3: What's he _____ _____?

16 Official 4: Birbal's _____!

17 Akbar: _____ _____ _____ say so?

18 Birbal: The person _____ pulled your hair _____ _____ your grandson. No one _____ could do _____ _____ _____.

19 Akbar: You are indeed correct, Birbal. I'm _____ glad _____ _____ someone _____ _____ you near me.

1 비르발 이야기

2 악바르는 무굴 제국의 제3대 황제로, 자신의 궁정에 많은 현명한 신하들이 있었다.

3 그 중 라자 비르발이라는 이름의 한 사람이 있었다.

4 그는 재빠른 재치로 유명했으며 말이 매우 지혜로웠다.

5 그래서, 황제는 언제나 비르발을 곁에 두기를 원했다.

6 달콤한 처벌

7 신하들의 지혜를 시험해 보기 위해, 악바르는 종종 그들에게 이상한 질문을 했다.

8 어느 날, 황제는 재미있는 질문이 생각났다.

9 악바르: 오늘 어떤 이가 내 머리에서 머리카락을 잡아당겼소. 이 자에게 무엇을 해야 하겠소?

10 신하 1: 당연히 처벌해야 합니다.

11 신하 2: 예, 그를 처벌하소서!

12 악바르가 비르발에게 돌아섰다.

13 악바르: 그대가 내 입장이라면 무엇을 하겠소, 비르발?

14 비르발: 소신이 폐하라면, 그에게 사탕을 주겠습니다.

15 신하 3: 저 사람은 무슨 말을 하는 건가?

16 신하 4: 비르발이 정신이 나갔어!

17 악바르: 왜 그렇게 말했소?

18 비르발: 폐하의 머리카락을 잡아당긴 사람은 폐하의 손자임이 분명합니다. 다른 그 누구도 그런 짓을 할 수 없지요.

19 악바르: 과연 그대의 말이 맞소, 비르발. 그대처럼 현명한 자를 옆에 두어 정말 기쁘오.

20 A _____ of _____

21 One day, the king of Persia sent an official _____ _____ _____ _____ .

22 Persian Official: I hear you have _____ _____ wise men in your country. _____ _____ by my king _____ _____ him _____ wisdom.

23 Official 5: That _____ _____ _____ ! How can we _____ wisdom _____ a pot?

24 Akbar: Can you bring him _____ _____ _____ wisdom, Birbal?

25 Birbal: It _____ _____ a problem.

26 Birbal: Could you please wait _____ _____ weeks?

27 Persian Official: Of course! Take _____ _____ you need.

28 _____ _____ weeks later, Birbal came back with two pots _____ necks were really narrow. He offered _____ to the Persian official.

29 Birbal: You can _____ this pot of wisdom to your king. Please ask him _____ _____ the pot to us after he takes the wisdom _____ _____ _____ .

30 Birbal: The pot is very precious, so please be careful _____ _____ _____ it. We only have two pots of wisdom.

31 The Persian official looked inside the pot and became _____ .

32 He thanked Birbal and _____ _____ his country.

33 Persian Official: It _____ _____ great _____ _____ a man _____ _____ _____ Birbal in our country.

34 After the Persian official left, Akbar asked Birbal _____ _____ inside the pot.

35 Birbal: Here is _____ _____ pot. You can see _____ _____ .

36 Akbar looked inside _____ _____ pot and found a pumpkin just _____ _____ _____ the pot.

37 Akbar: I see! The pumpkin _____ _____ _____ out _____ _____ the pot. How did you do it?

38 Birbal: I put the pots _____ pumpkin flowers and waited until the pumpkins grew _____ _____ _____ the pots.

39 Akbar: Hahaha! This certainly is _____ _____ _____ wisdom!

20 한 항아리만큼의 지혜

21 어느 날, 페르시아의 왕이 이상한 요청과 함께 신하를 보냈다.

22 페르시아의 신하: 폐하의 나라에 현명한 자들이 많다고 들었습니다. 저는 저의 왕으로부터 한 항아리의 지혜를 왕께 가지고 오라는 명을 받았습니다.

23 신하 5: 저건 말이 안 되오! 어떻게 지혜를 항아리에 넣을 수 있단 말이오?

24 악바르: 그에게 지혜 한 항아리를 가져다줄 수 있겠소, 비르발?

25 비르발: 문제될 것이 없사옵니다.

26 비르발: 몇 주만 기다려 주시겠습니까?

27 페르시아의 신하: 물론이오! 필요한 만큼 얼마든지 시간을 가지시오.

28 몇 주 후, 비르발은 목이 매우 좁은 두 항아리를 들고 돌아왔다. 그는 하나를 페르시아의 신하에게 줬다.

29 비르발: 이 지혜의 항아리를 그대의 왕께 가져다 드리십시오. 왕께서 이 항아리에서 지혜를 꺼내신 후에는 항아리를 우리에게 돌려달라 전해 주십시오.

30 비르발: 그 항아리는 매우 귀중한 것이니, 그것을 깨지 않도록 조심해 주십시오. 우리는 오직 두 개의 지혜의 항아리만 갖고 있습니다.

31 페르시아 신하는 항아리 안을 들여다보곤 말을 잃었다.

32 그는 비르발에게 감사를 표한 뒤 그의 나라로 떠났다.

33 페르시아의 신하: 우리 나라에도 비르발처럼 현명한 자가 있다면 정말 좋을 텐데.

34 페르시아의 신하가 떠난 뒤, 악바르는 비르발에게 항아리 속에 무엇이 있었는지를 물었다.

35 비르발: 여기 또 다른 항아리가 있습니다. 직접 살펴보시지요.

36 악바르는 또 다른 항아리 안을 보고 꼭 항아리만큼 큰 호박을 발견했다.

37 악바르: 그렇군! 항아리를 깨지 않고는 호박을 꺼낼 수가 없구려! 어떻게 한 것이오?

38 비르발: 항아리를 호박꽃에 덮어 놓은 후 호박이 항아리만큼 클 때까지 기다렸습니다.

39 악바르: 하하하! 이건 정말로 지혜의 항아리구려!

● 우리말을 참고하여 본문을 영작하시오.

1 비르발 이야기
➡ _____

2 악바르는 무굴 제국의 제3대 황제로, 자신의 궁정에 많은 현명한 신하들이 있었다.
➡ _____

3 그 중 라자 비르발이라는 이름의 한 사람이 있었다.
➡ _____

4 그는 재빠른 재치로 유명했으며 말이 매우 지혜로웠다.
➡ _____

5 그래서, 황제는 언제나 비르발을 곁에 두기를 원했다.
➡ _____

6 달콤한 처벌
➡ _____

7 신하들의 지혜를 시험해 보기 위해, 악바르는 종종 그들에게 이상한 질문을 했다.
➡ _____

8 어느 날, 황제는 재미있는 질문이 생각났다.
➡ _____

9 악바르: 오늘 어떤 이가 내 머리에서 머리카락을 잡아당겼소. 이 자에게 무엇을 해야 하겠소?
➡ _____

10 신하 1: 당연히 처벌해야 합니다.
➡ _____

11 신하 2: 예, 그를 처벌하소서!
➡ _____

12 악바르가 비르발에게 돌아섰다.
➡ _____

13 악바르: 그대가 내 입장이라면 무엇을 하겠소, 비르발?
➡ _____

14 비르발: 소신이 폐하라면, 그에게 사탕을 주겠습니다.
➡ _____

15 신하 3: 저 사람은 무슨 말을 하는 건가?
➡ _____

16 신하 4: 비르발이 정신이 나갔어!
➡ _____

17 악바르: 왜 그렇게 말했소?
➡ _____

18 비르발: 폐하의 머리카락을 잡아당긴 사람은 폐하의 손자임이 분명합니다. 다른 그 누구도 그런 짓을 할 수 없지요.
➡ _____

19 악바르: 과연 그대의 말이 맞소, 비르발. 그대처럼 현명한 자를 옆에 두어 정말 기쁘오.
➡ _____

20 한 항아리만큼의 지혜
➡ _____

21 어느 날, 페르시아의 왕이 이상한 요청과 함께 신하를 보냈다.
➡ _____

22 페르시아의 신하: 폐하의 나라에 현명한 자들이 많다고 들었습니다. 저는 저의 왕으로부터 한 항아리의 지혜를 왕께 가지고 오라는 명을 받았습니다.
➡ _____

23 신하 5: 저건 말이 안 되오! 어떻게 지혜를 항아리에 넣을 수 있단 말이오?
➡ _____

24 악바르: 그에게 지혜 한 항아리를 가져다줄 수 있겠소, 비르발?
➡ _____

25 비르발: 문제될 것이 없사옵니다.
➡ _____

26 몇 주만 기다려 주시겠습니까?
➡ _____

27 페르시아의 신하: 물론이오! 필요한 만큼 얼마든지 시간을 가지시오.
➡ _____

28 몇 주 후, 비르발은 목이 매우 좁은 두 항아리를 들고 돌아왔다. 그는 하나를 페르시아의 신하에게 줬다.
➡ _____

29 비르발: 이 지혜의 항아리를 그대의 왕께 가져다 드리십시오. 왕께서 이 항아리에서 지혜를 꺼내신 후에는 항아리를 우리에게 돌려달라 전해 주십시오.
➡ _____

30 비르발: 그 항아리는 매우 귀중한 것이니, 그것을 깨지 않도록 조심해 주십시오. 우리는 오직 두 개의 지혜의 항아리만 갖고 있습니다.
➡ _____

31 페르시아 신하는 항아리 안을 들여다보곤 말을 잃었다.
➡ _____

32 그는 비르발에게 감사를 표한 뒤 그의 나라로 떠났다.
➡ _____

33 페르시아의 신하: 우리 나라에도 비르발처럼 현명한 자가 있다면 정말 좋을 텐데.
➡ _____

34 페르시아의 신하가 떠난 뒤, 악바르는 비르발에게 항아리 속에 무엇이 있었는지를 물었다.
➡ _____

35 비르발: 여기 또 다른 항아리가 있습니다. 직접 살펴보시지요.
➡ _____

36 악바르는 또 다른 항아리 안을 보고 꼭 항아리만큼 큰 호박을 발견했다.
➡ _____

37 악바르: 그렇군! 항아리를 깨지 않고는 호박을 꺼낼 수가 없구려! 어떻게 한 것이오?
➡ _____

38 비르발: 항아리를 호박꽃에 덮어 놓은 후 호박이 항아리만큼 클 때까지 기다렸습니다.
➡ _____

39 악바르: 하하하! 이건 정말로 지혜의 항아리구려!
➡ _____

[01~03] 다음 글을 읽고 물음에 답하시오.

Akbar, the third Mogul emperor, had a number of wise officials at his court. Among them was a man whose name was Raja Birbal. He was famous for his quick wit and was very ⓐwise with his words. Thus, the emperor always liked to have Birbal near him.

Sweet Punishment

To ⓑtest his officials' wisdom, Akbar often asked them strange questions. One day, he came up with an ⓒinteresting question.

Akbar: Someone pulled a hair from my head today. What should I do to him?

Official 1: He should be punished, of course.

Official 2: Yes, punish him!

Akbar turned to Birbal.

Akbar: What would you do if you were in my place, Birbal?

Birbal: If I were you, I would give him sweets.

Official 3: What's he talking about?

Official 4: Birbal's ___(A)___ !

Akbar: What made you say so?

Birbal: The person who pulled your hair ⓓ should be your grandson. No one else could do such a thing.

Akbar: You are indeed correct, Birbal. I'm so ⓔglad to have someone as wise as you near me.

01 위 글의 빈칸 (A)에 들어갈 알맞은 말을 고르시오.

① reasonable   ② crazy

③ sensible   ④ fair

⑤ logical

02 위 글의 밑줄 친 ⓐ~ⓔ 중 잘못 쓰인 것을 고르시오.

① ⓐ   ② ⓑ   ③ ⓒ   ④ ⓓ   ⑤ ⓔ

03 According to the passage, which is NOT true?

① Akbar was the third Mogul emperor.

② Raja Birbal was famous for his quick wit and was very wise with his words.

③ One day, Akbar said that someone pulled a hair from his head.

④ Birbal said that he would give sweets to the man who had pulled his hair.

⑤ Officials asked Akbar to praise the man who had pulled his hair.

[04~06] 다음 글을 읽고 물음에 답하시오.

One day, ①the king of Persia sent an official with a strange favor.

Persian Official: I hear you have ⓐa lot of wise men in your country. I've been asked by my king to bring ②him a potful of wisdom.

Official 5: That makes no sense! How can we put wisdom in a pot?

Akbar: Can you bring ③him a potful of wisdom, Birbal?

Birbal: It won't be a problem.

Birbal: Could you please wait a few weeks?

Persian Official: Of course! Take as much time as you need.

A few weeks later, Birbal came back with two pots ___(A)___ necks were really narrow. ④He offered one to the Persian official.

Birbal: You can take this pot of wisdom to your king. Please ask ⑤him to return the pot to us after he takes the wisdom out of it.

04 위 글의 빈칸 (A)에 들어갈 알맞은 말을 고르시오.

① what   ② who   ③ whose
④ which   ⑤ that

05 위 글의 밑줄 친 ⓐa lot of 대신 쓸 수 없는 것을 고르시오.

① a deal of   ② lots of
③ a number of   ④ many
⑤ plenty of

중요

06 위 글의 밑줄 친 ①~⑤ 중에서 가리키는 대상이 다른 것을 고르시오.

①   ②   ③   ④   ⑤

[07~09] 다음 글을 읽고 물음에 답하시오.

Birbal: The pot is very precious, so please be careful not to break it. We only have two pots of wisdom.
The Persian official looked inside the pot and became ____ⓐ____.
He thanked Birbal and left for his country.
Persian Official: It would be great if there were a man as wise as Birbal in our country.
After the Persian official left, Akbar asked Birbal what was inside the pot.
Birbal: Here is the other pot. (①)
Akbar looked inside the other pot and found a pumpkin just as big as the pot.
Akbar: I see! (②) ⓑThe pumpkin can't take out without breaking the pot. How did you do it? (③)
Birbal: I put the pots over pumpkin flowers and waited until the pumpkins grew as big as the pots. (④)
Akbar: Hahaha! (⑤) This certainly is a potful of wisdom!

서답형

07 주어진 영영풀이를 참고하여 빈칸 ⓐ에 철자 s로 시작하는 단어를 쓰시오.

temporarily unable to speak

➡ _____

중요

08 위 글의 흐름으로 보아, 주어진 문장이 들어가기에 가장 적절한 곳은?

You can see for yourself.

①   ②   ③   ④   ⑤

서답형

09 위 글의 밑줄 친 ⓑ에서 어색한 것을 찾아 바르게 고치시오.

_____ ➡ _____

[10~13] 다음 글을 읽고 물음에 답하시오.

To test his officials' wisdom, Akbar often asked them strange questions. One day, he ⓐcame up with an interesting question.
Akbar: Someone pulled a hair from my head today. What should I do to him?
Official 1: He should be punished, of course.
Official 2: Yes, punish him!
Akbar turned to Birbal.
Akbar: What would you do if you were in my place, Birbal?
Birbal: If I (A)[am / were] you, I would give him sweets.
Official 3: What's he talking about?
Official 4: Birbal's crazy!
Akbar: ⓑ왜 그렇게 말했소?
Birbal: The person (B)[which / who] pulled your hair must be your grandson. No one else could do such a thing.
Akbar: You are indeed correct, Birbal. I'm so glad to have someone as (C)[wise / wiser] as you near me.

서답형

10 위 글의 괄호 (A)~(C)에서 어법상 알맞은 낱말을 골라 쓰시오.

➡ (A) _____ (B) _____ (C) _____

중요

11 Which question CANNOT be answered after reading the passage?

① Why did Akbar often ask strange questions of his officials?

② Did Official 1,2,3,4 answer correctly?

③ Why did Akbar's grandson pull his hair?

④ Who pulled Akbar's hair?

⑤ Why was Akbar glad?

12 위 글의 밑줄 친 @came up with와 다른 의미로 쓰인 것을 고르시오.

① I can't come up with any creative ideas.

② I must come up with an excuse.

③ I hope you can come up with a better idea than this.

④ How long does it take for you to come up with a song?

⑤ How soon can you come up with the money?

서답형

13 위 글의 밑줄 친 ⓑ의 우리말을 make를 이용하여 5 단어로 영작하시오.

➡ _____

[14~16] 다음 글을 읽고 물음에 답하시오.

One day, the king of Persia sent an official with a strange favor.

Persian Official: I hear you have a lot of wise men in your country. I've been asked by my king @to bring him a potful of wisdom.

Official 5: That makes no sense! How can we put wisdom in a pot?

Akbar: Can you bring him a potful of wisdom, Birbal?

Birbal: _____ (A)

Birbal: Could you please wait a few weeks?

Persian Official: Of course! Take as __(B)__ as you need.

14 위 글의 빈칸 (A)에 들어갈 말로 적절한 것은?

① How can I do that?

② It won't be a problem.

③ Why do you think I can do it?

④ Don't ask me such a question.

⑤ It can't be done.

중요

15 위 글의 빈칸 (B)에 들어갈 말로 알맞은 것은?

① much time   ② more time

③ less time   ④ few time

⑤ little time

16 〈보기〉에서 밑줄 친 @to bring과 문법적 쓰임이 같은 것의 개수를 고르시오.

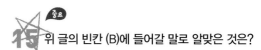

┌─ 보기 ┐

① Don't forget to bring your books with you.

② I didn't know how much to bring.

③ We went there to bring the equipment.

④ It is the first step to bring you success.

⑤ It is better not to bring the matter up.

└─────────┘

① 1개   ② 2개   ③ 3개   ④ 4개   ⑤ 5개

[17~21] 다음 글을 읽고 물음에 답하시오.

A few weeks later, Birbal came back with two pots whose necks were really narrow. He offered one to the Persian official.

Birbal: You can take this pot of wisdom to your king. Please ask him to return the pot to us after he takes the wisdom out of it.

Birbal: The pot is very precious, so please be careful not to break it. We only have two pots of wisdom.

The Persian official looked inside the pot and became speechless.

He thanked Birbal and left ___ⓐ___ his country.

Persian Official: (A)우리 나라에도 비르발처럼 현명한 자가 있다면 정말 좋을 텐데.

After the Persian official left, Akbar asked Birbal what was inside the pot.

Birbal: Here is ___ⓑ___ pot. You can see for yourself.

Akbar looked inside ___ⓑ___ pot and found a pumpkin just as big as the pot.

Akbar: I see! The pumpkin can't be taken out without breaking the pot. How did you do it?

Birbal: I put the pots over pumpkin flowers and waited until the pumpkins grew as big as the pots.

Akbar: Hahaha! This certainly is a potful of wisdom!

17 다음 중 위 글의 빈칸 ⓐ에 들어갈 말과 같은 말이 들어가는 것은?

① Everyone is worried _____ their food.

② A boy needs a father he can look up _____.

③ I always think of you _____ one of my family.

④ She was tired _____ hearing about their trip to India.

⑤ She moved back home to care _____ her elderly parents.

18 위 글의 빈칸 ⓑ에 공통으로 들어갈 말로 알맞은 것은?

① other ② the another ③ others
④ the other ⑤ the others

서답형

19 What did Birbal ask the Persian official to do? (Two things.)

➡ _____

_____

서답형

20 위 글의 밑줄 친 (A)의 우리말에 맞게 주어진 어휘를 알맞게 배열하여 영작하시오.

> Birbal, in our country, it, a man, if, be, were, would, wise, great, there, as, as

➡ _____

_____

중요

21 According to the passage, which is NOT true?

① The Persian official became speechless when he took a look at the inside of the pot.

② The Persian official wished to have a wise man like Birbal.

③ Birbal asked the Persian official to be careful not to break the pot as they had only one.

④ The pumpkin couldn't be taken out without breaking the pot.

⑤ Birbal put the pots over pumpkin flowers and waited until the pumpkins grew as big as the pots.

[01~03] 다음 글을 읽고 물음에 답하시오.

Akbar, the third Mogul emperor, had a number of wise officials at his court. Among them was a man whose name was Raja Birbal. He was famous for his quick wit and was very wise with his words. Thus, the emperor always liked to have Birbal near him.

Sweet Punishment

To test his officials' wisdom, Akbar often asked them strange questions. One day, he came up with an interesting question.

Akbar: Someone pulled a hair from my head today. What should I do to him?

Official 1: He should be punished, of course.

Official 2: Yes, punish him!

Akbar turned to Birbal.

Akbar: What would you do if you were ⓐ내 입장이라면, Birbal?

Birbal: ⓑ소신이 폐하라면, 그에게 사탕을 주겠습니다. (I, you, were, give sweets)

Official 3: What's he talking about?

Official 4: Birbal's crazy!

Akbar: What made you say so?

Birbal: The person who pulled your hair <u>must</u> be your grandson. No one else could do such a thing.

Akbar: You are indeed correct, Birbal. I'm so glad to have someone as wise as you near me.

01 밑줄 친 ⓐ의 우리말에 맞게 place를 이용하여 세 단어를 쓰시오.

➡ _____

02 밑줄 친 ⓑ의 우리말에 맞게 주어진 어휘를 이용하여 9 단어로 영작하시오.

➡ _____

03 Who pulled Akbar's hair? Answer in English with 5 words.

➡ _____

[04~06] 다음 글을 읽고 물음에 답하시오.

One day, the king of Persia sent an official with a strange favor.

Persian Official: I hear you have a lot of wise men in your country. I've been asked by my king to bring him a potful of wisdom.

Official 5: ⓐThat makes no sense!
_____(A)_____

Akbar: Can you bring him a potful of wisdom, Birbal?

Birbal: It won't be a problem.

Birbal: Could you please wait a few weeks?

Persian Official: Of course! Take as much time as you need.

04 위 글의 빈칸 (A)에 'We can't put wisdom in a pot.'이라는 의미의 말을 how를 이용한 의문문으로 쓰시오.

➡ _____

05 위 글의 밑줄 친 ⓐThat이 가리키는 것을 20자 내외의 우리말로 쓰시오.

➡ _____

06 What was the Persian official asked to do by his king?

➡ _____

[07~10] 다음 글을 읽고 물음에 답하시오.

A few weeks later, Birbal came back with two pots whose necks were really narrow. He offered one to the Persian official.

Birbal: You can take this pot of wisdom to your king. Please ask him ⓐ_____ the pot to us after he takes the wisdom out of it.

Birbal: The pot is very precious, so please be careful not to break it. We only have two pots of wisdom.

The Persian official looked inside the pot and became speechless.

He thanked Birbal and left for his country.

Persian Official: ⓑIt would be great if there were a man as wise as Birbal in our country.

After the Persian official left, Akbar asked Birbal what was inside the pot.

Birbal: Here is the other pot. You can see for yourself.

Akbar looked inside the other pot and found a pumpkin just as big as the pot.

Akbar: I see! The pumpkin can't be taken out without breaking the pot. How did you do it?

Birbal: I put the pots over pumpkin flowers and waited until the pumpkins grew as big as the pots.

Akbar: Hahaha! This certainly is a potful of wisdom!

07 빈칸 ⓐ에 return을 알맞은 형태로 쓰시오.

➡ _____

08 위 글의 밑줄 친 ⓑ를 as를 이용하여 고쳐 쓰시오.

➡ _____

_____

09 What was inside the pot when Akbar looked inside the other pot?

➡ _____

10 위 글의 내용과 일치하도록 다음 빈칸 (A)와 (B)에 알맞은 단어를 쓰시오.

Birbal offered the Persian official a pot which (A)_____ _____ was in. When the Persian official looked inside the pot he (B)_____ _____.

[11~13] 다음 글을 읽고 물음에 답하시오.

Tales of Birbal

Akbar, the third Mogul emperor, had a number of wise officials at his court. ⓐ그 중 Raja Birbal이라는 이름의 한 사람이 있었다.(Among으로 시작, name) He was famous for his quick wit and was very wise with his words. _(A)_, the emperor always liked to have Birbal near him.

11 위 글의 빈칸 (A)에 알맞은 말을 한 단어로 쓰시오.

➡ _____

12 위 글의 밑줄 친 ⓐ의 우리말을 주어진 어휘를 이용하여 10 단어로 영작하시오.

➡ _____

_____

13 What was Birbal famous for?

➡ _____

Link

A Shorter Line

One day, Emperor Akbar drew a line on the ground and asked his officials.

Akbar: Make this line shorter without touching it.
전치사 뒤에 동명사

Official 1: Without touching it?
= the line that Emperor Akbar drew

Official 2: How can we do that?
= make the line shorter without touching it

Birbal smiled.

Birbal: That's too easy.
부사(너무)

Birbal drew a longer line next to the line that Akbar had drawn.
주격 관계대명사   대과거

Birbal: Your line is now shorter than mine.
= my line

Akbar: You did it, Birbal!

Official 3: I wish I were as wise as Birbal.
가정법   동등 비교

구문해설 • **next to:** ~ 옆에 • **wise:** 현명한

해석

더 짧은 선

어느 날, 악바르 황제는 땅에 선을 그린 뒤 그의 신하들에게 물었다.

악바르: 이 선을 건드리지 않은 채 더 짧게 만들어 보게.

신하 1: 건드리지 않고 말씀입니까?

신하 2: 어떻게 그렇게 할 수 있습니까?

비르발은 미소를 지었다.

비르발: 너무 쉽군요.

비르발은 악바르가 그린 선 옆에 더 긴 선을 그렸다.

비르발: 폐하의 선이 이제 제 선보다 짧습니다.

악바르: 그대가 해냈소, 비르발!

신하 3: 제가 비르발만큼 지혜롭다면 좋겠군요.

Write

Dear Jaeha,

Time flies. I cannot believe that it is time to say goodbye. I still remember the
형용사적 용법
time when we went camping together. I really liked the movie we watched that
관계부사(= at which)   목적격 관계대명사 that 또는 which 생략
night. I also loved playing basketball with you after school. I really want to
= to play
thank you for teaching me basketball skills. If I could turn back time, I would
전치사 뒤에 나온 동명사   가정법 과거 = As I can't turn back time. I won't ~.
spend more time with you. I hope we keep in touch even after we graduate.

Best,

Jake

구문해설 • **go ~ing:** ~하러 가다 • **thank A for B:** B에 대하여 A에게 감사하다
• **spend time with A:** A와 시간을 보내다 • **graduate:** 졸업하다

재하에게,

시간 정말 빠르다. 작별 인사를 해야 할 시간이라는 게 믿어지지 않아. 아직도 우리가 함께 캠핑을 갔던 때가 생각나. 우리가 그날 밤에 봤던 영화를 정말 좋아했는데. 너와 방과 후에 농구를 하는 것도 정말로 좋아했어. 농구 기술들을 가르쳐 줘서 정말로 고맙다고 말하고 싶어. 시간을 되돌아갈 수 있다면, 너와 함께 더 많은 시간을 보낼 거야. 우리가 졸업한 뒤에도 계속 연락을 하면 좋겠다.

Jake가.

Culture Project

When my brother failed his driving test seven times, he was very disappointed.
감정(과거분사)
Kento, his friend from Japan, said to him, "If I were you, I wouldn't give up.
동격   가정법 과거
Fall seven times, stand up eight." It's a Japanese saying that means "Do not
주격 관계대명사+동사 (meaning으로 전환 가능)
give up." My brother tried again and finally passed.
과거시제 병렬구조

구문해설 • **saying:** 격언, 속담 • **finally:** 마침내

내 오빠가 운전 면허 시험에서 일곱 번 떨어졌을 때, 그는 매우 실망했습니다. 일본에서 온 그의 친구 Kento는 그에게, "내가 너라면, 포기하지 않을 거야. 일곱 번 넘어져도 여덟 번 일어나야지."하고 말했습니다. 이것은 "포기하지 마라."라는 뜻의 일본 격언입니다. 오빠는 다시 도전해 마침내 통과했습니다.

Words & Expressions

01 〈보기〉의 밑줄 친 어휘와 같은 의미로 쓰인 것을 고르시오.

> ┤ 보기 ├
> Akbar, the third Mogul emperor, had a number of wise officials at his court.

① They often performed for the royal court.

② Prisoners are taken to court under police escort.

③ They marked out a tennis court on the lawn.

④ You must court an opportunity.

⑤ The court judged him guilty.

02 다음 영영풀이에 해당하는 단어를 주어진 철자로 시작하여 빈칸에 쓰고, 알맞은 것을 골라 문장을 완성하시오.

> • h_____ : the quality of being honest
> • w_____ : the ability to use your experience and knowledge in order to make sensible decisions or judgments

(1) She is a woman of great _____.

(2) Where is there dignity unless there is _____?

03 다음 빈칸에 〈영영풀이〉에 해당하는 어휘를 주어진 철자로 시작하여 쓰시오.

> Would you do me a f_____?

> 〈영영풀이〉 something that you do for someone in order to help them or be kind to them

➡ _____

04 괄호 안에 주어진 어휘를 이용하여 빈칸에 알맞게 쓰시오.

> • Even things that appear _____ have their use. (worth)
> • A number of _____ works of art were stolen from the gallery. (price)

05 다음 문장에 공통으로 들어갈 말을 고르시오.

> • Phone them up and find _____ when they are coming.
> • The report turned _____ to be false information.
> • I can't figure _____ how to do this.

① from　　② with　　③ out

④ to　　⑤ of

Conversation

[06~07] 다음 대화를 읽고 물음에 답하시오.

> B: Wow, you play the guitar so well.
> (A) (a)굉장한 가족이다! I wish I could play the guitar like you.
> (B) Really? Does your father play the guitar, too?
> (C) Yes. He was in a famous band.
> (D) Thanks. I love playing the guitar. I learned it from my dad.

06 주어진 문장에 이어질 대화의 순서로 알맞은 것은?

① (B) – (A) – (C) – (D)
② (C) – (B) – (A) – (D)
③ (C) – (B) – (D) – (A)
④ (D) – (B) – (A) – (C)
⑤ (D) – (B) – (C) – (A)

07 위 대화의 밑줄 친 (a)의 우리말을 3 단어로 영작하시오.

➡ _____

08 다음 중 짝지어진 대화가 어색한 것은?

① A: Don't judge a book by its cover.
  B: Do you mean we should not judge others by their looks?
② A: The early bird catches the worm.
  B: No. The early bird gets tired quickly.
③ A: People say, "Yesterday is history, tomorrow is a mystery, and today is a gift. That's why it's called the present."
  B: Now I see. You know so many great expressions. You're as wise as my grandma.
④ A: You look worried. Is something wrong?
  B: I handed in my science report in time.
⑤ A: Do you mean everyone has a chance for success?
  B: Yes, that's what I mean.

[09~11] 다음 대화를 읽고 물음에 답하시오.

> B: Wow, you really dance well.
> G: Thanks. I love dancing. Everyone in my family (A)[is / are] good at dancing.
> B: Really? Your parents dance well, (B)[either / too]?
> G: Yes. They're also good singers.
> B: What a family! I (C)[want / wish] I could dance like you.

09 위 대화의 괄호 (A)~(C)에서 알맞은 말을 고르시오.

➡ (A) _____ (B) _____ (C) _____

10 What does everyone in the girl's family do well?

➡ _____

11 What does the boy wish?

➡ _____

Grammar

12 다음 주어진 두 문장을 관계대명사를 사용해서 하나의 문장으로 바르게 고친 것을 고르시오.

- Sammy has a rabbit.
- The rabbit's tail is very short.

① Sammy has a rabbit which tail is very short.
② Sammy has a rabbit whose tail is very short.
③ Sammy has a rabbit of which tail is very short.
④ Sammy has a rabbit that tail is very short.
⑤ Sammy has a rabbit which of the tail is very short.

13 다음 중 밑줄 친 부분의 쓰임이 〈보기〉와 같은 것은?

┤ 보기 ├
I couldn't finish it if it were not for your help.

① Janet will ask me if Seohyun is in good condition.
② They wonder if Charles is at home.
③ Our country would be in trouble if there were no wise man.
④ Carol used to wonder if God exists.
⑤ We don't know if the soccer finals will be canceled because of the weather.

14 다음 주어진 문장을 가정법으로 바르게 고친 것은?

As my daughters didn't return the books to the library, I had to pay the late fee.

① If my daughters returned the books to the library, I wouldn't have to pay the late fee.
② If my daughters returned the books to the library, I would have had to pay the late fee.
③ If my daughters had returned the books to the library, I wouldn't have to pay the late fee.
④ If my daughters had returned the books to the library, I wouldn't have had to pay the late fee.
⑤ If my daughters had returned the books to the library, I would have had to pay the late fee.

15 다음 〈보기〉와 같이 직설법 문장을 가정법으로 고치시오.

> ── 보기 ──
> As I am not rich, I can't buy the bike.
> → If I were rich, I could buy the bike.

(1) As I am not Birbal, I can't answer the difficult question of the king.

➡ _____

_____

(2) As Bentley doesn't wear a skirt, he won't look like a girl.

➡ _____

(3) As there is no kettle, I can't boil and drink my tea.

➡ _____

(4) As Michelle has the glasses, it is easy for her to read the books.

➡ _____

_____

[16~17] 다음 우리말에 맞게 영작한 것을 고르시오.

16
> Teddy는 아버지가 완고한 여자 친구와 결혼하려고 결심했다.

① Teddy decided to marry the girl friend whose father was strict.
② Teddy decided to marry the girl friend who was her father strict.
③ Teddy decided to marry the girl friend of whom father was strict.
④ Teddy decided to marry the girl friend with whose father being strict.
⑤ Teddy decided to marry the girl friend the father of whom was strict.

17
> 비가 충분히 온다면 가뭄 걱정을 덜 수 있을 텐데.

① If it didn't rain enough, we could ease our concern for drought.
② If it had rained enough, we could have eased our concern for drought.
③ Had it rained enough, we could ease our concern for drought.
④ Did it rain enough, we can ease our concern for drought.
⑤ If it rained enough, we could ease our concern for drought.

18 다음 문장의 빈칸 (A)~(C)에 들어갈 말로 가장 적절한 것은?

> • If I (A)_____ a boyfriend, I would not eat alone.
> • If it were not for the thick trees, the bitter wind (B)_____ blow the house to pieces.
> • If the waiting time (C)_____ over, I will take part in the battle.

	(A)	(B)	(C)
①	have	will	will be
②	have	would	were
③	had	could	were
④	had	would	is
⑤	have had	will	is

Reading

[19~21] 다음 글을 읽고 물음에 답하시오.

_____(A)_____

To test his officials' wisdom, Akbar often asked them strange questions. One day, he came up with an interesting question.

Akbar: Someone pulled a hair from my head today. What should I do to him?

Official 1: He should be punished, of course.

Official 2: Yes, punish him!

Akbar turned to Birbal.

Akbar: (B)그대가 내 입장이라면 무엇을 하겠소, Birbal?

Birbal: If I were you, I would give him sweets.

Official 3: ⓐWhat's he talking about?

Official 4: ⓑBirbal's crazy!

Akbar: What made you say so?

Birbal: The person who pulled your hair must be your grandson. No one else could do such a thing.

Akbar: You are indeed correct, Birbal. I'm so glad to have someone as wise as you near me.

19 위 글의 빈칸 (A)에 제목으로 알맞은 것을 고르시오.

① Whom to Blame
② Sweet Punishment
③ How to Test Wisdom
④ Harsh Punishment
⑤ Crazy Birbal

20 위 글의 밑줄 친 (B)의 우리말에 맞게 주어진 어휘를 이용하여 10 단어로 영작하시오.

place, would, if, in

➡ _____

21 밑줄 친 ⓐ와 ⓑ가 의미하는 것을 sense를 이용하여 4 단어의 영어로 쓰시오.

➡ _____

[22~24] 다음 글을 읽고 물음에 답하시오.

A Potful of Wisdom

One day, the king of Persia sent an official with a strange ⓐfavor.

Persian Official: I hear you have ①a deal of wise men in your country. I've been asked by my king to bring him a potful of wisdom.

Official 5: That makes ②sense! How can we put wisdom in a pot?

Akbar: Can you bring him a potful of wisdom, Birbal?

Birbal: It won't be a ③matter.

Birbal: Could you please wait ④a little weeks?

Persian Official: Of course! Take as ⑤many time as you need.

22 위 글의 밑줄 친 ⓐfavor와 같은 의미로 쓰인 것을 고르시오.

① Could you do me a favor and pick up Sam from school today?
② Many countries favor a presidential system of government.
③ I offer you my heartfelt thanks for your favor.
④ The ladies received compacts as favors at the banquet.
⑤ He escaped under favor of night.

23 위 글의 밑줄 친 ①~⑤에서 흐름상 어색하지 <u>않은</u> 것을 고르시오.

①   ②   ③   ④   ⑤

24 According to the passage, which is NOT true?

① The Persian official came with a strange favor.

② The king of Persia told the Persian official to bring him a potful of wisdom.

③ Official 5 thought that putting wisdom in a pot was impossible.

④ Birbal thought he could bring the Persian official a potful of wisdom.

⑤ The Persian official allowed little time to take.

[25~27] 다음 글을 읽고 물음에 답하시오.

Dear Jaeha,

Time flies. I cannot believe that it is time to say goodbye. I still remember the time when we went camping together. I really liked the movie we watched that night. I also loved

playing basketball with you after school. I really want to thank you for teaching me basketball skills. (A)시간을 되돌아갈 수 있다면, 너와 함께 더 많은 시간을 보낼 거야.(turn back, time, spend) I hope we ____ⓐ____ even after we graduate.

Best,
Jake

25 주어진 영영풀이에 해당하는 표현을 빈칸 ⓐ에 touch를 포함하여 3 단어로 써 넣으시오.

communicate with somebody regularly

➡ _____

26 위 글의 밑줄 친 (A)의 우리말에 맞게 괄호 안에 주어진 어휘를 이용하여 13 단어로 영작하시오.

➡ _____
_____

27 What does Jake still remember?

➡ _____
_____

01 출제율 95%

다음 중 짝지어진 단어의 관계가 나머지와 다른 것은?

① hopeful – hopeless
② valueless – priceless
③ valuable – precious
④ powerful – powerless
⑤ useful – useless

02 출제율 100%

밑줄 친 부분의 의미로 알맞지 않은 것은?

① This is your last chance to enter the correct password. (맞는, 정확한)
② The restaurant offers traditional home cooking. (내놓다, 제공하다)
③ Parents should punish their children in a proper way. (칭찬하다)
④ He wanted to become the emperor of Rome. (황제)
⑤ I've been asked by my king to bring him a potful of wisdom. (한 항아리만큼의)

03 출제율 95%

다음 밑줄 친 단어와 바꿔 쓸 수 있는 것은?

> Priceless antiques were destroyed in the fire.

① worthless   ② valueless
③ useless   ④ cheap
⑤ invaluable

04 출제율 95%

다음 주어진 우리말에 맞게 빈칸을 채우시오. (철자가 주어진 경우 주어진 철자로 시작할 것)

(1) 그것을 다시 하는 것은 이해가 안 된다.
➡ It doesn't make _____ to do it again.

(2) 경험은 지혜의 아버지이고 기억의 어머니이다.
➡ Experience is the father of _____ and the mother of memory.

(3) 그 상점은 매월 무료 선물을 제공한다.
➡ The store p_____ a free gift every month.

[05~07] 다음 대화를 읽고 물음에 답하시오.

Anna: What's wrong? You don't look so good.
Suho: I'm still thinking about our soccer match last week.
Anna: Do you mean the game you lost last week?
Suho: Yes. I wish I could forget about it, but I can't.
Anna: Well, (A)넌 항상 오늘을 위해 살아야 해.
Suho: Do you mean I should forget the past and focus on the present?
Anna: (①) People say, "Yesterday is history, tomorrow is a mystery, and today is a gift. (②) That's why it's called the present."
Suho: Now I see. (③) You know so many great expressions. (④) You're as wise as my grandma. (⑤)

05 출제율 95%

위 대화의 (①)~(⑤) 중에서 주어진 글이 들어가기에 가장 적절한 곳은?

> Yes, exactly.

①   ②   ③   ④   ⑤

06 위 대화의 밑줄 친 우리말 (A)에 맞게 should를 이용하여 6 단어로 영작하시오.
출제율 95%

➡ _____

07 When did Suho lose his soccer match?
출제율 90%

➡ _____

[08~10] 다음 대화를 읽고 물음에 답하시오.

> G: You look worried. Is something wrong?
> B: I had to hand in my science report by yesterday, but I didn't.
> G: _____ (A)
> B: Do you mean it's better to hand it in __(B)__ it's late?
> G: Yes, exactly. You should always finish what you've started.

08 위 대화의 빈칸 (A)에 알맞은 말을 고르시오.
출제율 90%

① Don't judge a book by its cover.
② It's better late than never.
③ Haste makes waste.
④ Honesty is the best policy.
⑤ Prevention is better than cure.

09 위 대화의 빈칸 (B)에 알맞은 말을 고르시오.
출제율 95%

① if   ② whether   ③ that
④ when   ⑤ even though

10 위 대화의 내용과 일치하지 않는 것은?
출제율 100%

① The boy looks worried.
② The boy didn't hand in his science report yesterday.
③ The girl thinks it's better for the boy to hand in the report though it's late.
④ The girl thinks we should always finish what we've started.
⑤ The boy will hand in his science report.

11 다음 각 문장의 빈칸에 들어갈 알맞은 말을 〈보기〉에서 기호를 골라 괄호 안에 써 넣으시오.
출제율 100%

┌─── 보기 ───┐
ⓐ who ⓑ whose ⓒ which ⓓ of which
└──────────┘

(1) We're going to buy a house _____ garden is beautiful. ( )
(2) We're going to buy a house _____ the garden is beautiful. ( )
(3) Dorothy met a tin man _____ heart was gone. ( )
(4) Brian is the one _____ car is orange red. ( )
(5) Brian is the one _____ has an orange red colored car. ( )
(6) I have to finish the project _____ the purpose is to market the new items. ( )
(7) I have to finish the project _____ has the purpose of marketing the new items. ( )
(8) I saw a building on _____ wall the ivy is growing. ( )
(9) I saw a wall on _____ the ivy is growing. ( )

12 다음 가정법 문장들 중 어법상 올바른 것을 고르면?

① The president would feel proud of them if they win the final match.
② What would you do if another war occurrs?
③ She will be puzzled if you left her.
④ What would the king do if Birbal brought the pot of wisdom?
⑤ If the official from Persia look inside the pot, he would be speechless.

13 다음 중 어법상 올바른 것을 고르시오.

① Naomi has a son whose the job is to write novels.
② Yuna bought the shoes colors of which are bright red and ocean blue.
③ The police arrested the artist the works of whom were all fake.
④ The reporter was covering the hospital whose the doctors are famous for cancer surgery.
⑤ While in college, Brad majored in Latin the grammar of which was too complex.

[14~16] 다음에 주어진 두 문장을 합쳐서 가정법의 한 문장으로 영작하되, 주어진 단어로 시작하시오.

14

• Mike wants to call her but he can't.
• He doesn't know her phone number.

➡ If _____

_____.

15

• Tom didn't catch the school bus this morning.
• He was late for school again.

➡ If _____

_____.

16

• In fact, I'm not as wise as Birbal.
• I want to be as wise as Birbal.

➡ I _____.

17 다음 중 어법상 올바른 문장의 개수는?

ⓐ The house whose roof was damaged has now been repaired.
ⓑ The trees of which branches are covered with snow are beautiful.
ⓒ They talked with a woman of whom husband was killed in an accident.
ⓓ The man whose dog I took care of is in New York.
ⓔ It is a novel the author of which is unknown.
ⓕ The prize will go to the team whose performance the judges like best.
ⓖ It is a movie whose the title she has never heard of.
ⓗ Those are firefighters whose job is to put out fires.

① 1개   ② 2개   ③ 3개
④ 4개   ⑤ 5개

[18~21] 다음 글을 읽고 물음에 답하시오.

_____(A)_____

One day, Emperor Akbar drew a line on the ground and asked his officials.

Akbar: Make this line shorter without touching it.

Official 1: Without touching it?

Official 2: _____(B)_____

Birbal smiled.

Birbal: That's too easy.

Birbal drew a longer line next to the line that Akbar ⓐhad drawn.

Birbal: Your line is now shorter than ⓑmine.

Akbar: You did it, Birbal!

Official 3: I wish I were as wise as Birbal.

18 위 글의 빈칸 (A)에 들어갈 알맞은 말을 고르시오.

① Great Idea
② A Shorter Line
③ Who Is Wise?
④ Drawing Without Touching
⑤ How Wonderful!

19 위 글의 빈칸 (B)에 'We can't do that.'이라는 의미의 말을 how를 이용한 의문문으로 쓰시오.

➡ _____

20 위 글의 밑줄 친 ⓐ와 같은 용법으로 쓰인 것을 고르시오.

① I could find the destination easily because of the map he had drawn.
② She had drawn the same picture twice.
③ Akbar had just drawn the line.
④ Terry had drawn pictures for 10 years.
⑤ Merriam had drawn the picture since that morning.

21 위 글의 밑줄 친 ⓑmine을 두 단어로 바꿔 쓰시오.

➡ _____

[22~24] 다음 글을 읽고 물음에 답하시오.

Dear Sumin,

Time flies. (①) I cannot believe that it is time to say goodbye. (②) I still remember the time when we had a party at my house. (③) I really liked talking with you about our worries and dreams all night long. (④) I really want to thank you for teaching me badminton skills. _____ⓐ_____ (⑤) I hope we remain best friends even after we graduate.

Best,
Minji

22 위 글의 빈칸 ⓐ에 다음 문장을 if를 이용하여 바꿔 쓰시오.

Since I cannot turn back time, I will not do more things together with you.

➡ _____

_____

23 위 글의 흐름으로 보아, 주어진 문장이 들어가기에 가장 적절한 곳은?

I also loved playing badminton with you after school.

① ② ③ ④ ⑤

24 What cannot Minji believe?

➡ _____

_____

[01~03] 다음 대화를 읽고 물음에 답하시오.

> G: You look tired this morning.
>
> B: I got up very early to study for the exam.
>
> G: Good for you. The early bird catches the warm.
>
> B: No. The early bird gets tired quickly.
>
> G: (A)Do you mean you don't like to get up early?
>
> B: Yes, that's exactly what I mean.

01 위 대화에서 어색한 어휘를 하나 찾아 바르게 고치시오.

_____ ➡ _____

02 Why does the boy look tired?

➡ _____

03 위 대화의 밑줄 친 (A)를 'saying'을 이용하여 바꿔 쓰시오.

➡ _____

_____

04 다음 〈보기〉에 주어진 단어들을 활용하여, 그림에 맞는 우리말과 일치하도록 어법상 알맞은 형태로 바꿔 영작하시오. (사용하지 않는 단어는 없어야 하며, 영작 시 줄임말 불가.)

┌─ 보기 ┐

Mina, families, cooking, grow longer, pay attention to, under 12, a lot of, lie, burn the food, more, visit, whose kids

- 미나가 요리에 더 신경을 쓴다면, 음식을 태우지 않을 텐데.
- 네가 거짓말을 하지 않았다면, 코가 더 길어지지 않았을 텐데.
- 아이들이 12살 이하인 많은 가족들이 동물원을 방문했다.

(1)

➡ _____

_____

(2)

➡ _____

_____

(3)

➡ _____

_____

A few weeks later, _____(A)_____ . He offered one to the Persian official.

Birbal: You can take this pot of wisdom to your king. Please ask him to return the pot to us after he takes the wisdom out of it.

Birbal: The pot is very precious, so please be careful not to break it. We only have two pots of wisdom.

The Persian official looked inside the pot and became speechless.

He thanked Birbal and left for his country.

Persian Official: It would be great if there were a man as wise as Birbal in our country.

After the Persian official left, Akbar asked Birbal what was inside the pot.

Birbal: Here is the other pot. You can see for yourself.

Akbar looked inside the other pot and found a pumpkin just as big as the pot.

Akbar: I see! The pumpkin can't be taken out without breaking the pot. How did you do it?

Birbal: I put the pots over pumpkin flowers and waited until the pumpkins grew as big as the pots.

Akbar: Hahaha! (B)This certainly is a potful of wisdom!

05 위 글의 빈칸 (A)에 다음의 두 문장을 한 문장으로 바꿔 써 넣으시오.(whose를 이용할 것)

> • Birbal came back with two pots.
> • Their necks were really narrow.

➡ _____

_____

06 What was offered to the Persian official by Birbal?

➡ _____

_____

A Shorter Line

One day, Emperor Akbar drew a line on the ground and asked his officials.

Akbar: Make this line shorter without touching it.

Official 1: Without touching it?

Official 2: How can we do that?

Birbal smiled.

Birbal: ⓐThat's too easy.

Birbal drew a longer line next to the line that Akbar had drawn.

Birbal: Your line is now shorter than mine.

Akbar: You did it, Birbal!

Official 3: ⓑ제가 비르발만큼 지혜롭다면 좋겠군요.
(wish, wise)

07 위 글의 밑줄 친 ⓐThat이 가리키는 것을 우리말로 쓰시오.

➡ _____

08 위 글의 밑줄 친 ⓑ의 우리말에 맞게 주어진 어휘를 이용하여 영작하시오.

➡ _____

09 본문의 내용과 일치하도록 다음 빈칸 (A)와 (B)에 알맞은 단어를 쓰시오.

> When Akbar drew a line on the ground and asked his officials to make the line shorter (A)_____ _____ _____, Birbal made the line shorter by drawing (B)_____ _____ _____ next to the line that Akbar had drawn.

01 다음 각 그림들을 보고, 〈보기〉와 같이 소유격 관계대명사가 들어가는 문장을 2개 이상 영작하시오.

┌── 보기 ──┐

Snow White rejected the witch whose apple didn't look yummy.

02 (A)의 어구를 이용하여 〈보기〉와 같이 다음 대화의 빈칸에 알맞은 말을 쓰시오.

┌── 보기 ──┐

You're good at singing.
I wish I could sing well like you.

You're good at _____.
I wish _____.

(A) draw / play soccer / dance / speak English

03 다음 〈보기〉의 속담을 바탕으로 만든 글의 빈칸을 주어진 어휘를 이용하여 알맞게 채우시오.

┌── 보기 ──┐

Fall seven times, stand up eight.

disappointed, give up, try

When my brother failed his driving test (A)_____, he was very (B)_____.
Kento, his friend from Japan, said to him, "If I were you, I wouldn't (C)_____.
Fall seven times, stand up (D)_____." It's a Japanese saying that means "Do not give up." My brother (E)_____ again and finally passed.

01 다음 짝지어진 단어의 관계가 같도록 빈칸에 알맞은 말을 쓰시오.

> precious – valuable : gift – _____

[02~03] 다음 주어진 영어 설명에 맞게 문장의 빈칸에 알맞은 말을 쓰시오.

02
> The _____ Theodosius ordered the temple to be closed.

> <영어 설명> the man who is the ruler of an empire

➡ _____

03
> Would you be so kind as to lock the door when you _____?

> <영어 설명> to go away from a place or a person

➡ _____

04 우리말과 일치하도록 주어진 단어를 배열하여 영작하시오.

(1) 왕은 그의 궁궐에서 많은 시간을 보냈다.
   (the king, time, court, lot, spent, a, his, at, of)
   ➡ _____

(2) 그의 부모님은 거짓말을 했다고 그를 벌 주셨다.
   (lying, his, him, parents, punished, for)
   ➡ _____

(3) 그녀의 책들은 재치와 지혜로 가득 차 있다.
   (her, books, and, full, of, her, wit, are, wisdom)
   ➡ _____

05 다음 빈칸에 알맞은 말로 짝지어진 것을 고르시오.

> • You can never wipe out the _____.
> • _____ your chair nearer the table.

① place – Push
② future – Push
③ future – Invent
④ past – Shake
⑤ past – Pull

[06~08] 다음 대화를 읽고 물음에 답하시오.

> B: Wow, you play the guitar so well.
> G: Thanks. I love ⓐplaying the guitar. I learned it from my dad.
> B: Really? Does your father play the guitar, too?
> G: Yes. He was in a ___(A)___ band.
> B: What a family! (B)I wish I could play the guitar like you.

06 다음 영영풀이에 해당하는 어휘를 빈칸 (A)에 쓰시오.

> being very well known

➡ _____

07 위 대화의 밑줄 친 (B)의 의도로 알맞은 것은?

① 걱정하기　　　② 의향 말하기
③ 이해 확인하기　④ 조언 구하기
⑤ 바람·소원 표현하기

08 다음 문장의 밑줄 친 부분이 위 대화의 밑줄 친 ⓐ와 문법적 쓰임이 같은 것은?

① How are you feeling now?

② No, it's an expression meaning I hope you do well.

③ Who is the man standing by the door?

④ Did you finish talking about your wishes?

⑤ I wish I could have a flying car.

[09~10] 다음 대화를 읽고 물음에 답하시오.

G: I have to sing at the school's English pop song contest.

B: Wow. (A)Break a leg!

G: What? Do you mean I have to break one of my legs?

B: No, (B)네가 잘하기를 바란다는 뜻의 표현이야. (do well, expression, it's, hope, mean).

09 밑줄 친 (A) 대신 쓸 수 있는 말을 고르시오.

① I'll keep my fingers crossed!

② Shake a leg!

③ Don't make a long face!

④ Don't let the cat out of the bag!

⑤ I wish I could have a green thumb!

10 밑줄 친 우리말 (B)를 주어진 어휘를 이용하여 9 단어로 영작하시오.

➡ _____

[11~13] 다음 대화를 읽고 물음에 답하시오.

Anna: What's wrong? You don't look so ① well.

Suho: I'm still thinking about our soccer match last week.

Anna: Do you mean the game you lost last week?

Suho: Yes. I wish I ②could forget about it, but I can't.

Anna: Well, you should always live for today.

Suho: Do you mean I should forget the past and focus ③on the present?

Anna: Yes, exactly. People say, "Yesterday is history, tomorrow is a mystery, and today is a gift. That's ④why it's called the present."

Suho: Now I see. You know so many great expressions. You're as ⑤wise as my grandma.

11 What is the problem with Suho? Answer with 10 words.

  _____

_____

12 위 대화의 내용과 일치하도록 다음 문장의 빈칸에 알맞은 말을 쓰시오.

Anna wants Suho to forget the (A)_____ and live for (B)_____.

13 위 대화의 밑줄 친 ①~⑤에서 어색한 것은?

①   ②   ③   ④   ⑤

14 다음 중 〈보기〉의 문장과 의미가 가장 가까운 것을 고르시오.

┌─ 보기 ─┐

If Brian were in good condition, he would make twice as many buzzer beaters as any other players.

① As Brian was in good condition, he made twice as many buzzer beaters as any other players.

② As Brian was not in good condition, he didn't make twice as many buzzer beaters as any other players.

③ As Brian is not in good condition, he didn't make twice as many buzzer beaters as any other players.

④ As Brian is not in good condition, he doesn't make twice as many buzzer beaters as any other players.

⑤ Though Brian were not in good condition, he made twice as many buzzer beaters as any other players.

15 다음 중 밑줄 친 whose의 쓰임이 나머지와 다른 하나는?

① My friend wants to marry the girl whose father is super rich.

② The author whose latest book sold well will speak in front of the politicians.

③ Is there any movie at your cinema whose title we have heard of?

④ Would you let me know whose pencil Samantha borrowed yesterday?

⑤ The old gentleman whose hobby is playing online shooting games is Yena's grandfather.

[16~17] 다음 각 문장과 가장 가까운 의미가 되도록, 가정법을 이용하여 괄호 안에 주어진 단어를 빈칸에 알맞게 배열해 넣으시오.

16

It is bad that there is no man as wise as Birbal in our country.

➡ It _____

_____.

(if, great, a man, our, were, country, be, there, would, as wise as, in, Birbal)

17

You have to break the pot to take out the pumpkin.

➡ Without _____

_____.

(could, the pot, taken out, not, breaking, the pumpkin, be)

18 다음 밑줄 친 부분 중 어법상 어색한 것을 모두 고르시오.

① Eagles have special eyelids of which move sideways.

② The people whose village my team visited last year were so kind and honest.

③ They raised pandas whose eating habits differed from other bear species.

④ Anna told me about a statue of which the sculptor was my father.

⑤ Greg is the professor the opinion of whom is respected by many students.

19 다음 중 내용상 〈보기〉의 밑줄 친 부분과 바꿔 쓸 때 의미가 다른 것은?

> ┤ 보기 ├
>
> If the athlete were not so short, he could join the national team for Olympics.

① Were the athlete not so short,

② Without the problem of the athlete's height,

③ If it were not for the problem of the athlete's height,

④ Had it not been for the athlete's height,

⑤ Were it not for the problem of the athlete's height,

[20~21] 다음 주어진 두 문장을 관계대명사를 사용해서 하나의 문장으로 만드시오.

20

> • The student is studying foreign languages very hard.
> • Her goal is to become a diplomat.

➡ The student _____

_____.

21

> • The lady's purse was stolen outside the department store.
> • The police came to question her.

➡ The police _____

_____.

[22~25] 다음 글을 읽고 물음에 답하시오.

___ⓐ___ weeks later, Birbal came back with two pots ①whose necks were really narrow. He offered one to the Persian official.

Birbal: You can take this pot of wisdom to your king. Please ask him to return the pot to us after he takes the wisdom out of it.

Birbal: The pot is very precious, so please be careful ②to not break it. We only have two pots of wisdom.

The Persian official looked inside the pot and became speechless.

He thanked Birbal and left for his country.

Persian Official: It would be great if there ③are a man as wise as Birbal in our country.

After the Persian official left, Akbar asked Birbal ④what was inside the pot.

Birbal: Here is ⑤the other pot. You can see for yourself.

Akbar looked inside the other pot and found a pumpkin just as big as the pot.

Akbar: I see! The pumpkin can't be taken out without breaking the pot. How did you do ⓑit?

Birbal: I put the pots over pumpkin flowers and waited until the pumpkins grew as big as the pots.

Akbar: Hahaha! (A)This certainly is a potful of wisdom!

22 위 글의 빈칸 ⓐ에 들어갈 말로 알맞은 것은?

① Few   ② A few

③ A lot   ④ Little

⑤ A little

23 위 글의 밑줄 친 ⓑ가 가리키는 것을 25자 내외의 우리말로 쓰시오.

➡ _____

24 위 글에서 악바르가 밑줄 친 (A)처럼 말한 이유를 알 수 있는 두 문장을 본문에서 찾아 쓰시오.

(1) _____

     _____

(2) _____

     _____

25 위 글의 밑줄 친 ①~⑤에서 어법상 어색한 것을 두 개 골라 바르게 고치고 그 이유를 밝히시오.

➡ _____

이유 _____

     _____

     _____

[26~28] 다음 글을 읽고 물음에 답하시오.

A Shorter Line

One day, Emperor Akbar drew a line on the ground and asked his officials.

Akbar: Make this line shorter without touching it.

Official 1: Without touching (A)it?

Official 2: How can we do that?

Birbal smiled.

Birbal: That's too easy.

Birbal drew a ____ⓐ____ line next to the line that Akbar ____ⓑ____ .

Birbal: Your line is now shorter than mine.

Akbar: You did it, Birbal!

Official 3: I wish I were as wise as Birbal.

26 위 글의 빈칸 ⓐ에 들어갈 말로 알맞은 것을 고르시오.

① equal   ② curved   ③ flat

④ longer   ⑤ shorter

27 위 글의 빈칸 ⓑ에 draw를 어법에 맞게 시간의 차가 드러나도록 쓰시오.

➡ _____

28 위 글의 밑줄 친 (A)가 가리키는 것을 6 단어의 영어로 쓰시오.

➡ _____

INSIGHT
on the textbook

교과서 파헤치기

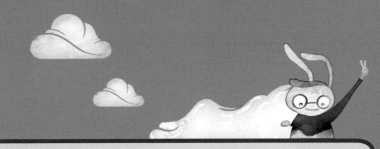

※ 다음 영어를 우리말로 쓰시오.

01	uniquely		22	honestly	
02	check		23	complain	
03	crush		24	passion	
04	unfortunately		25	finish	
05	surely		26	pay	
06	appreciate		27	innovative	
07	fantastic		28	throughout	
08	fix		29	provide	
09	grand		30	form	
10	happen		31	slice	
11	completely		32	fresh	
12	inconvenience		33	gladly	
13	pursue		34	successful	
14	customer		35	fill out	
15	inventor		36	scare away	
16	reason		37	now that	
17	creative		38	as a result	
18	role		39	of all time	
19	real		40	put up	
20	rare		41	be used to	
21	satisfied		42	do one's best	
			43	take charge of	

※ 다음 우리말을 영어로 쓰시오.

01 열정, 흥미 _____

02 진가를 알아보다, 고마워하다 _____

03 계산서 _____

04 ～ 동안 내내 _____

05 덜 익은, 살짝 익힌 _____

06 지불하다, 지급하다 _____

07 수리하다 _____

08 서류 _____

09 확실히, 분명히 _____

10 불편, 애로 _____

11 완전하게 _____

12 기꺼이 _____

13 추구하다, 추진하다 _____

14 이유 _____

15 역할, 배역 _____

16 일어나다 _____

17 불평하다 _____

18 장식하다, 꾸미다 _____

19 환상적인 _____

20 식사 _____

21 신선한 _____

22 솔직하게, 솔직히 _____

23 창의적인, 창조적인 _____

24 으깨다 _____

25 획기적인 _____

26 한 조각, 일부 _____

27 성공적인 _____

28 불행하게도 _____

29 웅장한, 위대한 _____

30 고객, 소비자 _____

31 독특하게 _____

32 만찬, 저녁 식사 _____

33 제공하다 _____

34 만족한 _____

35 ～에 익숙하다 _____

36 작성하다 _____

37 더 이상 아니다 _____

38 결과적으로 _____

39 역대, 지금껏 _____

40 최선을 다하다 _____

41 ～할 마음이 나다 _____

42 내붙이다, 게시하다 _____

43 겁주어 쫓아내다 _____

※ 다음 영영풀이에 알맞은 단어를 <보기>에서 골라 쓴 후, 우리말 뜻을 쓰시오.

1 _____ : the character played by an actor: _____

2 _____ : cooked a short time; still red inside: _____

3 _____ : the foods eaten or prepared for eating at one time: _____

4 _____ : to supply something that is wanted or needed: _____

5 _____ : an informal meal that people eat in the evening: _____

6 _____ : during the whole period of time of something: _____

7 _____ : a bill for the food and drinks that are served in a restaurant: _____

8 _____ : to like something because one recognizes its good qualities: _____

9 _____ : to press something so hard that it breaks or is damaged: _____

10 _____ : someone who buys goods or services from a shop, company, etc.: _____

11 _____ : to make something look more nice by putting something pretty on it: _____

12 _____ : to repair something that is broken or not working properly: _____

13 _____ : an official document with spaces where you write information: _____

14 _____ : a person who has invented something or whose job is inventing things: _____

15 _____ : to say that you are annoyed, not satisfied, or unhappy about something or someone: _____

16 _____ : to make efforts to achieve a particular aim or result, often over a long period of time: _____

보기			
complain	inventor	meal	throughout
crush	decorate	check	rare
pursue	form	provide	role
fix	customer	supper	appreciate

※ 다음 우리말과 일치하도록 빈칸에 알맞은 말을 쓰시오.

Listen & Speak 1 A-1

B: Wow! Did you _____ this?

G: I _____. Do you like _____?

B: Yes, the bread and the milk _____ _____ _____. I _____ _____ _____ _____ _____ _____ _____ _____ _____ the bread.

G: Thanks, but _____ _____ _____ _____ it. It's not _____.

B: I don't think _____. I think it's a _____ _____.

B: 우와! 이거 네가 그린 거야?
G: 내가 그렸어. 마음에 들어?
B: 응, 빵이랑 우유가 정말 진짜 같아. 빵을 한 입 먹고 싶어지는데.
G: 고마워, 하지만 이건 만족스럽진 않아. 독창적이지 않아.
B: 난 그렇게 생각 안 해. 정말 멋진 그림인 것 같아.

Listen & Speak 1 A-2

M: Hello, ma'am. _____ _____ I _____ you?

W: I _____ this phone _____ _____ _____ _____ _____, but it _____ _____ _____ _____ _____ _____.

M: Oh, I see. May I _____ _____ _____ _____ it? (*Pause*) We're sorry for the _____. It'll _____ a _____ _____ _____ _____ it.

W: _____ _____ _____ _____ _____ the phone. I'd _____ a new _____.

M: Of _____. I just need to _____ _____ this _____.

M: 안녕하세요, 고객님. 무엇을 도와드릴까요?
W: 이 휴대전화를 겨우 일주일 전에 샀는데, 가끔 저절로 꺼져요.
M: 오, 그렇군요. 제가 좀 봐도 될까요? 불편을 드려 죄송합니다. 고치는 데 몇 시간 정도 걸릴 거예요.
W: 그 휴대전화가 만족스럽지 않아요. 새것을 원해요.
M: 물론이죠. 이 서류만 작성하면 됩니다.

Listen & Speak 2 A-1

G: Wow, I like this blueberry jam. Where _____ you _____ it?

B: I made it _____.

G: Really? This is _____ _____ _____ _____ _____ _____ I've ever had. You _____ _____ _____ _____.

B: Do you think people _____ want _____ _____ this?

G: Of course. _____ _____ _____ _____ your first customer.

G: 우와, 이 블루베리 잼 마음에 든다. 어디서 샀어?
B: 직접 만든 거야.
G: 정말? 내가 지금껏 먹어본 잼 중에 제일 좋아. 팔아도 되겠어.
B: 사람들이 이걸 사길 원할 거라고 생각해?
G: 물론이지. 내가 너의 첫 손님이 되겠다고 약속할게.

Listen & Speak 2 A-2

B: Mom, I want to go to an arts high school. I want to become an actor.

W: What? I _____ you _____ _____ _____ science.

B: I was but _____ _____. I _____ _____ _____ _____ a movie star.

W: _____ you _____ you want to be an actor?

B: Yes, I'll learn _____ _____ _____ _____. _____ _____ _____ _____.

B: 엄마, 저 예술 고등학교에 가고 싶어요. 배우가 되고 싶어요.
W: 뭐라고? 네가 과학에 관심이 있다고 생각했는데.
B: 그랬었는데 더는 아니에요. 저는 영화배우가 되고 싶어요.
W: 배우가 되고 싶은 게 확실하니?
B: 네, 연기하는 방법을 배울 거예요. 최선을 다하겠다고 약속할게요.

Communicate A

Man: Are you enjoying _____ _____?

Woman: Well, the bread was _____, and the salad was _____.

Man: How _____ your steak?

Woman: Honestly, _____ _____ _____ _____ the steak. It's too _____ for me.

Man: I'm sorry. _____ you _____ me _____ _____ you _____ _____?

Woman: That's O.K. I need to _____ _____. Let me just _____ the _____, please.

Man: I'm really sorry. You _____ _____ _____ the steak.

Woman: O.K. Thanks.

Man: _____ _____ _____ _____ you _____ a better _____ next time you visit.

Progress Check 1

M: Hello, ma'am. _____ _____ _____ help you?

W: I _____ this hat _____ a gift yesterday, but _____ _____ _____ _____ the color.

M: Oh, I see. We have this hat _____ _____ _____.

W: Do you have _____ _____ _____?

M: Yes, we _____. I'll _____ _____ for you.

W: Thanks.

Progress Check 2

B: Mom, I want to _____ cooking _____.

W: What? I thought you were _____ _____ sports.

B: I was but _____ _____. I want to become a _____.

W: Are you sure? Cooking is _____ _____.

B: Don't _____. _____ _____ _____ _____ _____ my best.

W: O.K., _____.

Progress Check 3

G: Dad, I want to watch a movie _____ TV now.

M: _____ you _____ your homework?

G: No, but _____ _____ _____ _____ _____ it after I watch TV.

남자: 식사가 마음에 드십니까?

여자: 음, 빵은 괜찮았고, 샐러드도 신선했어요.

남자: 스테이크는 어떠세요?

여자: 솔직히, 스테이크는 만족스럽지 않아요. 제겐 너무 덜 익었어요.

남자: 죄송합니다. 다른 것으로 가져다 드릴까요?

여자: 괜찮아요. 가봐야 해서요. 그냥 계산서 좀 갖다주세요.

남자: 정말 죄송합니다. 스테이크 값은 지불하지 않으셔도 됩니다.

여자: 알겠습니다. 감사해요.

남자: 다음에 방문하실 때는 더 좋은 경험을 드릴 것을 약속드릴게요.

M: 안녕하세요, 고객님. 무엇을 도와드릴까요?

W: 어제 이 모자를 선물 받았는데, 색상이 마음에 들지 않아요.

M: 오, 그렇군요. 이 모자로 다른 색상도 있습니다.

W: 파란 것도 있나요?

M: 네, 있습니다. 하나 가져다 드릴게요.

W: 고맙습니다.

B: 엄마, 저 요리 수업을 듣고 싶어요.

W: 뭐? 네가 스포츠에 관심이 있다고 생각했는데.

B: 그랬는데 더는 아니에요. 저는 요리사가 되고 싶어요.

W: 정말이니? 요리는 힘든 일이란다.

B: 걱정하지 마세요. 최선을 다하겠다고 약속할게요.

W: 그래, 그럼.

G: 아빠, 저 지금 TV에서 영화를 보고 싶어요.

M: 숙제는 끝냈니?

G: 아니요, 하지만 TV를 보고 나서 끝낼 것을 약속드릴게요.

※ 다음 우리말에 맞도록 대화를 영어로 쓰시오.

Listen & Speak 1 A-1

B: _____

G: _____

B: _____

G: _____

B: _____

B: 우와! 이거 네가 그린 거야?

G: 내가 그렸어. 마음에 들어?

B: 응, 빵이랑 우유가 정말 진짜 같아. 빵을 한 입 먹고 싶어지는데.

G: 고마워, 하지만 이건 만족스럽진 않아. 독창적이지 않아.

B: 난 그렇게 생각 안 해. 정말 멋진 그림인 것 같아.

Listen & Speak 1 A-2

M: _____

W: _____

M: _____

W: _____

M: _____

M: 안녕하세요, 고객님. 무엇을 도와드릴까요?

W: 이 휴대전화를 겨우 일주일 전에 샀는데, 가끔 저절로 꺼져요.

M: 오, 그렇군요. 제가 좀 봐도 될까요? 불편을 드려 죄송합니다. 고치는 데 몇 시간 정도 걸릴 거예요.

W: 그 휴대전화가 만족스럽지 않아요. 새것을 원해요.

M: 물론이죠. 이 서류만 작성하면 됩니다.

Listen & Speak 2 A-1

G: _____

B: _____

G: _____

B: _____

G: _____

G: 우와, 이 블루베리 잼 마음에 든다. 어디서 샀어?

B: 직접 만든 거야.

G: 정말? 내가 지금껏 먹어본 잼 중에 제일 좋아. 팔아도 되겠어.

B: 사람들이 이걸 사길 원할 거라고 생각해?

G: 물론이지. 내가 너의 첫 손님이 되겠다고 약속할게.

Listen & Speak 2 A-2

B: _____

W: _____

B: _____

W: _____

B: _____

B: 엄마, 저 예술 고등학교에 가고 싶어요. 배우가 되고 싶어요.

W: 뭐라고? 네가 과학에 관심이 있다고 생각했는데.

B: 그랬었는데 더는 아니에요. 저는 영화 배우가 되고 싶어요.

W: 배우가 되고 싶은 게 확실하니?

B: 네, 연기하는 방법을 배울 거예요. 최선을 다하겠다고 약속할게요.

Communicate A

Man: _____

Woman: _____

Man: _____

Woman: _____

Man: _____

Woman: _____

Man: _____

Woman: _____

Man: _____

남자: 식사가 마음에 드십니까?
여자: 음, 빵은 괜찮았고, 샐러드도 신선했어요.
남자: 스테이크는 어떠세요?
여자: 솔직히, 스테이크는 만족스럽지 않아요. 제겐 너무 덜 익었어요.
남자: 죄송합니다. 다른 것으로 가져다 드릴까요?
여자: 괜찮아요. 가봐야 해서요. 그냥 계산서 좀 갖다주세요.
남자: 정말 죄송합니다. 스테이크 값은 지불하지 않으셔도 됩니다.
여자: 알겠습니다. 감사해요.
남자: 다음에 방문하실 때는 더 좋은 경험을 드릴 것을 약속드릴게요.

Progress Check 1

M: _____

W: _____

M: _____

W: _____

M: _____

W: _____

M: 안녕하세요, 고객님. 무엇을 도와드릴까요?
W: 어제 이 모자를 선물 받았는데, 색상이 마음에 들지 않아요.
M: 오, 그렇군요. 이 모자로 다른 색상도 있습니다.
W: 파란 것도 있나요?
M: 네, 있습니다. 하나 가져다 드릴게요.
W: 고맙습니다.

Progress Check 2

B: _____

W: _____

B: _____

W: _____

B: _____

W: _____

B: 엄마, 저 요리 수업을 듣고 싶어요.
W: 뭐? 네가 스포츠에 관심이 있다고 생각했는데.
B: 그랬는데 더는 아니에요. 저는 요리사가 되고 싶어요.
W: 정말이니? 요리는 힘든 일이란다.
B: 걱정하지 마세요. 최선을 다하겠다고 약속할게요.
W: 그래, 그럼.

Progress Check 3

G: _____

M: _____

G: _____

G: 아빠, 저 지금 TV에서 영화를 보고 싶어요.
M: 숙제는 끝냈니?
G: 아니요, 하지만 TV를 보고 나서 끝낼 것을 약속드릴게요.

※ 다음 우리말과 일치하도록 빈칸에 알맞은 것을 골라 쓰시오.

1 Da _____ _____ _____

A. Cook   B. the   C. Vinci

2 Leonardo da Vinci is _____ _____ one of the _____ painters of all _____.

A. time   B. known   C. greatest   D. as

3 He was _____ a great _____, scientist, and _____.

A. inventor   B. musician   C. also

4 Very _____ people, _____, know _____ da Vinci was also a _____ cook.

A. creative   B. however   C. few   D. that

5 _____ 1473, twenty-year-old da Vinci _____ _____ a cook _____ a restaurant in Florence, Italy.

A. as   B. in   C. worked   D. at

6 When he _____ _____ of the kitchen, da Vinci _____ the menu _____.

A. changed   B. charge   C. completely   D. took

7 He made _____ but _____ dishes _____ fish with a few carrot _____.

A. slices   B. simple   C. like   D. artistic

8 Some _____ were _____ _____ _____ flowers.

A. decorated   B. dishes   C. with   D. even

9 Customers, however, were unhappy _____ they were _____ to dishes _____ big _____ of meat.

A. servings   B. used   C. with   D. because

10 _____ a _____, da Vinci _____ his _____.

A. lost   B. as   C. job   D. result

11 A _____ years _____, da Vinci _____ a restaurant _____ his friend Sandro Botticelli.

A. opened   B. later   C. few   D. with

12 He wanted to _____ a place _____ people could _____ his _____ food.

A. innovative   B. create   C. try   D. where

13 They _____ _____ a beautifully painted sign and made a _____ _____ menu.

A. uniquely   B. up   C. written   D. put

14 Da Vinci _____ that people would soon _____ his _____ _____.

A. appreciate   B. believed   C. cooking   D. creative

15 _____, that _____ _____.

A. happened   B. unfortunately   C. never

---

1 요리사 다빈치

2 레오나르도 다빈치는 역대 가장 위대한 화가들 중의 한 명으로 알려져 있다.

3 그는 또한 위대한 발명가, 과학자, 그리고 음악가였다.

4 하지만, 극히 소수의 사람들만이 또한 그가 창의적인 요리사였다는 것을 안다.

5 1473년, 스무 살의 레오나르도 다빈치는 이탈리아 플로렌스에 있는 음식점에서 요리사로 일했다.

6 그가 부엌을 책임지게 되었을 때, 다빈치는 메뉴를 완전히 바꿔 버렸다.

7 그는 약간의 당근 조각을 곁들인 생선과 같이 간단하지만 예술적인 음식을 만들었다.

8 몇몇 음식들은 심지어 꽃으로 장식되었다.

9 하지만, 손님들은 많은 양의 고기 요리에 익숙했었기 때문에 불만족스러워했다.

10 그 결과, 다빈치는 그의 직업을 잃었다.

11 몇 년 후, 다빈치는 그의 친구인 산드로 보티첼리와 함께 음식점을 열었다.

12 그는 사람들이 그의 획기적인 음식을 먹어 볼 수 있는 장소로 만들기를 원했다.

13 그들은 아름답게 그려진 간판을 내걸었고 독특하게 써진 메뉴를 만들었다.

14 다빈치는 사람들이 곧 그의 창의적인 요리의 진가를 알아볼 것이라고 믿었다.

15 불행히도, 그런 일은 결코 일어나지 않았다.

16 _____ the _____ 1480s, da Vinci began to _____ _____ Ludovico Sforza in Milan.

    A. work   B. early   C. for   D. in

17 He was given many _____ _____, _____ _____ a musician, a painter, and an engineer.

    A. as   B. different   C. such   D. roles

18 He was also _____ _____ _____ _____ the kitchen.

    A. of   B. put   C. charge   D. in

19 He was happy to be given _____ _____ to _____ his _____ for cooking.

    A. pursue   B. passion   C. chance   D. another

20 Da Vinci did not _____ _____ _____ _____ dishes.

    A. creative   B. stop   C. cooking   D. at

21 He wanted to cook _____ _____ _____ and _____.

    A. easily   B. more   C. much   D. quickly

22 _____, he _____ new _____ for his kitchen.

    A. machines   B. invented   C. thus

23 He _____ machines that could _____ _____ and _____ spaghetti.

    A. crush   B. created   C. pull   D. vegetables

24 He even made a _____ that could _____ frogs _____ the water tank.

    A. from   B. scare   C. device   D. away

25 Surely, they were all very _____, but _____ of them were too big or _____ difficult _____ use.

    A. too   B. innovative   C. most   D. to

26 In 1495, Sforza asked da Vinci to make a _____ painting, which was _____ _____ the last supper of Jesus, on the _____ of a church in Milan.

    A. based   B. wall   C. grand   D. on

27 Da Vinci gladly _____ on the project _____ he had always _____ _____ in food.

    A. interested   B. took   C. been   D. because

28 He _____ a lot of time cooking all _____ of food to decide _____ to _____ on the table in his picture.

    A. kinds   B. what   C. spent   D. put

29 "Da Vinci has _____ his time in the kitchen for _____ a year. That's the _____ why he hasn't finished the painting yet," _____ the people from the church to Sforza.

    A. over   B. complained   C. reason   D. wasted

30 _____ da Vinci never became a _____ cook, he showed great _____ in cooking _____ his life.

    A. throughout   B. successful   C. interest   D. although

31 He was _____ _____ _____ a great painter _____ _____ a creative cook.

    A. also   B. not   C. but   D. only

32 Now _____ you know all about his _____ passion for cooking, you will never look at *The Last Supper* the _____ _____.

    A. same   B. secret   C. that   D. way

16 1480년대 초반에, 다빈치는 밀라노에서 루도비코 스포르차를 위해 일하기 시작했다.

17 그는 음악가, 화가, 그리고 공학자와 같은 많은 역할들을 부여받았다.

18 그는 또한 주방을 책임지게 되었다.

19 그는 요리를 향한 그의 열정을 추구할 또 다른 기회를 얻게 되어 행복했다.

20 다빈치는 창의적인 요리를 만드는 것에 멈추지 않았다.

21 그는 훨씬 더 빠르고 쉽게 요리하고 싶어했다.

22 따라서, 그는 그의 주방에서 사용할 새로운 기계들을 발명하였다.

23 그는 채소를 으깨고 스파게티를 뽑는 기계들을 만들었다.

24 그는 심지어 개구리를 겁주어 물탱크에서 쫓아낼 수 있는 기구도 만들었다.

25 확실히 그것들은 모두 매우 획기적이었지만, 그것들 중 대부분은 사용하기에 너무 크거나 너무 어려웠다.

26 1495년, 스포르차는 다빈치에게 웅장한 그림을 밀라노에 있는 교회의 벽에 그려 달라고 부탁했는데, 그것은 예수의 최후의 만찬을 바탕으로 한 것이었다.

27 다빈치는 기꺼이 그 작업을 맡았는데, 그가 항상 음식에 흥미를 가졌기 때문이었다.

28 그는 그림 속 식탁 위에 어떤 음식을 올릴지 결정하기 위해 모든 종류의 음식을 요리하느라 많은 시간을 썼다.

29 "다빈치는 1년 넘게 부엌에서 시간을 낭비해 오고 있습니다. 그것이 그가 아직도 그림을 끝내지 못한 이유입니다."라고 교회 사람들이 스포르차에게 불평을 했다.

30 다빈치는 결코 성공적인 요리사는 되지 못했지만 그는 그의 생애 내내 요리에 대한 큰 흥미를 보여 주었다.

31 그는 훌륭한 화가일 뿐만 아니라 창의적인 요리사였다.

32 이제 여러분은 요리에 대한 그의 비밀스런 열정을 모두 알게 되었기 때문에 〈최후의 만찬〉을 절대 같은 식으로는 보지 않을 것이다.

Step2

※ 다음 우리말과 일치하도록 빈칸에 알맞은 것을 골라 쓰시오.

1 Da Vinci _____ _____

2 Leonardo da Vinci _____ _____ _____ one of the _____
_____ _____ _____ _____.

3 He was _____ a great _____, _____, and musician.

4 Very _____ people, _____, know that da Vinci was also a
_____ _____.

5 In 1473, _____ da Vinci worked _____ _____
_____ at a restaurant in Florence, Italy.

6 When he _____ _____ _____ the kitchen, da Vinci
_____ the menu _____.

7 He made simple _____ artistic dishes _____ fish with
_____ _____ _____ _____.

8 Some dishes _____ _____ _____ _____ flowers.

9 Customers, _____, were unhappy because they _____
_____ _____ dishes _____ big _____ of meat.

10 _____ _____ _____, da Vinci lost his job.

11 _____ _____ years _____, da Vinci opened a restaurant
with his friend Sandro Botticelli.

12 He wanted _____ _____ a place _____ people could try
his _____ food.

13 They _____ _____ a _____ _____ sign and made a
_____ _____ menu.

14 Da Vinci believed that people _____ soon _____ his _____
cooking.

15 _____, that never _____.

1 요리사 다빈치

2 레오나르도 다빈치는 역대 가장 위대한 화가들 중의 한 명으로 알려져 있다.

3 그는 또한 위대한 발명가, 과학자, 그리고 음악가였다.

4 하지만, 극히 소수의 사람들만이 또한 그가 창의적인 요리사였다는 것을 안다.

5 1473년, 스무 살의 레오나르도 다빈치는 이탈리아 플로렌스에 있는 음식점에서 요리사로 일했다.

6 그가 부엌을 책임지게 되었을 때, 다빈치는 메뉴를 완전히 바꿔 버렸다.

7 그는 약간의 당근 조각을 곁들인 생선과 같이 간단하지만 예술적인 음식을 만들었다.

8 몇몇 음식들은 심지어 꽃으로 장식되었다.

9 하지만, 손님들은 많은 양의 고기 요리에 익숙했었기 때문에 불만족스러워했다.

10 그 결과, 다빈치는 그의 직업을 잃었다.

11 몇 년 후, 다빈치는 그의 친구인 산드로 보티첼리와 함께 음식점을 열었다.

12 그는 사람들이 그의 획기적인 음식을 먹어 볼 수 있는 장소로 만들기를 원했다.

13 그들은 아름답게 그려진 간판을 내걸었고 독특하게 써진 메뉴를 만들었다.

14 다빈치는 사람들이 곧 그의 창의적인 요리의 진가를 알아볼 것이라고 믿었다.

15 불행히도, 그런 일은 결코 일어나지 않았다.

16 In the _____ 1480s, da Vinci began _____ _____ for Ludovico Sforza in Milan.

17 He _____ _____ many different _____, _____ _____ a musician, a painter, and an engineer.

18 He _____ also _____ _____ _____ _____ the kitchen.

19 He was happy _____ _____ _____ _____ chance _____ _____ his _____ for cooking.

20 Da Vinci did not _____ cooking creative dishes.

21 He wanted to cook _____ _____ quickly and easily.

22 _____, he _____ new machines for his kitchen.

23 He created machines _____ could _____ vegetables and pull spaghetti.

24 He even made a device _____ could _____ frogs _____ _____ the water tank.

25 Surely, they were all very innovative, but most of them _____ _____ big or _____ difficult _____ _____.

26 In 1495, Sforza asked da Vinci _____ _____ a grand painting, _____ _____ _____ _____ the last supper of Jesus, on the wall of a church in Milan.

27 Da Vinci gladly _____ _____ the project because he _____ always _____ _____ _____ food.

28 He spent _____ _____ _____ time _____ all kinds of food to decide _____ _____ _____ on the table in his picture.

29 "Da Vinci has wasted his time in the kitchen _____ _____ a year. That's the reason _____ he hasn't finished the painting yet," complained the people from the church _____ Sforza.

30 _____ da Vinci never became a successful cook, he showed great _____ _____ cooking _____ his life.

31 He was _____ _____ a great painter _____ _____ _____ a _____ _____.

32 _____ _____ you know all about his _____ _____ for cooking, you will never look at *The Last Supper* _____ _____ _____.

16 1480년대 초반에, 다빈치는 밀라노에서 루도비코 스포르차를 위해 일하기 시작했다.

17 그는 음악가, 화가, 그리고 공학자와 같은 많은 역할들을 부여받았다.

18 그는 또한 주방을 책임지게 되었다.

19 그는 요리를 향한 그의 열정을 추구할 또 다른 기회를 얻게 되어 행복했다.

20 다빈치는 창의적인 요리를 만드는 것에 멈추지 않았다.

21 그는 훨씬 더 빠르고 쉽게 요리하고 싶어했다.

22 따라서, 그는 그의 주방에서 사용할 새로운 기계들을 발명하였다.

23 그는 채소를 으깨고 스파게티를 뽑는 기계들을 만들었다.

24 그는 심지어 개구리를 겁주어 물탱크에서 쫓아낼 수 있는 기구도 만들었다.

25 확실히 그것들은 모두 매우 획기적이었지만, 그것들 중 대부분은 사용하기에 너무 크거나 너무 어려웠다.

26 1495년, 스포르차는 다빈치에게 웅장한 그림을 밀라노에 있는 교회의 벽에 그려 달라고 부탁했는데, 그것은 예수의 최후의 만찬을 바탕으로 한 것이었다.

27 다빈치는 기꺼이 그 작업을 맡았는데, 그가 항상 음식에 흥미를 가졌기 때문이었다.

28 그는 그림 속 식탁 위에 어떤 음식을 올릴지 결정하기 위해 모든 종류의 음식을 요리하느라 많은 시간을 썼다.

29 "다빈치는 1년 넘게 부엌에서 시간을 낭비해 오고 있습니다. 그것이 그가 아직도 그림을 끝내지 못한 이유입니다."라고 교회 사람들이 스포르차에게 불평을 했다.

30 다빈치는 결코 성공적인 요리사는 되지 못했지만 그는 그의 생애 내내 요리에 대한 큰 흥미를 보여 주었다.

31 그는 훌륭한 화가일 뿐만 아니라 창의적인 요리사였다.

32 이제 여러분은 요리에 대한 그의 비밀스런 열정을 모두 알게 되었기 때문에 〈최후의 만찬〉을 절대 같은 식으로는 보지 않을 것이다.

※ 다음 문장을 우리말로 쓰시오.

1 Da Vinci the Cook
➡ _____

2 Leonardo da Vinci is known as one of the greatest painters of all time.
➡ _____

3 He was also a great inventor, scientist, and musician.
➡ _____

4 Very few people, however, know that da Vinci was also a creative cook.
➡ _____

5 In 1473, twenty-year-old da Vinci worked as a cook at a restaurant in Florence, Italy.
➡ _____

6 When he took charge of the kitchen, da Vinci changed the menu completely.
➡ _____

7 He made simple but artistic dishes like fish with a few carrot slices.
➡ _____

8 Some dishes were even decorated with flowers.
➡ _____

9 Customers, however, were unhappy because they were used to dishes with big servings of meat.
➡ _____

10 As a result, da Vinci lost his job.
➡ _____

11 A few years later, da Vinci opened a restaurant with his friend Sandro Botticelli.
➡ _____

12 He wanted to create a place where people could try his innovative food.
➡ _____

13 They put up a beautifully painted sign and made a uniquely written menu.
➡ _____

14 Da Vinci believed that people would soon appreciate his creative cooking.
➡ _____

15 Unfortunately, that never happened.
➡ _____

16 In the early 1480s, da Vinci began to work for Ludovico Sforza in Milan.
➡ _____

17 He was given many different roles, such as a musician, a painter, and an engineer.
➡ _____

18 He was also put in charge of the kitchen.

➡ _____

19 He was happy to be given another chance to pursue his passion for cooking.

➡ _____

20 Da Vinci did not stop at cooking creative dishes.

➡ _____

21 He wanted to cook much more quickly and easily.

➡ _____

22 Thus, he invented new machines for his kitchen.

➡ _____

23 He created machines that could crush vegetables and pull spaghetti.

➡ _____

24 He even made a device that could scare frogs away from the water tank.

➡ _____

25 Surely, they were all very innovative, but most of them were too big or too difficult to use.

➡ _____

26 In 1495, Sforza asked da Vinci to make a grand painting, which was based on the last supper of Jesus, on the wall of a church in Milan.

➡ _____

_____

27 Da Vinci gladly took on the project because he had always been interested in food.

➡ _____

28 He spent a lot of time cooking all kinds of food to decide what to put on the table in his picture.

➡ _____

29 "Da Vinci has wasted his time in the kitchen for over a year. That's the reason why he hasn't finished the painting yet," complained the people from the church to Sforza.

➡ _____

_____

30 Although da Vinci never became a successful cook, he showed great interest in cooking throughout his life.

➡ _____

31 He was not only a great painter but also a creative cook.

➡ _____

32 Now that you know all about his secret passion for cooking, you will never look at *The Last Supper* the same way.

➡ _____

_____

※ 다음 괄호 안의 단어들을 우리말에 맞도록 바르게 배열하시오.

1 (Vinci / Da / Cook / the)

➡ _____

2 (da / Leonardo / Vinci / known / is / one / as / the / of / painters / greatest / all / of / time.)

➡ _____

3 (was / he / also / a / inventor, / great / musician. / and / scientist,)

➡ _____

4 (few / very / people, / know / however, / that / Vinci / da / also / was / a / cook. / creative)

➡ _____

5 (1473, / in / twenty-year-old / da / worked / Vinci / a / as / cook / a / at / restaurant / in / Italy. / Florence,)

➡ _____
_____

6 (he / when / took / of / charge / kitchen, / the / Vinci / da / the / changed / completely. / menu)

➡ _____

7 (made / he / simple / artistic / but / like / dishes / with / fish / few / a / slices. / carrot)

➡ _____

8 (dishes / some / even / were / with / decorated / flowers.)

➡ _____

9 (however, / customers, / unhappy / were / they / because / were / used / dishes / to / big / with / of / servings / meat.)

➡ _____
_____

10 (a / as / result, / Vinci / da / his / lost / job.)

➡ _____

11 (few / a / later, / years / Vinci / da / a / opened / restaurant / his / with / Sandro / friend / Botticelli.)

➡ _____

1 요리사 다빈치

2 레오나르도 다빈치는 역대 가장 위대한 화가들 중의 한 명으로 알려져 있다.

3 그는 또한 위대한 발명가, 과학자, 그리고 음악가였다.

4 하지만, 극히 소수의 사람들만이 또한 그가 창의적인 요리사였다는 것을 안다.

5 1473년, 스무 살의 레오나르도 다빈치는 이탈리아 플로렌스에 있는 음식점에서 요리사로 일했다.

6 그가 부엌을 책임지게 되었을 때, 다빈치는 메뉴를 완전히 바꿔 버렸다.

7 그는 약간의 당근 조각을 곁들인 생선과 같이 간단하지만 예술적인 음식을 만들었다.

8 몇몇 음식들은 심지어 꽃으로 장식되었다.

9 하지만, 손님들은 많은 양의 고기 요리에 익숙했기 때문에 불만족스러워했다.

10 그 결과, 다빈치는 그의 직업을 잃었다.

11 몇 년 후, 다빈치는 그의 친구인 산드로 보티첼리와 함께 음식점을 열었다.

12 (wanted / he / create / to / place / a / where / could / people / his / try / food. / innovative)

➡ _____

_____

13 (put / they / up / beautifully / a / painted / and / sign / made / uniquely / a / menu. / written)

➡ _____

_____

14 (Vinci / da / believed / people / that / soon / would / appreciate / creative / his / cooking.)

➡ _____

_____

15 (that / unfortunately, / happened. / never)

➡ _____

16 (the / in / 1480s, / early / Vinci / da / to / began / for / work / Sforza / Ludovico / Milan. / in)

➡ _____

17 (was / he / many / given / roles, / different / as / such / musician, / a / painter, / a / and / engineer. / an)

➡ _____

18 (was / he / put / also / charge / in / the / of / kitchen.)

➡ _____

19 (was / he / to / happy / given / be / chance / another / pursue / to / passion / his / cooking. / for)

➡ _____

_____

20 (Vinci / da / not / did / at / stop / creative / cooking / dishes.)

➡ _____

21 (wanted / he / cook / to / more / much / easily. / and / quickly)

➡ _____

12 그는 사람들이 그의 획기적인 음식을 먹어 볼 수 있는 장소로 만들기를 원했다.

13 그들은 아름답게 그려진 간판을 내걸었고 독특하게 써진 메뉴를 만들었다.

14 다빈치는 사람들이 곧 그의 창의적인 요리의 진가를 알아볼 것이라고 믿었다.

15 불행히도, 그런 일은 결코 일어나지 않았다.

16 1480년대 초반에, 다빈치는 밀라노에서 루도비코 스포르차를 위해 일하기 시작했다.

17 그는 음악가, 화가, 그리고 공학자와 같은 많은 역할들을 부여받았다.

18 그는 또한 주방을 책임지게 되었다.

19 그는 요리를 향한 그의 열정을 추구할 또 다른 기회를 얻게 되어 행복했다.

20 다빈치는 창의적인 요리를 만드는 것에 멈추지 않았다.

21 그는 훨씬 더 빠르고 쉽게 요리하고 싶어했다.

Step4

22 (he / thus, / iinvented / machines / new / his / for / kitchen.)

➡ _____

23 (created / he / that / machines / crush / could / vegetables / pull / and / spaghetti.)

➡ _____

24 (even / he / a / made / that / device / scare / could / away / frogs / the / from / tank. / water)

➡ _____

25 (they / surely, / were / very / all / innovative, / of / but / most / them / too / were / big / too / or / difficult / use. / to)

➡ _____

26 (1495, / in / asked / Sforza / Vinci / da / make / to / grand / a / painting, / was / which / on / based / the / supper / last / Jesus, / of / the / on / wall / a / of / in / church / Milan.)

➡ _____

27 (Vinci / da / took / gladly / the / on / because / project / had / he / been / always / interested / food. / in)

➡ _____

28 (spent / he / lot / a / of / cooking / time / all / of / kinds / to / food / what / decide / to / on / put / table / the / his / in / picture.)

➡ _____

29 (Vinci / "da / wasted / has / time / his / the / in / for / kitchen / over / year. / a // the / that's / why / reason / hasn't / he / the / finished / yet," / painting / `complained / people / the / from / church / the / Sforza. / to)

➡ _____

30 (da / although / Vinci / became / never / a / cook, / successful / showed / he / interest / great / cooking / in / his / throughout / life.)

➡ _____

31 (was / he / only / not / great / a / but / painter / also / creative / a / cook.)

➡ _____

32 (that / now / know / you / about / all / secret / his / for / passion / cooking, / will / you / look / never / *The* / at / *Supper* / *Last* / same / the / way.)

➡ _____

_____

22 따라서, 그는 그의 주방에서 사용할 새로운 기계들을 발명하였다.

23 그는 채소를 으깨고 스파게티를 뽑는 기계들을 만들었다.

24 그는 심지어 개구리를 겁주어 물탱크에서 쫓아낼 수 있는 기구도 만들었다.

25 확실히 그것들은 모두 매우 획기적이었지만, 그것들 중 대부분은 사용하기에 너무 크거나 너무 어려웠다.

26 1495년, 스포르차는 다빈치에게 웅장한 그림을 밀라노에 있는 교회의 벽에 그려 달라고 부탁했는데, 그것은 예수의 최후의 만찬을 바탕으로 한 것이었다.

27 다빈치는 기꺼이 그 작업을 맡았는데, 그가 항상 음식에 흥미를 가졌기 때문이었다.

28 그는 그림 속 식탁 위에 어떤 음식을 올릴지 결정하기 위해 모든 종류의 음식을 요리하느라 많은 시간을 썼다.

29 "다빈치는 1년 넘게 부엌에서 시간을 낭비해 오고 있습니다. 그것이 그가 아직도 그림을 끝내지 못한 이유입니다."라고 교회 사람들이 스포르차에게 불평을 했다.

30 다빈치는 결코 성공적인 요리사는 되지 못했지만 그는 그의 생애 내내 요리에 대한 큰 흥미를 보여 주었다.

31 그는 훌륭한 화가일 뿐만 아니라 창의적인 요리사였다.

32 이제 여러분은 요리에 대한 그의 비밀스런 열정을 모두 알게 되었기 때문에 〈최후의 만찬〉을 절대 같은 식으로는 보지 않을 것이다.

※ 다음 우리말을 영어로 쓰시오.

1 요리사 다빈치

➡ _____

2 레오나르도 다빈치는 역대 가장 위대한 화가들 중의 한 명으로 알려져 있다.

➡ _____

3 그는 또한 위대한 발명가, 과학자, 그리고 음악가였다.

➡ _____

4 하지만, 극히 소수의 사람들만이 또한 그가 창의적인 요리사였다는 것을 안다.

➡ _____

5 1473년, 스무 살의 레오나르도 다빈치는 이탈리아 플로렌스에 있는 음식점에서 요리사로 일했다.

➡ _____

6 그가 부엌을 책임지게 되었을 때, 다빈치는 메뉴를 완전히 바꿔 버렸다.

➡ _____

7 그는 약간의 당근 조각을 곁들인 생선과 같이 간단하지만 예술적인 음식을 만들었다.

➡ _____

8 몇몇 음식들은 심지어 꽃으로 장식되었다.

➡ _____

9 하지만, 손님들은 많은 양의 고기 요리에 익숙했었기 때문에 불만족스러워했다.

➡ _____

10 그 결과, 다빈치는 그의 직업을 잃었다.

➡ _____

11 몇 년 후, 다빈치는 그의 친구인 산드로 보티첼리와 함께 음식점을 열었다.

➡ _____

12 그는 사람들이 그의 획기적인 음식을 먹어 볼 수 있는 장소로 만들기를 원했다.

➡ _____

13 그들은 아름답게 그려진 간판을 내걸었고 독특하게 써진 메뉴를 만들었다.

➡ _____

14 다빈치는 사람들이 곧 그의 창의적인 요리의 진가를 알아볼 것이라고 믿었다.

➡ _____

15 불행히도, 그런 일은 결코 일어나지 않았다.

➡ _____

16 1480년대 초반에, 다빈치는 밀라노에서 루도비코 스포르차를 위해 일하기 시작했다.

➡ _____

17 그는 음악가, 화가, 그리고 공학자와 같은 많은 역할들을 부여받았다.

➡ _____

18 그는 또한 주방을 책임지게 되었다.
➡ _____

19 그는 요리를 향한 그의 열정을 추구할 또 다른 기회를 얻게 되어 행복했다.
➡ _____

20 다빈치는 창의적인 요리를 만드는 것에 멈추지 않았다.
➡ _____

21 그는 훨씬 더 빠르고 쉽게 요리하고 싶어했다.
➡ _____

22 따라서, 그는 그의 주방에서 사용할 새로운 기계들을 발명하였다.
➡ _____

23 그는 채소를 으깨고 스파게티를 뽑는 기계들을 만들었다.
➡ _____

24 그는 심지어 개구리를 겁주어 물탱크에서 쫓아낼 수 있는 기구도 만들었다.
➡ _____

25 확실히 그것들은 모두 매우 획기적이었지만, 그것들 중 대부분은 사용하기에 너무 크거나 너무 어려웠다.
➡ _____

26 1495년, 스포르차는 다빈치에게 웅장한 그림을 밀라노에 있는 교회의 벽에 그려 달라고 부탁했는데, 그것은 예수의 최후의 만찬을 바탕으로 한 것이었다.
➡ _____
_____

27 다빈치는 기꺼이 그 작업을 맡았는데, 그가 항상 음식에 흥미를 가졌기 때문이었다.
➡ _____

28 그는 그림 속 식탁 위에 어떤 음식을 올릴지 결정하기 위해 모든 종류의 음식을 요리하느라 많은 시간을 썼다.
➡ _____

29 "다빈치는 1년 넘게 부엌에서 시간을 낭비해 오고 있습니다. 그것이 그가 아직도 그림을 끝내지 못한 이유입니다."라고 교회 사람들이 스포르차에게 불평을 했다.
➡ _____

30 다빈치는 결코 성공적인 요리사는 되지 못했지만 그는 그의 생애 내내 요리에 대한 큰 흥미를 보여 주었다.
➡ _____

31 그는 훌륭한 화가일 뿐만 아니라 창의적인 요리사였다.
➡ _____

32 이제 여러분은 요리에 대한 그의 비밀스런 열정을 모두 알게 되었기 때문에 〈최후의 만찬〉을 절대 같은 식으로는 보지 않을 것이다.
➡ _____
_____

※ 다음 우리말과 일치하도록 빈칸에 알맞은 말을 쓰시오.

Write

1. My name is Kim Jieun. I am _____ _____ _____ _____
   _____.

2. There was a _____ _____ when I _____ _____ _____
   _____ to be.

3. _____ _____ 2030, I made a _____ _____ _____
   _____.

4. It was a _____ _____ _____ _____ about _____
   _____ for arts.

5. Thus, I _____ _____ go to a _____ _____ _____.

6. _____ I _____ _____ high school, I _____ Korea Art
   College and _____ more about _____ and _____.

7. _____ _____, I _____ my first _____.

8. I _____ very _____ _____ my life.

1. 내 이름은 김지은이다. 나는 기술을 사용하는 예술가다.
2. 내가 예술가가 되기로 결심했을 때 특별한 순간이 있었다.
3. 2030년에, 나는 기술을 사용해 작은 동상을 만들었다.
4. 그것은 예술을 위한 기술을 배우는 데에 아주 좋은 기회였다.
5. 따라서, 나는 기술 고등학교에 진학하기로 결심했다.
6. 고등학교를 졸업한 뒤, 나는 한국 예술 대학에 입학해서 예술과 기술에 대해 더 배웠다.
7. 올해, 나는 내 첫 전시회를 열었다.
8. 나는 내 인생에 매우 만족한다.

Link

1. Some people think creativity is _____ _____
   _____ _____ when they _____ _____ _____.

2. They like to _____ _____ _____ new ideas and _____
   _____ _____.

3. Thus, they want to _____ _____ _____ _____ _____
   they can _____ _____ _____.

1. 어떤 사람들은 직업을 선택할 때 고려해야 할 가장 중요한 것은 창의력이라고 생각한다.
2. 그들은 새로운 아이디어를 떠올리고 새로운 것들을 구상하기를 좋아한다.
3. 따라서, 그들은 그들의 창의력을 발휘할 수 있는 곳에서 일하기를 원한다.

Watch and Think Share

1. Winston Churchill _____ _____ _____ _____ the Prime
   Minister of the United Kingdom _____ World War II.

2. Very _____ _____, _____, know that he was also a _____,
   a _____, and a _____.

3. He even _____ the _____ _____ _____ _____ in
   1953.

1. Winston Churchill은 제 2차 세계대전 중 영국의 수상이었던 것으로 알려져 있다.
2. 하지만, 극소수의 사람들은 그가 또한 사학자이며, 화가이자, 작가임을 알고 있다.
3. 심지어 그는 1953년에 노벨 문학상을 수상하기도 했다.

※ 다음 우리말을 영어로 쓰시오.

Write

1. 내 이름은 김지은이다. 나는 기술을 사용하는 예술가다.
   ➡ _____

2. 내가 예술가가 되기로 결심했을 때 특별한 순간이 있었다.
   ➡ _____

3. 2030년에, 나는 기술을 사용해 작은 동상을 만들었다.
   ➡ _____

4. 그것은 예술을 위한 기술을 배우는 데에 아주 좋은 기회였다.
   ➡ _____

5. 따라서, 나는 기술 고등학교에 진학하기로 결심했다.
   ➡ _____

6. 고등학교를 졸업한 뒤, 나는 한국 예술 대학에 입학해서 예술과 기술에 대해 더 배웠다.
   ➡ _____
   _____

7. 올해, 나는 내 첫 전시회를 열었다.
   ➡ _____

8. 나는 내 인생에 매우 만족한다.
   ➡ _____

Link

1. 어떤 사람들은 직업을 선택할 때 고려해야 할 가장 중요한 것은 창의력이라고 생각한다.
   ➡ _____

2. 그들은 새로운 아이디어를 떠올리고 새로운 것들을 구상하기를 좋아한다.
   ➡ _____

3. 따라서, 그들은 그들의 창의력을 발휘할 수 있는 곳에서 일하기를 원한다.
   ➡ _____

Watch and Think Share

1. Winston Churchill은 제 2차 세계대전 중 영국의 수상이었던 것으로 알려져 있다.
   ➡ _____

2. 하지만, 극소수의 사람들은 그가 또한 사학자이며, 화가이자, 작가임을 알고 있다.
   ➡ _____

3. 심지어 그는 1953년에 노벨 문학상을 수상하기도 했다.
   ➡ _____

※ 다음 영어를 우리말로 쓰시오.

01	precious	_____
02	correct	_____
03	exactly	_____
04	official	_____
05	potful	_____
06	honesty	_____
07	indeed	_____
08	among	_____
09	break	_____
10	journey	_____
11	strange	_____
12	match	_____
13	wise	_____
14	wit	_____
15	narrow	_____
16	offer	_____
17	court	_____
18	emperor	_____
19	worm	_____
20	policy	_____
21	sweet	_____

22	punish	_____
23	pumpkin	_____
24	return	_____
25	expression	_____
26	favor	_____
27	speechless	_____
28	thus	_____
29	wisdom	_____
30	present	_____
31	certainly	_____
32	must	_____
33	pull	_____
34	exam	_____
35	for oneself	_____
36	hand in	_____
37	come up with	_____
38	thanks to	_____
39	focus on	_____
40	in one's place	_____
41	make sense	_____
42	be famous for	_____
43	a potful of	_____

※ 다음 우리말을 영어로 쓰시오.

01 지혜로운, 현명한 _____

02 표현 _____

03 청, 부탁 _____

04 ~ 중에, ~의 사이에 _____

05 틀림없이, 분명히 _____

06 선물 _____

07 정직 _____

08 처벌하다, 벌주다 _____

09 좁은 _____

10 귀중한, 값비싼 _____

11 맞는, 정확한 _____

12 현재, 지금 _____

13 고위 공무원, 관리 _____

14 이상한 _____

15 정말, 확실히 _____

16 정책 _____

17 여행, 여정 _____

18 (땅속에 사는) 벌레 _____

19 경기, 시합 _____

20 호박 _____

21 깨지다, 부러뜨리다 _____

22 황제 _____

23 대궐, 궁궐 _____

24 (화나거나 놀라서) 말을 못 하는 _____

25 시험 _____

26 기지, 재치 _____

27 과거 _____

28 정확하게 _____

29 되돌려주다 _____

30 사탕, 단것 _____

31 그러므로 _____

32 지혜, 슬기, 현명함 _____

33 한 항아리의 양 _____

34 내놓다, 제공하다 _____

35 제출하다 _____

36 ~에 주력하다, 집중하다 _____

37 다시 한 번 _____

38 ~의 처지에서, ~의 상황에서 _____

39 혼자서, 스스로 _____

40 ~을 찾아내다, ~을 떠올리다 _____

41 ~로 유명하다 _____

42 ~ 덕분에 _____

43 타당하다, 말이 되다 _____

※ 다음 영영풀이에 알맞은 단어를 <보기>에서 골라 쓴 후, 우리말 뜻을 쓰시오.

1 _____ : the quality of being honest:

2 _____ : existing or happening now: _____

3 _____ : rare and worth a lot of money: _____

4 _____ : to go away from a place or a person: _____

5 _____ : the man who is the ruler of an empire: _____

6 _____ : accurate or true, without any mistakes: _____

7 _____ : the place where a king or queen lives and works: _____

8 _____ : a large round vegetable with thick orange skin: _____

9 _____ : an occasion when you travel from one place to another: _____

10 _____ : an organized sport event between two teams or people: _____

11 _____ : a long, thin creature with a soft body and no bones or legs: _____

12 _____ : measuring only a small distance from one side to the other, not wide: _____

13 _____ : someone who is in a position of authority in an organization: _____

14 _____ : a thing that you give to somebody, especially on a special occasion or to say thank you: _____

15 _____ : to make somebody suffer because they have broken the law or done something wrong: _____

16 _____ : not able to speak, especially because you are extremely angry or surprised: _____

보기			
precious	honesty	worm	match
speechless	gift	pumpkin	emperor
leave	present	narrow	journey
official	punish	correct	court

※ 다음 우리말과 일치하도록 빈칸에 알맞은 말을 쓰시오.

Listen & Speak 1 A-1

G: You _____ _____ this morning.

B: I _____ _____ very early _____ _____ for the exam.

G: _____ _____ you. The _____ _____ catches the _____.

B: No. The early bird _____ _____ quickly.

G: _____ _____ _____ you don't like to get up early?

B: Yes, that's _____ _____ _____ _____.

> G: 오늘 아침 너 피곤해 보인다.
> B: 시험 공부를 하려고 아주 일찍 일어났거든.
> G: 잘했어. 일찍 일어나는 새가 벌레를 잡는 법이지.
> B: 아니. 일찍 일어나는 새가 빨리 지쳐.
> G: 일찍 일어나는 게 싫다는 말이야?
> B: 응, 정확히 그런 뜻이야.

Listen & Speak 1 A-2

G: I _____ _____ sing at the school's English pop song contest.

B: Wow. Break _____ _____!

G: What? _____ _____ _____ I have to _____ _____ of my _____?

B: No, it's an _____ _____ I hope _____ _____ _____.

> G: 나는 학교의 영어 팝송 부르기 대회에서 노래를 해야 해.
> B: 우와. 행운을 빌어!
> G: 뭐? 내가 내 다리 한 쪽을 부러뜨려야 한다는 말이야?
> B: 아니, 네가 잘하길 빈다는 뜻의 표현이야.

Listen & Speak 2 A-1

B: Wow, you really _____ _____.

G: Thanks. I love dancing. _____ in my family _____ _____ _____ dancing.

B: Really? Your parents dance well, _____?

G: Yes. They're also _____ _____.

B: _____ _____ family! _____ _____ _____ dance _____ you.

> B: 우와, 너 춤 정말 잘 춘다.
> G: 고마워. 나 춤추는 거 정말 좋아해. 우리 가족 모두가 춤을 잘 춰.
> B: 정말? 너희 부모님도 춤을 잘 추시니?
> G: 맞아. 노래도 잘하셔.
> B: 굉장한 가족이다! 나도 너처럼 춤을 출 수 있으면 좋겠어.

Listen & Speak 2 A-2

B: Hello, everyone! Time flies. I _____ _____ it's time _____ _____ goodbye. _____ _____ my teachers and friends, I was really happy here. _____ _____ _____ _____ go _____ _____ my first year and live these years over again, but it's time _____ _____ a _____ _____ to high school. I hope I can see you again. Thank you.

> B: 안녕, 모두들! 시간이 참 빠르네요. 이제 작별 인사를 해야 할 시간이라는 게 믿어지지 않아요. 선생님들과 친구들 덕분에, 이곳에서 정말 행복했어요. 첫 해로 돌아가서 이 해들을 다시 지낼 수 있다면 좋겠지만, 이제는 고등학교로 새로운 여행을 떠나야 할 시간이에요. 여러분을 다시 볼 수 있다면 좋겠어요. 고맙습니다.

Communicate A

Anna: What's _____? You don't _____ so _____.

Suho: I'm still _____ _____ our soccer match last week.

Anna: _____ _____ _____ the game you _____ last week?

Suho: Yes. _____ _____ _____ _____ forget about it, but I can't.

Anna: Well, you should always _____ _____ _____.

Suho: _____ _____ _____ I should forget the past and _____ _____ the present?

Anna: Yes, _____. People say, "Yesterday is history, tomorrow is a mystery, and today is a _____. That's _____ it's _____ the present."

Suho: Now I see. You know so many great _____. You're _____ _____ _____ my grandma.

Progress Check 1

G: You _____ _____. Is something _____?

B: I had to _____ _____ my science report _____ yesterday, but I didn't.

G: It's _____ _____ _____ _____.

B: _____ _____ _____ it's better to _____ _____ _____ _____ _____ it's _____?

G: Yes, exactly. You should always finish _____ you've started.

Progress Check 2

B: Wow, you _____ _____ _____ so well.

G: Thanks. I love playing the guitar. I learned _____ from my dad.

B: Really? Does your father play the guitar, _____?

G: Yes. He was _____ a famous band.

B: _____ _____ family! _____ _____ I _____ play the guitar _____ you.

Progress Check 3

M: You _____ your friend's phone, and you don't know _____ _____ _____. _____ friend says to you, "_____ is the best _____." You don't know _____ _____ _____ exactly.

※ 다음 우리말에 맞도록 대화를 영어로 쓰시오.

Listen & Speak 1 A-1

G: _____

B: _____

G: _____

B: _____

G: _____

B: _____

G: 오늘 아침 너 피곤해 보인다.
B: 시험 공부를 하려고 아주 일찍 일어났거든.
G: 잘했어. 일찍 일어나는 새가 벌레를 잡는 법이지.
B: 아니. 일찍 일어나는 새가 빨리 지쳐.
G: 일찍 일어나는 게 싫다는 말이야?
B: 응, 정확히 그런 뜻이야.

Listen & Speak 1 A-2

G: _____

B: _____

G: _____

B: _____

G: 나는 학교의 영어 팝송 부르기 대회에서 노래를 해야 해.
B: 우와. 행운을 빌어!
G: 뭐? 내가 내 다리 한 쪽을 부러뜨려야 한다는 말이야?
B: 아니, 네가 잘하길 빈다는 뜻의 표현이야.

Listen & Speak 2 A-1

B: _____

G: _____

B: _____

G: _____

B: _____

B: 우와, 너 춤 정말 잘 춘다.
G: 고마워. 나 춤추는 거 정말 좋아해. 우리 가족 모두가 춤을 잘 춰.
B: 정말? 너희 부모님도 춤을 잘 추시니?
G: 맞아. 노래도 잘하셔.
B: 굉장한 가족이다! 나도 너처럼 춤을 출 수 있으면 좋겠어.

Listen & Speak 2 A-2

B: _____

_____

_____

B: 안녕, 모두들! 시간이 참 빠르네요. 이제 작별 인사를 해야 할 시간이라는 게 믿어지지 않아요. 선생님들과 친구들 덕분에, 이곳에서 정말 행복했어요. 첫 해로 돌아가서 이 해들을 다시 지낼 수 있다면 좋겠지만, 이제는 고등학교로 새로운 여행을 떠나야 할 시간이에요. 여러분을 다시 볼 수 있다면 좋겠어요. 고맙습니다.

Communicate A

Anna: _____

Suho: _____

Anna: _____

Suho: _____

Anna: _____

Suho: _____

Anna: _____
_____

Suho: _____
_____

Anna: 무슨 일 있니? 별로 좋아 보이질 않네.
수호: 지난주 우리의 축구 시합을 어진 히 생각하고 있어.
Anna: 지난주에 진 게임 말이니?
수호: 응. 그걸 잊을 수 있음 좋겠는데, 못하겠네.
Anna: 음, 넌 항상 오늘을 살아야 해.
수호: 과거는 잊고 현재에 집중해야 한 다는 뜻이니?
Anna: 그래, 바로 그거야. 사람들이 "어 제는 역사, 내일은 미스터리, 그 리고 오늘은 선물이다. 그게 바 로 오늘을 선물이라 부르는 이 유."라고 하잖아.
수호: 그렇구나. 넌 정말 좋은 표현들을 많이 알고 있구나. 넌 우리 할머니 만큼 현명해.

Progress Check 1

G: _____

B: _____

G: _____

B: _____

G: _____

G: 걱정이 있는 것 같아 보인다. 무슨 문제 있니?
B: 어제까지 과학 보고서를 냈어야 했는 데, 내지 않았어.
G: 늦더라도 안 하는 것보다는 낫지.
B: 늦었더라도 내는 게 낫다는 뜻이야?
G: 맞아, 정확해. 언제나 시작을 했으면 끝을 봐야지.

Progress Check 2

B: _____

G: _____

B: _____

G: _____

B: _____

B: 우와, 너 기타 정말 잘 친다.
G: 고마워. 나 기타 치는 거 정말 좋아 해. 아버지께 배웠어.
B: 정말? 너희 아버지도 기타를 치시니?
G: 응. 유명한 밴드에 계셨어.
B: 굉장한 가족이다! 나도 너처럼 기타 를 칠 수 있다면 좋겠어.

Progress Check 3

M: _____
_____
_____

M: 여러분은 친구의 휴대전화를 부수었 고, 어떻게 해야 할지 모릅니다. 다 른 친구가 여러분에게, "정직이 최선 의 방책이야."라고 말합니다. 여러분 은 그것이 정확히 무슨 뜻인지 모릅 니다.

※ 다음 우리말과 일치하도록 빈칸에 알맞은 것을 골라 쓰시오.

1 _____ _____ Birbal
A. of   B. tales

2 Akbar, the third Mogul _____, had a _____ of wise _____ at his _____.
A. court   B. emperor   C. officials   D. number

3 _____ them was a man _____ _____ was Raja Birbal.
A. whose   B. among   C. name

4 He was _____ _____ his quick wit and was very wise _____ his _____.
A. for   B. with   C. words   D. famous

5 _____, the _____ always liked to _____ Birbal _____ him.
A. near   B. thus   C. have   D. emperor

6 _____ _____
A. Punishment B. Sweet

7 To _____ his officials' _____, Akbar often _____ them _____ questions.
A. wisdom   B. strange   C. test   D. asked

8 _____ day, he _____ _____ _____ an interesting question.
A. up   B. one   C. with   D. came

9 Akbar: Someone _____ a _____ from my _____ today. What _____ I do to him?
A. should   B. pulled   C. head   D. hair

10 Official 1: He should _____ _____, of _____.
A. course   B. punished   C. be

11 Official 2: Yes, _____ _____!
A. him   B. punish

12 Akbar _____ _____ Birbal.
A. to   B. turned

13 Akbar: What _____ you _____ if you _____ in my _____, Birbal?
A. were   B. would   C. place   D. do

14 Birbal: _____ I _____ you, I _____ _____ him sweets.
A. give   B. were   C. if   D. would

15 Official 3: What's he _____ _____?
A. about   B. talking

16 Official 4: _____ _____!
A. crazy   B. Birbal's

---

1 비르발 이야기

2 악바르는 무굴 제국의 제3대 황제로, 자신의 궁정에 많은 현명한 신하들이 있었다.

3 그 중 라자 비르발이라는 이름의 한 사람이 있었다.

4 그는 재빠른 재치로 유명했으며 말이 매우 지혜로웠다.

5 그래서, 황제는 언제나 비르발을 곁에 두기를 원했다.

6 달콤한 처벌

7 신하들의 지혜를 시험해 보기 위해, 악바르는 종종 그들에게 이상한 질문을 했다.

8 어느 날, 황제는 재미있는 질문이 생각났다.

9 악바르: 오늘 어떤 이가 내 머리에서 머리카락을 잡아당겼소. 이 자에게 무엇을 해야 하겠소?

10 신하 1: 당연히 처벌해야 합니다.

11 신하 2: 예, 그를 처벌하소서!

12 악바르가 비르발에게 돌아섰다.

13 악바르: 그대가 내 입장이라면 무엇을 하겠소, 비르발?

14 비르발: 소신이 폐하라면, 그에게 사탕을 주겠습니다.

15 신하 3: 저 사람은 무슨 말을 하는 건가?

16 신하 4: 비르발이 정신이 나갔어!

17 Akbar: _____ _____ you _____ _____ ?

    A. made   B. so   C. what   D. say

18 Birbal: The person who pulled your hair _____ _____ your grandson. No one _____ could do _____ a thing.

    A. such   B. be   C. else   D. must

19 Akbar: You are indeed _____ , Birbal. I'm _____ glad to have someone as _____ as you _____ me.

    A. wise   B. correct   C. near   D. so

20 A _____ of _____

    A. Wisdom   B. Potful

21 One day, the king of Persia _____ an official _____ a _____ _____ .

    A. favor   B. sent   C. with   D. strange

22 Persian Official: I hear you have a lot of wise men in your country. I've _____ _____ by my king to _____ him a _____ of wisdom.

    A. bring   B. asked   C. potful   D. been

23 Official 5: That _____ no _____ ! How can we _____ wisdom _____ a pot?

    A. put   B. makes   C. in   D. sense

24 Akbar: Can you _____ him a _____ of _____ , Birbal?

    A. wisdom   B. bring   C. potful

25 Birbal: It _____ _____ a _____ .

    A. be   B. won't   C. problem

26 Birbal: Could you please _____ _____ _____ _____ ?

    A. a   B. wait   C. weeks   D. few

27 Persian Official: Of course! Take as _____ _____ _____ you _____ .

    A. time   B. as   C. much   D. need

28 A _____ weeks later, Birbal came _____ with two pots _____ necks were really _____ . He offered one to the Persian official.

    A. narrow   B. back   C. few   D. whose

29 Birbal: You can _____ this pot of wisdom to your king. Please ask him to _____ the pot to us _____ he takes the wisdom _____ of it.

    A. return   B. out   C. take   D. after

17 악바르: 왜 그렇게 말했소?

18 비르발: 폐하의 머리카락을 잡아당긴 사람은 폐하의 손자임이 분명합니다. 다른 그 누구도 그런 짓을 할 수 없지요.

19 악바르: 과연 그대의 말이 맞소, 비르발. 그대처럼 현명한 자를 옆에 두어 정말 기쁘오.

20 한 항아리만큼의 지혜

21 어느 날, 페르시아의 왕이 이상한 요청과 함께 신하를 보냈다.

22 페르시아의 신하: 폐하의 나라에 현명한 자들이 많다고 들었습니다. 저는 저의 왕으로부터 한 항아리의 지혜를 왕께 가지고 오라는 명을 받았습니다.

23 신하 5: 저건 말이 안 되오! 어떻게 지혜를 항아리에 넣을 수 있단 말이오?

24 악바르: 그에게 지혜 한 항아리를 가져다줄 수 있겠소, 비르발?

25 비르발: 문제될 것이 없사옵니다.

26 비르발: 몇 주만 기다려 주시겠습니까?

27 페르시아의 신하: 물론이오! 필요한 만큼 얼마든지 시간을 가지시오.

28 몇 주 후, 비르발은 목이 매우 좁은 두 항아리를 들고 돌아왔다. 그는 하나를 페르시아의 신하에게 줬다.

29 비르발: 이 지혜의 항아리를 그대의 왕께 가져다 드리십시오. 왕께서 이 항아리에서 지혜를 꺼내신 후에는 항아리를 우리에게 돌려달라 전해 주십시오.

30 Birbal: The pot is very _____, so please be _____ not to _____ it. We only have two pots of _____.

    A. break   B. precious   C. wisdom   D. careful

31 The Persian _____ looked _____ the pot and _____ _____.

    A. inside   B. speechless   C. official   D. became

32 He _____ Birbal and _____ _____ his _____.

    A. for   B. thanked   C. country   D. left

33 Persian Official: It would _____ great _____ there _____ a man _____ wise as Birbal in our country.

    A. be   B. as   C. if   D. were

34 _____ the Persian official _____, Akbar asked Birbal _____ was _____ the pot.

    A. what   B. left   C. inside   D. after

35 Birbal: Here is _____ _____ pot. You can see _____.

    A. for   B. other   C. yourself   D. the

36 Akbar looked inside the _____ pot and _____ a pumpkin just as _____ _____ the pot.

    A. big   B. as   C. other   D. found

37 Akbar: I see! The pumpkin can't _____ _____ out _____ _____ the pot. How did you do it?

    A. breaking   B. be   C. without   D. taken

38 Birbal: I _____ the pots _____ pumpkin flowers and waited _____ the pumpkins _____ as big as the pots.

    A. until   B. over   C. grew   D. put

39 Akbar: Hahaha! This _____ is a _____ _____ _____!

    A. wisdom   B. certainly   C. of   D. potful

---

30 비르발: 그 항아리는 매우 귀중한 것이니, 그것을 깨지 않도록 조심해 주십시오. 우리는 오직 두 개의 지혜의 항아리만 갖고 있습니다.

31 페르시아 신하는 항아리 안을 들여다보곤 말을 잃었다.

32 그는 비르발에게 감사를 표한 뒤 그의 나라로 떠났다.

33 페르시아의 신하: 우리 나라에도 비르발처럼 현명한 자가 있다면 정말 좋을 텐데.

34 페르시아의 신하가 떠난 뒤, 악바르는 비르발에게 항아리 속에 무엇이 있었는지를 물었다.

35 비르발: 여기 또 다른 항아리가 있습니다. 직접 살펴보시지요.

36 악바르는 또 다른 항아리 안을 보고 꼭 항아리만큼 큰 호박을 발견했다.

37 악바르: 그렇군! 항아리를 깨지 않고는 호박을 꺼낼 수가 없구려! 어떻게 한 것이오?

38 비르발: 항아리를 호박꽃에 덮어 놓은 후 호박이 항아리만큼 클 때까지 기다렸습니다.

39 악바르: 하하하! 이건 정말로 지혜의 항아리구려!

※ 다음 우리말과 일치하도록 빈칸에 알맞은 것을 골라 쓰시오.

1 _____ _____ Birbal

2 Akbar, the third Mogul emperor, had _____ _____ _____ _____ _____ at his _____.

3 _____ them _____ a man _____ _____ was Raja Birbal.

4 He was famous _____ his quick _____ and was very wise _____ his words.

5 _____, the _____ always liked _____ _____ Birbal _____ him.

6 Sweet_____

7 _____ _____ his _____ _____, Akbar often _____ _____ _____ _____.

8 One day, he _____ _____ _____ an interesting question.

9 Akbar: Someone pulled _____ _____ from my head today. What _____ _____ _____ _____ him?

10 Official 1: He should _____ _____, of _____.

11 Official 2: Yes, _____ him!

12 Akbar _____ _____ Birbal.

13 Akbar: What _____ you _____ _____ you _____ _____ _____ _____, Birbal?

14 Birbal: _____ I _____ _____, I _____ _____ him _____.

15 Official 3: What's he _____ _____?

16 Official 4: Birbal's _____!

17 Akbar: _____ _____ _____ say so?

18 Birbal: The person _____ pulled your hair _____ _____ your grandson. No one _____ could do _____ _____.

19 Akbar: You are _____ _____, Birbal. I'm _____ glad _____ _____ someone _____ _____ _____ you near me.

1	비르발 이야기
2	악바르는 무굴 제국의 제3대 황제로, 자신의 궁정에 많은 현명한 신하들이 있었다.
3	그 중 라자 비르발이라는 이름의 한 사람이 있었다.
4	그는 재빠른 재치로 유명했으며 말이 매우 지혜로웠다.
5	그래서, 황제는 언제나 비르발을 곁에 두기를 원했다.
6	달콤한 처벌
7	신하들의 지혜를 시험해 보기 위해, 악바르는 종종 그들에게 이상한 질문을 했다.
8	어느 날, 황제는 재미있는 질문이 생각났다.
9	악바르: 오늘 어떤 이가 내 머리에서 머리카락을 잡아당겼소. 이 자에게 무엇을 해야 하겠소?
10	신하 1: 당연히 처벌해야 합니다.
11	신하 2: 예, 그를 처벌하소서!
12	악바르가 비르발에게 돌아섰다.
13	악바르: 그대가 내 입장이라면 무엇을 하겠소, 비르발?
14	비르발: 소신이 폐하라면, 그에게 사탕을 주겠습니다.
15	신하 3: 저 사람은 무슨 말을 하는 건가?
16	신하 4: 비르발이 정신이 나갔어!
17	악바르: 왜 그렇게 말했소?
18	비르발: 폐하의 머리카락을 잡아당긴 사람은 폐하의 손자임이 분명합니다. 다른 그 누구도 그런 짓을 할 수 없지요.
19	악바르: 과연 그대의 말이 맞소, 비르발. 그대처럼 현명한 자를 옆에 두어 정말 기쁘오.

20 A _____ of _____

21 One day, the king of Persia sent an official _____ _____ _____ _____.

22 Persian Official: I hear you have _____ _____ _____ wise men in your country. _____ _____ by my king _____ _____ him _____ _____ _____ _____.

23 Official 5: That _____ _____ _____! How can we _____ wisdom _____ _____ _____?

24 Akbar: Can you bring him _____ _____ _____ wisdom, Birbal?

25 Birbal: It _____ _____ a problem.

26 Birbal: Could you please wait _____ _____ _____ _____?

27 Persian Official: Of course! Take _____ _____ _____ you need.

28 _____ _____ weeks later, Birbal came back with two pots _____ necks were really _____. He offered _____ to the Persian _____.

29 Birbal: You can _____ this pot of wisdom to your king. Please ask him _____ _____ the pot to us after he takes the wisdom _____ _____ _____ _____.

30 Birbal: The pot is very precious, so please be careful _____ _____ _____ it. We only have two pots of wisdom.

31 The Persian official looked inside the pot and became _____.

32 He _____ Birbal and _____ _____ his country.

33 Persian Official: It _____ _____ great _____ _____ _____ a man _____ _____ _____ _____ Birbal in our country.

34 _____ the Persian official _____, Akbar asked Birbal _____ _____ inside the pot.

35 Birbal: Here is _____ _____ pot. You can see _____ _____.

36 Akbar looked inside _____ _____ pot and found a pumpkin just _____ _____ _____ the pot.

37 Akbar: I see! The pumpkin _____ _____ _____ out _____ _____ the pot. How did you do it?

38 Birbal: I put the pots _____ pumpkin flowers and waited _____ the pumpkins grew _____ _____ the pots.

39 Akbar: Hahaha! This _____ is _____ _____ _____!

20 한 항아리만큼의 지혜

21 어느 날, 페르시아의 왕이 이상한 요청과 함께 신하를 보냈다.

22 페르시아의 신하: 폐하의 나라에 현명한 자들이 많다고 들었습니다. 저는 저의 왕으로부터 한 항아리의 지혜를 왕께 가지고 오라는 명을 받았습니다.

23 신하 5: 저건 말이 안 되오! 어떻게 지혜를 항아리에 넣을 수 있단 말이오?

24 악바르: 그에게 지혜 한 항아리를 가져다줄 수 있겠소, 비르발?

25 비르발: 문제될 것이 없사옵니다.

26 비르발: 몇 주만 기다려 주시겠습니까?

27 페르시아의 신하: 물론이오! 필요한 만큼 얼마든지 시간을 가지시오.

28 몇 주 후, 비르발은 목이 매우 좁은 두 항아리를 들고 돌아왔다. 그는 하나를 페르시아의 신하에게 줬다.

29 비르발: 이 지혜의 항아리를 그대의 왕께 가져다 드리십시오. 왕께서 이 항아리에서 지혜를 꺼내신 후에는 항아리를 우리에게 돌려달라 전해 주십시오.

30 비르발: 그 항아리는 매우 귀중한 것이니, 그것을 깨지 않도록 조심해 주십시오. 우리는 오직 두 개의 지혜의 항아리만 갖고 있습니다.

31 페르시아 신하는 항아리 안을 들여다보곤 말을 잃었다.

32 그는 비르발에게 감사를 표한 뒤 그의 나라로 떠났다.

33 페르시아의 신하: 우리 나라에도 비르발처럼 현명한 자가 있다면 정말 좋을 텐데.

34 페르시아의 신하가 떠난 뒤, 악바르는 비르발에게 항아리 속에 무엇이 있었는지를 물었다.

35 비르발: 여기 또 다른 항아리가 있습니다. 직접 살펴보시지요.

36 악바르는 또 다른 항아리 안을 보고 꼭 항아리만큼 큰 호박을 발견했다.

37 악바르: 그렇군! 항아리를 깨지 않고는 호박을 꺼낼 수가 없구려! 어떻게 한 것이오?

38 비르발: 항아리를 호박꽃에 덮어 놓은 후 호박이 항아리만큼 클 때까지 기다렸습니다.

39 악바르: 하하하! 이건 정말로 지혜의 항아리구려!

※ 다음 문장을 우리말로 쓰시오.

1 Tales of Birbal
➡ _____

2 Akbar, the third Mogul emperor, had a number of wise officials at his court.
➡ _____

3 Among them was a man whose name was Raja Birbal.
➡ _____

4 He was famous for his quick wit and was very wise with his words.
➡ _____

5 Thus, the emperor always liked to have Birbal near him.
➡ _____

6 Sweet Punishment
➡ _____

7 To test his officials' wisdom, Akbar often asked them strange questions.
➡ _____

8 One day, he came up with an interesting question.
➡ _____

9 Akbar: Someone pulled a hair from my head today. What should I do to him?
➡ _____

10 Official 1: He should be punished, of course.
➡ _____

11 Official 2: Yes, punish him!
➡ _____

12 Akbar turned to Birbal.
➡ _____

13 Akbar: What would you do if you were in my place, Birbal?
➡ _____

14 Birbal: If I were you, I would give him sweets.
➡ _____

15 Official 3: What's he talking about?
➡ _____

16 Official 4: Birbal's crazy!
➡ _____

17 Akbar: What made you say so?
➡ _____

18 Birbal: The person who pulled your hair must be your grandson. No one else could do such a thing.
➡ _____

19 Akbar: You are indeed correct, Birbal. I'm so glad to have someone as wise as you near me.
➡ _____

20 A Potful of Wisdom
➡ _____

21 One day, the king of Persia sent an official with a strange favor.
➡ _____

22 Persian Official: I hear you have a lot of wise men in your country. I've been asked by my king to bring him a potful of wisdom.
➡ _____

23 Official 5: That makes no sense! How can we put wisdom in a pot?
➡ _____

24 Akbar: Can you bring him a potful of wisdom, Birbal?
➡ _____

25 Birbal: It won't be a problem.
➡ _____

26 Could you please wait a few weeks?
➡ _____

27 Persian Official: Of course! Take as much time as you need.
➡ _____

28 A few weeks later, Birbal came back with two pots whose necks were really narrow. He offered one to the Persian official.
➡ _____

29 Birbal: You can take this pot of wisdom to your king. Please ask him to return the pot to us after he takes the wisdom out of it.
➡ _____

30 Birbal: The pot is very precious, so please be careful not to break it. We only have two pots of wisdom.
➡ _____

31 The Persian official looked inside the pot and became speechless.
➡ _____

32 He thanked Birbal and left for his country.
➡ _____

33 Persian Official: It would be great if there were a man as wise as Birbal in our country.
➡ _____

34 After the Persian official left, Akbar asked Birbal what was inside the pot.
➡ _____

35 Birbal: Here is the other pot. You can see for yourself.
➡ _____

36 Akbar looked inside the other pot and found a pumpkin just as big as the pot.
➡ _____

37 Akbar: I see! The pumpkin can't be taken out without breaking the pot. How did you do it?
➡ _____

38 Birbal: I put the pots over pumpkin flowers and waited until the pumpkins grew as big as the pots.
➡ _____

39 Akbar: Hahaha! This certainly is a potful of wisdom!
➡ _____

※ 다음 괄호 안의 단어들을 우리말에 맞도록 바르게 배열하시오.

1 (of / Birbal / Tales)
➡ _____

2 (the / Akbar, / Mogul / third / emperor, / a / had / of / number / wise / at / officials / court. / his)
➡ _____
_____

3 (them / among / a / was / man / name / whose / was / Birbal. / Raja)
➡ _____

4 (was / he / for / famous / quick / his / and / wit / was / wise / very / his / with / words.)
➡ _____

5 (the / thus, / always / emperor / to / liked / Birbal / have / him. / near)
➡ _____

6 (Punishment / Sweet)
➡ _____

7 (test / to / officials' / his / Akbar / wisdom, / asked / often / strange / them / questions.)
➡ _____

8 (day, / one / came / he / with / up / interesting / an / question.)
➡ _____

9 (Akbar: / pulled / someone / a / from / hair / head / my / today. // should / what / do / I / him? / to)
➡ _____
_____

10 (Official 1: / should / he / punished, / be / course. / of)
➡ _____

11 (Official 2: / punish / yes, / him!)
➡ _____

12 (turned / Akbar / Birbal. / to)
➡ _____

13 (Akbar: / would / what / do / you / if / were / you / in / Bribal? / place,)
➡ _____

14 (Birbal: / I / if / you, / were / would / I / him / give / sweets.)
➡ _____

15 (Official 3: / he / what's / about? / talking)
➡ _____

16 (Official 3: / crazy! / Birbal's)
➡ _____

1 비르빌 이야기

2 악바르는 무굴 제국의 제3대 황제로, 자신의 궁정에 많은 현명한 신하들이 있었다.

3 그 중 라자 비르발이라는 이름의 한 사람이 있었다.

4 그는 재빠른 재치로 유명했으며 말이 매우 지혜로웠다.

5 그래서, 황제는 언제나 비르발을 곁에 두기를 원했다.

6 달콤한 처벌

7 신하들의 지혜를 시험해 보기 위해, 악바르는 종종 그들에게 이상한 질문을 했다.

8 어느 날, 황제는 재미있는 질문이 생각났다.

9 악바르: 오늘 어떤 이가 내 머리에서 머리카락을 잡아당겼소. 이 자에게 무엇을 해야 하겠소?

10 신하 1: 당연히 처벌해야 합니다.

11 신하 2: 예, 그를 처벌하소서!

12 악바르가 비르발에게 돌아섰다.

13 악바르: 그대가 내 입장이라면 무엇을 하겠소, 비르발?

14 비르발: 소신이 폐하라면, 그에게 사탕을 주겠습니다.

15 신하 3: 저 사람은 무슨 말을 하는 건가?

16 신하 4: 비르발이 정신이 나갔어!

17 (Akbar: / made / what / say / you / so?)

➡ _____

18 (Birbal: / person / the / pulled / who / hair / your / be / must / grandson. / your // one / no / could / else / such / do / thing. / a)

➡ _____

19 (Akbar: / are / you / indeed / Birbal. / correct, // I'm / glad / so / to / someone / have / as / as / wise / you / me. / near)

➡ _____

20 (Potful / A / Wisdom / of)

➡ _____

21 (day, / one / king / the / Persia / of / an / sent / official / a / with / favor. / strange)

➡ _____

22 (Persian Official: / hear / I / have / you / a / of / lot / wise / in / men / country. / your // I've / asked / been / my / by / king / bring / to / him / potful / a / wisdom. / of)

➡ _____

23 (Official 5: / makes / that / sense! / no // how / we / can / wisdom / put / in / pot? / a)

➡ _____

24 (Akbar: / you / can / him / bring / a / of / potful / Birbal? / wisdom,)

➡ _____

25 (Birbal: / won't / it / a / be / problem.)

➡ _____

26 (Birbal: / you / could / please / a / wait / weeks? / few)

➡ _____

27 (Persian Official: / course! / of // take / much / as / time / you / as / need.)

➡ _____

28 (few / a / later, / weeks / came / Birbal / with / back / pots / two / necks / whose / really / were / narrow. // offered / he / to / one / the / official. / Persian)

➡ _____

29 (Birbal: / can / you / take / pot / this / of / to / wisdom / king. / your // ask / please / to / him / the / return / pot / us / to / he / after / takes / wisdom / the / out / it. / of)

➡ _____

17 악바르: 왜 그렇게 말했소?

18 비르발: 폐하의 머리카락을 잡아당긴 사람은 폐하의 손자임이 분명합니다. 다른 그 누구도 그런 짓을 할 수 없지요.

19 악바르: 과연 그대의 말이 맞소. 비르발. 그대처럼 현명한 자를 옆에 두어 정말 기쁘오.

20 한 항아리만큼의 지혜

21 어느 날, 페르시아의 왕이 이상한 요청과 함께 신하를 보냈다.

22 페르시아의 신하: 폐하의 나라에 현명한 자들이 많다고 들었습니다. 저는 저의 왕으로부터 한 항아리의 지혜를 왕께 가지고 오라는 명을 받았습니다.

23 신하 5: 저건 말이 안 되오! 어떻게 지혜를 항아리에 넣을 수 있단 말이오?

24 악바르: 그에게 지혜 한 항아리를 가져다줄 수 있겠소, 비르발?

25 비르발: 문제될 것이 없사옵니다.

26 비르발: 몇 주만 기다려 주시겠습니까?

27 페르시아의 신하: 물론이오! 필요한 만큼 얼마든지 시간을 가지시오.

28 몇 주 후, 비르발은 목이 매우 좁은 두 항아리를 들고 돌아왔다. 그는 하나를 페르시아의 신하에게 줬다.

29 비르발: 이 지혜의 항아리를 그대의 왕께 가져다 드리십시오. 왕께서 이 항아리에서 지혜를 꺼내신 후에는 항아리를 우리에게 돌려달라 전해 주십시오.

30 (Birbal: / pot / the / is / precious, / very / please / so / careful / be / to / not / it. / break // we / have / only / pots / two / wisdom. / of)

➡ _____

_____

31 (Persian / the / looked / official / the / inside / pot / and / speechless. / became)

➡ _____

32 (thanked / he / and / Birbal / left / his / for / country.)

➡ _____

33 (Persian Official: / would / it / be / if / great / were / there / man / a / as / as / wise / in / Birbal / country. / our)

➡ _____

34 (the / after / offical / Persian / left, / asked / Akbar / what / Birbal / was / the / inside / pot.)

➡ _____

35 (Birbal: / is / here / other / the / pot. // can / you / see / yourself. / for)

➡ _____

36 (looked / Akbar / the / inside / pot / other / and / a / found / just / pumpkin / as / big / the / as / pot.)

➡ _____

_____

37 (Akbar: / see! / I // the / can't / pumpkin / taken / be / without / out / breaking / pot. / the // did / how / do / you / it?)

➡ _____

_____

38 (Birbal: / put / I / pots / the / pumpkin / over / flowers / and / until / waited / pumpkins / the / as / grew / big / the / as / pots.)

➡ _____

_____

39 (Akbar: / hahaha! // certainly / this / a / is / of / potful / wisdom!)

➡ _____

30 비르발: 그 항아리는 매우 귀중한 것이니, 그것을 깨지 않도록 조심해 주십시오. 우리는 오직 두 개의 지혜의 항아리만 갖고 있습니다.

31 페르시아 신하는 항아리 안을 들여다보곤 말을 잃었다.

32 그는 비르발에게 감사를 표한 뒤 그의 나라로 떠났다.

33 페르시아의 신하: 우리 나라에도 비르발처럼 현명한 자가 있다면 정말 좋을 텐데.

34 페르시아의 신하가 떠난 뒤, 악바르는 비르발에게 항아리 속에 무엇이 있었는지를 물었다.

35 비르발: 여기 또 다른 항아리가 있습니다. 직접 살펴보시지요.

36 악바르는 또 다른 항아리 안을 보고 꼭 항아리만큼 큰 호박을 발견했다.

37 악바르: 그렇군! 항아리를 깨지 않고는 호박을 꺼낼 수가 없구려! 어떻게 한 것이오?

38 비르발: 항아리를 호박꽃에 덮어 놓은 후 호박이 항아리만큼 클 때까지 기다렸습니다.

39 악바르: 하하하! 이건 정말로 지혜의 항아리구려!

※ **다음 우리말을 영어로 쓰시오.**

1 비르발 이야기
➡ _____

2 악바르는 무굴 제국의 제3대 황제로, 자신의 궁정에 많은 현명한 신하들이 있었다.
➡ _____

3 그 중 라자 비르발이라는 이름의 한 사람이 있었다.
➡ _____

4 그는 재빠른 재치로 유명했으며 말이 매우 지혜로웠다.
➡ _____

5 그래서, 황제는 언제나 비르발을 곁에 두기를 원했다.
➡ _____

6 달콤한 처벌
➡ _____

7 신하들의 지혜를 시험해 보기 위해, 악바르는 종종 그들에게 이상한 질문을 했다.
➡ _____

8 어느 날, 황제는 재미있는 질문이 생각났다.
➡ _____

9 악바르: 오늘 어떤 이가 내 머리에서 머리카락을 잡아당겼소. 이 자에게 무엇을 해야 하겠소?
➡ _____

10 신하 1: 당연히 처벌해야 합니다.
➡ _____

11 신하 2: 예, 그를 처벌하소서!
➡ _____

12 악바르가 비르발에게 돌아섰다.
➡ _____

13 악바르: 그대가 내 입장이라면 무엇을 하겠소, 비르발?
➡ _____

14 비르발: 소신이 폐하라면, 그에게 사탕을 주겠습니다.
➡ _____

15 신하 3: 저 사람은 무슨 말을 하는 건가?
➡ _____

16 신하 4: 비르발이 정신이 나갔어!
➡ _____

17 악바르: 왜 그렇게 말했소?
➡ _____

18 비르발: 폐하의 머리카락을 잡아당긴 사람은 폐하의 손자임이 분명합니다. 다른 그 누구도 그런 짓을 할 수 없지요.
➡ _____

19 악바르: 과연 그대의 말이 맞소, 비르발. 그대처럼 현명한 자를 옆에 두어 정말 기쁘오.
➡ _____

20 한 항아리만큼의 지혜
➡ _____

21 어느 날, 페르시아의 왕이 이상한 요청과 함께 신하를 보냈다.
➡ _____

22 페르시아의 신하: 폐하의 나라에 현명한 자들이 많다고 들었습니다. 저는 저의 왕으로부터 한 항아리의 지혜를 왕께 가지고 오라는 명을 받았습니다.
➡ _____

23 신하 5: 저건 말이 안 되오! 어떻게 지혜를 항아리에 넣을 수 있단 말이오?
➡ _____

24 악바르: 그에게 지혜 한 항아리를 가져다줄 수 있겠소, 비르발?
➡ _____

25 비르발: 문제될 것이 없사옵니다.
➡ _____

26 비르발: 몇 주만 기다려 주시겠습니까?
➡ _____

27 페르시아의 신하: 물론이오! 필요한 만큼 얼마든지 시간을 가지시오.
➡ _____

28 몇 주 후, 비르발은 목이 매우 좁은 두 항아리를 들고 돌아왔다. 그는 하나를 페르시아의 신하에게 줬다.
➡ _____

29 비르발: 이 지혜의 항아리를 그대의 왕께 가져다 드리십시오. 왕께서 이 항아리에서 지혜를 꺼내신 후에는 항아리를 우리에게 돌려달라 전해 주십시오.
➡ _____

30 비르발: 그 항아리는 매우 귀중한 것이니, 그것을 깨지 않도록 조심해 주십시오. 우리는 오직 두 개의 지혜의 항아리만 갖고 있습니다.
➡ _____

31 페르시아 신하는 항아리 안을 들여다보곤 말을 잃었다.
➡ _____

32 그는 비르발에게 감사를 표한 뒤 그의 나라로 떠났다.
➡ _____

33 페르시아의 신하: 우리 나라에도 비르발처럼 현명한 자가 있다면 정말 좋을 텐데.
➡ _____

34 페르시아의 신하가 떠난 뒤, 악바르는 비르발에게 항아리 속에 무엇이 있었는지를 물었다.
➡ _____

35 비르발: 여기 또 다른 항아리가 있습니다. 직접 살펴보시지요.
➡ _____

36 악바르는 또 다른 항아리 안을 보고 꼭 항아리만큼 큰 호박을 발견했다.
➡ _____

37 악바르: 그렇군! 항아리를 깨지 않고는 호박을 꺼낼 수가 없구려! 어떻게 한 것이오?
➡ _____

38 비르발: 항아리를 호박꽃에 덮어 놓은 후 호박이 항아리만큼 클 때까지 기다렸습니다.
➡ _____

39 악바르: 하하하! 이건 정말로 지혜의 항아리구려!
➡ _____

※ 다음 우리말과 일치하도록 빈칸에 알맞은 말을 쓰시오.

Link

1. A _____ _____
2. One day, Emperor Akbar _____ _____ _____ on the ground and _____ _____ _____.
3. Akbar: _____ this line _____ _____ _____ it.
4. Official 1: _____ _____ it?
5. Official 2: _____ can we do _____?
6. Birbal _____.
7. Birbal: That's _____ _____.
8. Birbal drew a longer line _____ _____ the line _____ Akbar _____ _____.
9. Birbal: Your line is now _____ _____ _____.
10. Akbar: You _____ _____, Birbal!
11. Official 3: I _____ I _____ _____ _____ _____ _____ Birbal.

1. 더 짧은 선
2. 어느 날, 악바르 황제는 땅에 선을 그린 뒤 그의 신하들에게 물었다.
3. 악바르: 이 선을 건드리지 않은 채 더 짧게 만들어 보게.
4. 신하 1: 건드리지 않고 말씀입니까?
5. 신하 2: 어떻게 그렇게 할 수 있습니까?
6. 비르발은 미소를 지었다.
7. 비르발: 너무 쉽군요.
8. 비르발은 악바르가 그린 선 옆에 더 긴 선을 그렸다.
9. 비르발: 폐하의 선이 이제 제 선보다 짧습니다.
10. 악바르: 그대가 해냈소, 비르발!
11. 신하 3: 제가 비르발만큼 지혜롭다면 좋겠군요.

Write

1. _____ Jaeha,
2. Time _____. I cannot believe that it is time _____ _____ _____.
3. I still remember _____ _____ _____ _____ _____ camping together.
4. I really liked _____ _____ _____ _____ that night.
5. I also loved _____ _____ _____ _____ you _____ _____.
6. I really want to thank you _____ _____ _____ _____ _____ _____.
7. If I _____ _____ _____ _____, I _____ _____ more time with you.
8. I hope we _____ _____ _____ even after we _____.
9. _____, Jake

1. 재하에게,
2. 시간 정말 빠르다. 작별 인사를 해야 할 시간이라는 게 믿어지지 않아.
3. 아직도 우리가 함께 캠핑을 갔던 때가 생각나.
4. 우리가 그날 밤에 봤던 영화를 정말 좋아했는데.
5. 너와 방과 후에 농구를 하는 것도 정말로 좋아했어.
6 농구 기술들을 가르쳐 줘서 정말로 고맙다고 하고 싶어.
7. 시간을 되돌아갈 수 있다면, 너와 함께 더 많은 시간을 보낼 거야.
8. 우리가 졸업한 뒤에도 계속 연락을 하면 좋겠다.
9. Jake가.

Culture Project

1. _____ my brother _____ his driving test _____ _____, he was very _____.
2. Kento, his friend _____ Japan, _____ him, "_____ _____ you, I _____ _____ _____."
3. _____ seven times, _____ _____ eight."
4. It's a _____ _____ that means "_____ _____ _____."
5. My brother _____ _____ and _____ _____.

1. 내 오빠가 운전 면허 시험에서 일곱 번 떨어졌을 때, 그는 매우 실망했습니다.
2. 일본에서 온 그의 친구 Kento는 그에게, "내가 너였다면, 포기하지 않을 거야.
3. 일곱 번 넘어져도 여덟 번 일어나야지."하고 말했습니다.
4. 이것은 "포기하지 마라."라는 뜻의 일본 격언입니다.
5. 오빠는 다시 도전해 마침내 통과했습니다.

※ 다음 우리말을 영어로 쓰시오.

Link

1. 더 짧은 선
➡

2. 어느 날, 악바르 황제는 땅에 선을 그린 뒤 그의 신하들에게 물었다.
➡

3. 악바르: 이 선을 건드리지 않은 채 더 짧게 만들어 보게.
➡

4. 신하 1: 건드리지 않고 말씀입니까?
➡

5. 신하 2: 어떻게 그렇게 할 수 있습니까?
➡

6. 비르발은 미소를 지었다.
➡

7. 비르발: 너무 쉽군요.
➡

8. 비르발은 악바르가 그린 선 옆에 더 긴 선을 그렸다.
➡

9. 비르발: 폐하의 선이 이제 제 선보다 짧습니다.
➡

10. 악바르: 그대가 해냈소, 비르발!
➡

11. 신하 3: 제가 비르발만큼 지혜롭다면 좋겠군요.
➡

Write

1. 재하에게,
➡

2. 시간 정말 빠르다. 작별 인사를 해야 할 시간이라는 게 믿어지지 않아.
➡

3. 아직도 우리가 함께 캠핑을 갔던 때가 생각나.
➡

4. 우리가 그날 밤에 봤던 영화를 정말 좋아했는데.
➡

5. 너와 방과 후에 농구를 하는 것도 정말로 좋아했어.
➡

6. 농구 기술들을 가르쳐 줘서 정말로 고맙다고 하고 싶어.
➡

7. 시간을 되돌아갈 수 있다면, 너와 함께 더 많은 시간을 보낼 거야.
➡

8. 우리가 졸업한 뒤에도 계속 연락을 하면 좋겠다.
➡

9. Jake가.
➡

Culture Project

1. 내 오빠가 운전 면허 시험에서 일곱 번 떨어졌을 때, 그는 매우 실망했습니다.
➡

2. 일본에서 온 그의 친구 Kento는 그에게, "내가 너였다면, 포기하지 않을 거야.
➡

3. 일곱 번 넘어져도 여덟 번 일어나야지."하고 말했습니다.
➡

4. 이것은 "포기하지 마라."라는 뜻의 일본 격언입니다.
➡

5. 오빠는 다시 도전해 마침내 통과했습니다.
➡

MEMO

MEMO

적중100

2학기

정답 및 해설

미래 | 최연희

중 **3**

영어 기출 문제집

적중100

2학기

정답 및 해설

미래 | 최연희

중 3

Find Your Passion

01 ⑤	02 pursue	03 ④	04 ①
05 ③	06 ②		

01 동의어 관계이다. check: 계산서, bill: 계산서, decide: 결정하다, determine: 결정하다

02 '종종 오랜 시간에 걸쳐, 어떤 특정 목표나 결과를 달성하기 위해 노력하다'는 'pursue(추구하다, 추진하다)'가 적절하다. 더 이상 논의할 필요가 없다.

03 ① promise: 약속하다, 다짐하다. 내가 뭘 할 수 있을지 보기는 하겠지만 아무것도 약속할 수는 없어요. ② fix: 수리하다. 전화를 수리하도록 기술자를 보내요. ③ slice: 한 조각, 일부. 나는 보통 매일 아침 빵 한 조각을 먹는다. ④ decorate: 장식하다, 꾸미다. 배우들의 사진이 그 레스토랑의 벽을 장식하고 있다. ⑤ provide: 제공하다. 교사들은 아동들에게 본뜰 수 있는 모델을 제시한다.

04 passion: 열정, 흥미 / 너만의 열정을 찾고 너의 꿈을 따라가라.

05 ① scare away: 겁주어 쫓아내다. 그들은 겁을 주어 그 곰들을 간신히 쫓았다. ② fill out: 작성하다. 이 양식들 좀 작성해 주세요. ③ be used to (동)명사: ~에 익숙하다. 저는 한 손으로 쟁반을 나르는 것에 익숙하지 못했어요. be used to 동사원형: ~에 사용되다 ④ take on: 떠맡다. 저는 새로운 책무를 맡을 준비가 안 되어 있는 것 같습니다. ⑤ take classes: 수업을 듣다. 이 수업을 들으려면 컴퓨터를 사용할 수 있어야 한다.

06 take charge of: ~의 책임을 지다, ~을 떠맡다. 네가 그 회사를 맡게 될 거야. of all time: 역대, 지금껏. 내 생각에는 그가 역대 최고의 코미디언 중 한 명인 것 같다. To my thinking: 내 생각에는

01 (1) complain   (2) customer
    (3) appreciate   (4) form

02 (1) complaint   (2) unnatural

03 (1) innovative   (2) decorate
    (3) device   (4) role

04 (1) I have a passion for fashion.
    (2) The new restaurant put up a bright and colorful sign.

(3) Thank you for your understanding and we apologize for any inconvenience.

(4) Now that it's winter, I'm going to go skiing every weekend.

01 (1) complain: 불평하다 / 무엇이나 누군가에 대해 짜증나거나 불만족스럽거나 불쾌하다고 말하다 (2) customer: 고객, 소비자 / 상점, 회사 등으로부터 상품이나 서비스를 구입하는 사람 (3) appreciate: 진가를 알아보다 / 어떤 것의 좋은 점을 인정하여 그것을 좋아하다 (4) form: 서류 / 당신이 정보를 적을 여백을 가진 공식적인 문서

02 (1) '동사 – 명사'의 관계이다. decide: 결정하다 – decision: 결정, complain: 불평하다 – complaint: 불평 (2) '반의어' 관계이다. completely: 완전하게 – incompletely: 불완전하게, natural: 자연스러운 – unnatural: 자연스럽지 않은

03 (1) innovative: 획기적인 (2) decorate: 장식하다 (3) device: 장치, 기구 (4) role: 역할 the main role: 주인공

04 (1) passion: 열정, passion을 추가한다. (2) put up: 세우다, 내붙이다, put을 추가한다. (3) inconvenience: 불편, 애로, thank A for B ~의 형태로 쓰이므로 for를 추가한다. (4) now that: ~이기 때문에, ~이므로, now that으로 접속사 역할을 하도록 that을 추가한다. go ~ing: ~하러 가다

[교과서]
Conversation

1 I'm not satisfied with the phone.

2 I promise I'll do my best.

교과서 대화문 익히기

1 F   2 T   3 F   4 T

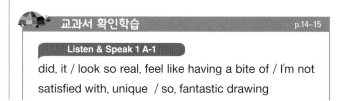
교과서 확인학습   p.14~15

Listen & Speak 1 A-1

did, it / look so real, feel like having a bite of / I'm not satisfied with, unique / so, fantastic drawing

Listen & Speak 1 A-2

How can, help / only a week ago, sometimes turns off by itself / have a look at, inconvenience, take, few hours to / I'm not satisfied with, one / fill out, form

Listen & Speak 2 A-1

myself / better than any other jam / it / would / I promise I'll be

Listen & Speak 2 A-2

were interested in / not anymore, want to / Are, sure / how to act, I promise I'll do

Communicate A

your meal / good, fresh / about / I'm not satisfied with, rare / to bring, another one / be going, have, check / won't have to / I promise we'll provide, with

Progress Check 1

How can I / got, as, I'm not satisfied with / in / one in blue / do, get one

Progress Check 2

take, classes / interested in / not anymore / worry, I promise I'll do / then

Progress Check 3

on / Have, finished / I promise I'll finish

시험대비 기본평가   p.16

01 ②   02 I promise I'll be your first customer.
03 (C) – (B) – (A) – (D)

01 뒤에 나오는 'It's not unique.'로 보아 ②번이 가장 적절하다. 'I'm not satisfied with it'은 불만족을 표현하는 말이다.

02 'I promise I'll be your first customer.'는 다짐을 말할 때 쓰는 표현이다. promise 뒤에는 구체적인 내용을 명사절을 써서 나타내며, "I promise to be your first customer."로 바꿔 쓸 수 있다.

03 '무엇을 도와드릴까요?'라는 주어진 글에 이어서 (C)에서 불만을 말하고, (B)에서 사과하며 '고치는 데 몇 시간 정도 걸릴 거예요.'라며 고쳐 주겠다고 하자, (A)에서 '새것을 원한다'는 말에, (D)에서 '물론.'이라며 '서류만 작성하면 된다.'고 말하는 순서가 적절하다.

시험대비 실력평가   p.17~18

01 ④   02 ①   03 Yes, we do.
04 Do you have one in blue?   05 ⑤
06 ⑤   07 not anymore
08 (C) – (B) – (A) – (D)   09 ④   10 one

---

01 'not anymore'로 보아 A와 B를 서로 바꾸는 것이 적절하다.

02 다음에 '다른 색상도 있습니다.'라는 말로 보아 색상이 가장 적절하다.

03 뒤에 이어서 남자가 'I'll get one for you.'라고 하고 있으므로 가지고 있다고 했음을 알 수 있다.

04 hat을 대신해서 쓰인 부정대명사 one을 이용하여 one in blue로 영작한다.

05 마지막의 one은 'a hat'을 대신하는 부정대명사이다.

06 빈칸 앞에서 '배우가 되고 싶은 게 확실하니?'라는 질문에 '네, 연기하는 방법을 배울 거예요.'라고 답하고 있으므로 '최선을 다하겠다고 약속할게요.'라는 말이 자연스럽다.

07 not anymore: 더 이상 ~아니다, 이젠 ~않다

08 손님을 맞이하는 주어진 글에 이어, (C)에서 마음에 들지 않는 색상에 대한 불만족을 말하고, (B)에서 다른 색상도 있음을 설명하고, (A)에서 원하는 색상을 말하고, (D)에서 있다며 하나 가져다 드리겠다고 한 후, 고맙다는 말로 마무리한다.

09 뒤에서 'It's too rare for me.'라고 하는 것으로 보아 불만족을 말하는 것이 적절하다.

10 steak를 대신하는 부정대명사 one이 적절하다.

11 남자가 스테이크를 항상 덜 익은 상태로 제공하는지는 대화를 통해 알 수 없다.

12 'next time'을 하나의 접속사처럼 생각한다.

13 밑줄 친 문장은 다짐을 말할 때 쓰는 표현이다.

서술형 시험대비   p.19

01 (D) → (B) → (C) → (A)
02 You won't have to pay for the steak.
03 Because the steak was too rare for her. 또는 The woman isn't satisfied with the steak because it was too rare for her.
04 I'm not satisfied with the phone.
05 by itself
06 (1) I was. → I did.
     (2) feel like to have → feel like having

---

01 빵과 샐러드에 대해 언급한 문장에 이어서, 스테이크는 어땠는지 묻는 (D)가 나오고, 스테이크에 대해 불만족을 언급하는 (B)가 나오고, 사과하며 다른 것으로 가져다 드릴지를 묻는 (C)가 나오고, 괜찮다며 가봐야 한다는 (A)로 이어지는 순서가 적절하다.

02 'not have to(~할 필요 없다)'와 'pay for(지불하다)'를 이용한다. 주어의 의지를 나타내는 will과 'not have to'를 'won't

have to'로 쓴다.

03 남자의 '스테이크는 어떠세요?'라는 질문에 여자가 '솔직히, 스테이크는 만족스럽지 않아요. 제겐 너무 덜 익었어요.'라고 하고 있다.

04 'be not satisfied with ~'는 불만족을 나타내는 표현이다.

05 by itself: 스스로, 저절로

06 (1) 일반동사 draw를 받는 대동사이므로 was가 아니라 did로 써야 한다. (2) feel like -ing: ~하고 싶다

[교과서] Grammar

핵심 Check
p.20~21

1 (1) why　(2) when
2 (1) However　(2) Thus

시험대비 기본평가
p.22

01 ③　　　　**02** (1) in which, where
(2) for which, why　　**03** ②
04 (1) However　(2) Thus　(3) however
(4) However　(5) Thus

01 콘서트가 취소된 것과 가수와 팬들이 실망한 것은 인과 관계이다.

02 '전치사+관계대명사'는 관계부사로 표현할 수도 있다. 선행사가 장소일 때 where, 선행사가 이유일 때는 why를 쓴다.

03 관계부사가 오면 뒤의 문장은 완전한 절의 형태여야 한다. 문미에 전치사 in이 남아 있으므로, 관계부사 where가 아닌 관계대명사 which로 고치는 것이 적절하다.

04 접속부사는 앞뒤 문장의 내용을 연결하는 역할을 한다. however는 '대조, 반대' 등의 '역접'을, thus는 '결과, 결론' 등의 '순접'을 의미한다. 해석을 통해 내용의 자연스러운 연결, 또는 반대 연결을 판단하여 어떤 종류의 접속부사로 문맥을 연결할지 결정하는 것이 중요하다.

시험대비 실력평가
p.23~25

01 ③　　**02** ④　　**03** ②　　**04** ⑤
05 ①　　**06** (1) For example　(2) Moreover
(3) Similarly　(4) However　(5) However　**07** ⑤
08 ③　　**09** ⑤　　**10** ③　　**11** where
12 when　　**13** mother was born in the year when
World War II broke out　　**14** why the subway has
not arrived for 30 minutes　　**15** ③
16 (1) couldn't understand about the way his mother
cut them straight
(2) to hear how I could be rich

01 선행사 the way와 관계부사 how는 함께 쓸 수 없다. 둘 중 하나를 삭제하면 옳은 문장이 된다.

02 William은 그 공원 옆에서 3년 동안 살았다. (그래서 → 그러나) 한 번도 그곳을 가 본 적이 없다. Thus를 However로 바꾸는 것이 적절하다.

03 그 영화는 실망스러웠다. (그러므로 → 그렇지만), 배우들의 연기는 훌륭했다. Therefore를 However로 바꾸는 것이 적절하다.

04 선행사가 the time이므로 '관계부사' when 또는 '전치사+관계대명사' at which 등으로 연결해서 표현 가능하다.

05 선행사가 the reason일 때, '전치사+관계대명사'로 받을 때는 for which를, '관계부사'로 받을 때는 why를 쓰는 것이 적절하며, the reason과 why 둘 중 하나만 쓰는 것도 가능하다. ④에는 which 앞에 the reason이 필요하다.

06 (1) Shakespeare가 단어들을 만들어 낸 사례들 (2) 추운데다가 바람까지 세차게 불었다. (3) 아들은 아버지를, 마찬가지로 딸은 엄마를 따른다. (4) 소극적인 성격이지만, 불쌍한 사람들을 위해서는 적극적인 Lily. (5) 세계 경제가 불황이라서 사람들이 실직하게 되었다.

07 ① However → Thus ② Thus → However ③ However → Thus ④ Thus → However

08 ① Thus → However ② However → Thus ④ However → Thus ⑤ Thus → However

09 선행사가 the reason일 때, '전치사+관계대명사' 표현은 'for which'가 적절하며, 관계부사 why는 the reason과 함께 써도 되고, 생략도 가능하다.

10 선행사가 the way일 때, 관계부사 how는 같이 쓰지 않으며, 관계부사 앞에 전치사 in을 쓰지도 않는다.

12 두 문장을 연결해 주는 빈칸 뒤에 완전한 문장이 오고, 선행사가 장소일 때는 관계부사 where를, 선행사가 시간일 때는 관계부사 when을 쓰는 것이 적절하다.

13 시간을 나타내는 선행사 the year 뒤에 관계부사 when을 쓴다.

14 이유는 the reason인데 관계부사 why와 함께 쓸 수도 있고, 둘 중 하나를 생략해도 된다. 보기에 the reason이 없으므로, why를 이용하여 알맞게 단어를 배열한다.

15 <보기>는 'Dahyun이 피자 다섯 조각과 햄버거 두 개를 먹었지만 여전히 배가 고프다.'라는 뜻이다. ③ '~에도 불구하고'의 양보 의미를 가진 접속사 Though로 표현된 문장이 가장 가까운 뜻이다.

16 (1) 석봉은 자신의 형편없는 글씨들을 보며, 어떻게 그의 어머니가 그것들을 똑바로 썰었는지 이해할 수 없었다. (2) 내 친구들은 내가 어떻게 부자가 될 수 있었는지 듣고 놀랐다.

01 However

02 (1) However, customers were unhappy because
they were used to

(2) Thus, he invented new machines for his kitchen.

(3) However, your mind can change your behavior
as well.

(4) Thus, she decided to take a day trip by herself.

03 (1) They found a special cave where their
ancestors spent the winter.

(2) The singer told me how she could be world
famous.

(3) My favorite season is spring when I can see
the life coming back.

(4) Please tell your mom the reason why you hid
the the letter from Grace.

(5) That is the soccer stadium where the Korean
national team beat Brazil.

(6) I remember the day when my first daughter
was born.

04 (1) the restaurant where she made a hamburger

(2) a charity box where a girl putsome money

(3) the cafe where we talked over teaand coffee

(4) a laptop where she wrote a marketing report

05 (A) However   (B) However
(C) However   (D) Thus

06 ④ Thus → However, ⑥ However → Thus

07 the summer vacation when she played in the pool
with

---

02 (1), (3)은 '역접' 관계이므로 접속부사 However를, (2), (4)
는 '순접' 관계이므로 접속부사 Thus를 쓰는 것이 적절하다. 그
외의 단어 배열은 의미와 어법에 알맞게 한다. *be used to: ~
에 익숙하다 *clear one's mind: 마음을 정리하다

03 (1) 그들은 그들의 조상이 겨울을 보냈던 특별한 동굴을 찾았
다. (2) 그 가수는 어떻게 그녀가 세계적으로 유명하게 되었는지
를 내게 말해줬다. (3) 내가 가장 좋아하는 계절은 생명이 되돌
아오는 것을 볼 수 있는 봄이다. (4) 제발 너의 엄마에게 왜 네가
Grace에게서 온 편지를 숨겼는지 그 이유를 말해라. (5) 저곳
이 한국 국가대표팀이 브라질을 이겼던 축구 경기장이다. (6) 나
는 나의 첫째 딸이 태어난 날을 기억한다.

04 (1) 그녀가 햄버거를 만든 식당에서 한 남자에게 영수증이 건
네졌다. (2) 한 소녀가 돈을 넣는 자선 상자가 있었다. (3) 이
곳은 우리가 차와 커피를 마시며 얘기를 나눴던 카페였다. (4)
Brenda는 그녀가 마케팅 보고서를 기록하는 노트북 한 대를 가
져왔다.

05 (A)~(C)는 모두 '역접'이다. 교과서의 원문에는 (A)에는

Unfortunately가, (B)에는 But이, (C)에는 접속사 Although를
이용한 표현이었다. (D)는 내용상 순접이고, Thus가 적절하다.

06 내용상 ④는 '역접'이므로 However를, ⑥은 '순접'이므로
Thus를 쓰는 것이 적절하다.

07 민주는 사촌들과 수영장에서 물놀이를 했던 여름방학을 결코 잊
을 수 없었다.

교과서
Reading

확인문제 p.28

1 T   2 F   3 T   4 F

확인문제 p.29

1 T   2 F   3 T   4 F

교과서 확인학습 A p.30~31

01 the Cook

02 is known as, painters of all time

03 also

04 few, however, creative

05 twenty-year-old, as

06 took charge of, completely   07 but, like, a few

08 were even decorated with

09 however, were used to, servings

10 As a result   11 A few

12 where, innovative

13 beautifully painted, uniquely written

14 would, appreciate, creative   15 happened

16 to work

17 was given, such as

18 was, put in charge of

19 to be given another, to pursue

20 stop at   21 much more

22 Thus   23 that

24 that, scare, away from   25 were too, too, to

26 to make, which was based on

27 took on, had, been

28 a lot of, cooking, what to put

29 for over, why, to

30 Although, throughout

31 not only, but also

32 Now that, the same way

1 Da Vinci the Cook

2 Leonardo da Vinci is known as one of the greatest painters of all time.

3 He was also a great inventor, scientist, and musician.

4 Very few people, however, know that da Vinci was also a creative cook.

5 In 1473, twenty-year-old da Vinci worked as a cook at a restaurant in Florence, Italy.

6 When he took charge of the kitchen, da Vinci changed the menu completely.

7 He made simple but artistic dishes like fish with a few carrot slices.

8 Some dishes were even decorated with flowers.

9 Customers, however, were unhappy because they were used to dishes with big servings of meat.

10 As a result, da Vinci lost his job.

11 A few years later, da Vinci opened a restaurant with his friend Sandro Botticelli.

12 He wanted to create a place where people could try his innovative food.

13 They put up a beautifully painted sign and made a uniquely written menu.

14 Da Vinci believed that people would soon appreciate his creative cooking.

15 Unfortunately, that never happened.

16 In the early 1480s, da Vinci began to work for Ludovico Sforza in Milan.

17 He was given many different roles, such as a musician, a painter, and an engineer.

18 He was also put in charge of the kitchen.

19 He was happy to be given another chance to pursue his passion for cooking.

20 Da Vinci did not stop at cooking creative dishes.

21 He wanted to cook much more quickly and easily.

22 Thus, he invented new machines for his kitchen.

23 He created machines that could crush vegetables and pull spaghetti.

24 He even made a device that could scare frogs away from the water tank.

25 Surely, they were all very innovative, but most of them were too big or too difficult to use.

26 In 1495, Sforza asked da Vinci to make a grand painting, which was based on the last supper of Jesus, on the wall of a church in Milan.

27 Da Vinci gladly took on the project because he had always been interested in food.

28 He spent a lot of time cooking all kinds of food to decide what to put on the table in his picture.

29 "Da Vinci has wasted his time in the kitchen for over a year. That's the reason why he hasn't finished the painting yet," complained the people from the church to Sforza.

30 Although da Vinci never became a successful cook, he showed great interest in cooking throughout his life.

31 He was not only a great painter but also a creative cook.

32 Now that you know all about his secret passion for cooking, you will never look at The Last Supper the same way.

01 ②   02 appreciate   03 ④   04 ③

05 ①   06 to use   07 ⑤

08 Now that   09 ③

10 (A) painters (B) a few (C) lost

11 ④   12 ②   13 ⑤

14 Da Vinci not only cooked creative dishes but also wanted to cook much more quickly and easily.

15 that could scare frogs away from the water tank

16 ②   17 ④

18 He spent a lot of time cooking all kinds of food to decide what to put on the table in his picture.

19 ①   20 pursue   21 ③   22 ①

01 이어지는 글에서 다빈치가 '음식점에서 요리사로 일했'고 하고 있으므로 '창의적인 요리사'가 적절하다.

02 appreciate: ~의 진가를 인정하다 <영영풀이: 그것의 좋은 특성 때문에 그것을 좋아하다>

03 '손님들은 많은 양의 고기 요리에 익숙했었기 때문에 불만족스러워했다. 그 결과, 다빈치는 그의 직업을 잃었다.'라고 하고 있다.

04 ⓐ for: [획득·추구·기대의 대상] ~을 얻기 위해[위한], ⓒ away from: ~에서 떠나서

05 앞 문장의 내용에 대한 결과가 이어지고 있으므로 Thus가 적절하다.

06 too ~ to ...: …하기에 너무 ~한, 너무 ~해서 …할 수 없다

07 (C)의 the project가 주어진 글의 a grand painting을 가리키므로 제일 먼저 오고 (B)에서 어떤 음식을 올릴지 결정하기 위해 모든 종류의 음식을 요리하느라 많은 시간을 쓰고 (A)에서 (B)의 시간 낭비에 대해 불평하는 것이 적절하다.

08 now that: ~이기 때문에, ~이므로

09 앞에서 '다빈치는 1년 넘게 부엌에서 시간을 낭비해 오고 있습니다.'라고 하고 있으므로 complained가 적절하다. complain: 불평하다, commend: 칭찬하다

10 (A) 'one of+최상급+복수 명사'의 형태로 쓰므로 painters가 적절하다. (B) 'a few+셀 수 있는 명사 복수, a little+셀 수 없는 명사 단수'이므로 a few가 적절하다. (C) '손님들은 많은 양의 고기 요리에 익숙했었기 때문에 불만족스러워했다.'고 했으므로 lost가 적절하다.

11 da Vinci가 얼마나 오래 요리사로 일했는지는 대답할 수 없다. ① No. ② A cook. ③ He changed the menu completely. ⑤ Customers didn't like the dishes that da Vinci made.

12 ① 두통은 스트레스의 징후일 수 있다. ② 많은 건물 간판이 영어로 쓰여 있다. ③ 그가 엄지손가락을 세우는 몸짓을 해 보였다. ④ 그는 나더러 뜰에 들어오라고 손짓했다. ⑤ 사람이 살고 있는 흔적이 없다.

13 ① common: 일반적인, 평범한 ② routine: 판에 박힌 ③ plain: 평이한 ④ traditional: 전통적인 ⑤ innovative: 혁신적인

14 '다빈치는 창의적인 요리를 만드는 것에 멈추지 않았다. 그는 훨씬 더 빠르고 쉽게 요리하고 싶어했다.'는 것은 '다빈치는 창의적인 요리를 만드는 것뿐만 아니라 훨씬 더 빠르고 쉽게 요리하고 싶어했다.'고 쓸 수 있으므로 'not only A but also B' 구문을 이용한다.

15 scare A away from B: A를 겁주어 B로부터 멀어지도록 하다, that은 주격 관계대명사이다.

16 뒤에서 '"그것이 그가 아직도 그림을 끝내지 못한 이유입니다." 라고 교회 사람들이 스포르차에게 불평을 했다.'라고 하고 있으므로 wasted가 적절하다.

17 주절의 내용과 상반되는 내용이므로 Although가 가장 적절하다.

18 spend+시간+~ing: ~하는 데 시간을 보내다, '의문사+to부정사(to put)'가 decide의 목적어가 되도록 배열한다.

19 다빈치가 스포르차에게 무엇을 하도록 요청했는지는 알 수 없다. ② It was based on the last supper of Jesus. ③ Because he had always been interested in food. ④ Da Vinci spend a lot of time cooking all kinds of food to decide what to put on the table in his picture. ⑤ Because we know all about da Vinci's secret passion for cooking.

20 pursue: 추구하다 <영영풀이: 종종 오랜 기간에 걸쳐 특정한 목적이나 결과를 달성하기 위해 노력하다>

21 (B)에서 also로 주어진 글의 내용에 추가되고 있으므로 제일 먼저 오고 (C)에서 Thus로 (B)의 내용에 대한 결과가 나오므로 (B) 다음에 (C)가 이어지고 (A)의 they가 (C)의 machines를 가리키므로 (C) 다음에 (A)가 나오는 것이 적절하다.

22 위 글에서는 과학자로서의 역할에 대해서는 언급하고 있지 않다.

🦉 서술형 시험대비   p.38~39

01 It's because customers were not satisfied with his creative dishes.

02 He wanted to create a place where people could try his innovative food.

03 people would soon appreciate his creative cooking

04 He invented new machines for his kitchen.

05 the other → another

06 new machines for his kitchen

07 and it

08 He was a creative cook as well as a great painter.

09 decide what to put on the table in hispicture

10 however

11 (A) completely (B) unhappy (C) appreciate

12 da Vinci, Sandro Botticelli

01 손님들이 그의 창의적인 요리에 불만족스러워했기 때문이었다.

02 a place를 선행사로 하는 관계부사 where를 이용하여 영작한다.

03 앞 문장의 내용을 가리킨다.

04 '그는 훨씬 더 빠르고 쉽게 요리하고 싶어했다. 따라서, 그는 그의 주방에서 사용할 새로운 기계들을 발명하였다.'라고 하고 있다

05 the other는 '두 개 중의 나머지 하나'를 일컬을 때 쓰므로 '또 다른 하나'를 말할 때 쓰는 another로 고치는 것이 적절하다.

06 '그의 주방에서 사용할 새로운 기계들'을 가리킨다.

07 계속적 용법의 관계대명사 = 접속사+대명사

08 not only A but also B = B as well as A

09 '그는 그림 속 식탁 위에 어떤 음식을 올릴지 결정하기 위해 모든 종류의 음식을 요리하느라 많은 시간을 썼다.'라고 하고 있다.

10 앞 문장의 내용과 상반되는 내용이며 문장의 중간에 콤마(,)로 삽입되어 있는 형식으로 쓰였으므로 however가 적절하다.

11 (A) 형용사로 쓰일 경우 수식하는 명사나 보어로서의 역할이 없으므로 동사 changed를 수식하는 completely가 적절하다. (B) 이어서 'As a result, da Vinci lost his job.'라는 것으로 보아 unhappy가 적절하다. (C) 이어서 'Unfortunately, that never happened.'라는 것으로 보아 appreciate가 적절하다. depreciate는 '평가 절하하다, 가치[평가]를 떨어뜨리다'라는 뜻이다.

12 다빈치와 그의 친구인 산드로 보티첼리를 가리킨다.

01 ①   02 decorate   03 unusual, Unfortunately

04 (r)eason, (r)are   (1) reason   (2) rare

05 purchase   06 put   07 ③

08 I promise I'll be your first customer.   09 ③

10 ②   11 ④   12 ③   13 ④

14 (1) However   (2) However   (3) Thus

    (4) However   (5) Thus   (6) Thus

15 (1) how da Vinci made his creative cooking

    (2) when I can have a delicious meal with my

      friends

16 ③   17 ①   18 ④   19 ④

20 ②   21 ③

22 He changed the menu completely.

23 such as   24 that[which]

25 most of them were too big or too difficult to use

26 ④   27 ①

28 It was based on the last supper of Jesus.

29 ①   30 where they can use their creativity

---

01 <보기>와 ①은 '계산서'의 뜻으로 쓰였다. ① 계산서 좀 갖다 주시겠어요? ② 그들은 공항에서 보안 점검을 실시했다. ③ 제가 이 카드를 잘 작성했는지 봐주시겠습니까? ④ 이 수표를 현금으로 바꾸고 싶습니다. ⑤ 자동차는 생산 라인에서 나올 때 점검을 받는다.

02 '어떤 예쁜 것을 올려놓아 어떤 것을 더 매력적으로 보이게 만들다'라는 의미로 'decorate(장식하다, 꾸미다)'가 적절하다.

03 (1) 형용사 usual에 un을 붙여 반의어가 된 어휘이다. unusual: 흔치 않은. 거대한 소행성이 지구에 너무 가까이 접근하는 것은 흔치 않은 일이다. (2) 문장 구성상 부사가 적절하다. unfortunately: 불행하게도. 형용사 fortunate에 un을 붙여 반대의 뜻을 갖는 형용사가 되고 거기에 ly를 붙여 부사가 된 어휘이다. 불행히도, 저는 그 회의에 참석할 수 없을 거예요.

04 (1) reason: 이유. 누군가가 어떤 것을 하기로 결정한 이유, 또는 일어난 어떤 것에 대한 원인이나 설명. 그렇게 늦은 것에 대한 이유가 있니? (2) rare: 덜 익은, 살짝 익힌. 잠깐 요리된; 속이 아직 붉은. 우리 아버지는 속이 약간 분홍빛이 도는 덜 익은 고기를 좋아하신다.

05 반의어 관계이다. rare: 덜 익은, well-done: 잘 익은, sell: 팔다, purchase: 구입하다

06 • put ... in charge of ~: …에게 ~의 책임을 맡기다 / 그들은 그에게 그 공원을 책임지게 했다. • put up: 내붙이다, 게시하다 / 그는 "반려동물 출입 금지"라는 팻말을 내걸었다. • put out: (불을) 끄다 / 소방차들이 화재를 진화하기 위해 도착했다. • put on: 입다 / 내게 네가 입을 수 있는 스웨터가 있어.

07 '배우가 되고 싶다'는 말에 '최선을 다하겠다고 약속한다'는 것이

08 'I promise ~'는 다짐을 말할 때 쓰는 표현으로 promise 뒤에는 구체적인 내용을 명사절을 써서 나타낸다.

09 (C)의 it이 주어진 글의 this blueberry를 가리키므로 가장 먼저 나오고, (B)에서 'Really?'로 (C)에서 한 말에 대해 놀라움을 나타내고, (A)에서 (B)에서 말한 '팔아도 되겠다'는 말에 대해 '사람들이 이걸 살 거라고 생각하는지' 묻고, (D)에서 '물론'이라는 말로 답하는 순서가 적절하다.

10 'I made it myself.(직접 만든 거야.)'라고 하고 있다.

11 '큰 아파트에 혼자 살고 있는 것'과 '거의 외로움을 느끼지 않는 것'은 '역접' 관계이다. '역접'의 접속부사 Nevertheless가 쓰인 문장이 적절하다.

12 which를 where로 바꾸거나 which 앞이나 stayed 다음에 in이 있어야 한다.

13 'space or building in which'에서 which 뒤의 절이 불완전하므로 in which를 which로 바꾸어야 한다.

15 (1) 사람들은 다빈치가 어떻게 그의 창의적인 요리를 만드는지 관심이 없었다. (2) 학교에서, 나는 친구들과 맛있는 식사를 할 수 있는 점심시간이 제일 좋다.

16 선행사 the way와 관계부사 how는 함께 쓸 수 없다.

17 관계부사 where 뒤에는 완전한 절의 구조가 와야 하는데, 전치사 in이 있으므로 where를 which로 고치는 것이 적절하다.

18 시간을 나타내는 선행사 뒤에 관계부사를 찾는 문제이다. ①은 부사절 접속사 ②, ③, ⑤는 의문사로 사용되었다.

19 '그의 설명이 명확하지 않아서 이해를 못했다'는 것은 '순접'의 인과 관계이다. Since, As, Because 등의 접속사를 이용해서 한 문장으로 만드는 것이 적절하다.

20 '(a) few+셀 수 있는 명사 복수, (a) little+셀 수 없는 명사 단수'이며 'few와 little'은 '부정'의 의미이고 'a few와 a little'은 '긍정'의 의미이므로 few가 적절하다. however로 앞부분과 상반되고 있음을 확인한다.

21 주어진 문장의 however에 주목한다. however로 앞 문장과 상반되는 내용이 나오므로 ③번이 적절하다. 또한 ③번 다음 문장에서 As a result로 주어진 문장의 결과가 나오고 있음에도 유의한다.

22 When he took charge of the kitchen, da Vinci changed the menu completely.

23 like = such as: ~와 같은

24 주격 관계대명사가 필요한 자리이다. 선행사가 사물이므로 that이나 which가 적절하다.

25 'too ~ to ...(…하기에 너무 ~한, 너무 ~해서 … 할 수 없다)' 구문을 이용한다. most of them: 그것들 중 대부분

26 '선행사로 the reason이 나와 있으므로 관계부사 why가 적절하다.

27 주어진 문장의 the project가 ①번 앞 문장에서 언급한 '웅장한 그림을 밀라노에 있는 교회의 벽에 그리는 것'을 말하고 있으므로 ①번이 적절하다.

28 '그것은 예수의 최후의 만찬을 바탕으로 한 것이었다.'라고 하고 있다.

29 ⓐ와 ①: 형용사적 용법 ②, ⑤ 부사적 용법 ③, ④ 명사적 용법

30 관계부사 where를 이용하여 'they can use their creativity'가 선행사 a place를 수식하도록 한다.

단원별 예상문제
p.47~51

01 ③ 02 ⑤ 03 charge
04 (1) of all (t)ime (2) (u)sed to (3) (u)nique
05 ② 06 ⑤
07 I feel like having a bite of the bread. 08 ①
09 She asks the man to let her just have the check.
10 ① 11 (1) however (2) Thus (3) Thus
(4) However (5) Thus 12 ③ 13 the reason why he hadn't finished the painting earlier
14 (1) Jamaica is a country where international reggae festivals take place every summer.
(2) Show your brother how you solved the puzzle in such a short time.
(3) Everyone but me knows the day when I will be transferred to Jeju island.
(4) Katherine won't tell her teacher the reason why she ran out of the classroom.
15 where people have to line up all night to eat pizza
16 He wanted to create a place where people could try his innovative food.
17 ② 18 ⑤ 19 at 20 ④
21 painting → cooking
22 most of them were so big or so difficult that people couldn't use them

01 ③번은 동의어 관계이다. 나머지는 모두 반의어 관계이다. check: 계산서, bill: 계산서 ① inconvenience: 불편, convenience: 편리함 ② sell: 팔다, purchase: 구매하다 ④ satisfied: 만족한, dissatisfied: 불만족한 ⑤ creative: 창의적인, uncreative: 창의적이지 않은

02 ① appreciate: 진가를 알아보다, 고마워하다 / 무엇이든 문제가 있으면 알려주시면 고맙겠습니다. ② feel like -ing: ~할 마음이 나다 / 정말 더 이상 일하고 싶지 않아요. ③ not ~ anymore: 더 이상 ~ 아니다 / 그곳은 더 이상 조용한 섬이 아니야. ④ have a bite of: 한 입 베어 물다 / 이 버거를 한 입 먹

어보고 싶지 않나요? ⑤ now that: ~이기 때문에, ~이므로 / 이제라도 내가 알았으니까 너를 챙겨 줄게.

03 • put ~ in charge of: ~에게 …의 책임을 맡기다 / 나는 사무실 책임자를 맡게 되었다. • take charge of: ~의 책임을 지다, ~을 떠맡다 / 아버지가 돌아가신 후 그가 농장을 책임지게[떠맡게] 되었다.

04 (1) of all time: 역대, 지금껏 (2) be used to 동명사: ~하는 것에 익숙하다 (3) unique: 독특한, 고유의, 특유의

05 look+형용사: ~처럼[하게] 보이다 really를 real로 고쳐야 한다.

06 소녀가 독창적이지 않다고 할 뿐 무엇이 독창적인지는 알 수 없다.

07 feel like ~ing: ~하고 싶다

08 ①을 제외한 모두는 불만족을 표현하고 있다. pitiful: 동정적인, 처량한

09 여자는 'Let me just have the check, please.'라고 말하고 있다.

10 여자는 '빵은 괜찮았고, 샐러드는 신선했어요.'라고 하고 있다.

11 (1) 레오나르도 다빈치는 역대 가장 위대한 화가들 중의 한 명이자 위대한 발명가, 과학자, 그리고 음악가로 알려졌다. 하지만, 극히 소수의 사람들만이 그가 창의적인 요리사였다는 것을 안다. (2) 다빈치의 창의적인 음식을 본 손님들은 많은 양의 고기 요리에 익숙했기 때문에 불만족스러워했다. 그래서, 다빈치는 그의 직업을 잃었다. (3) 다빈치는 창의적인 요리를 더 빠르고 더 쉽게 요리하고 싶어 했다. 따라서, 그는 채소를 으깨고 스파게티를 뽑을 수 있는 새로운 기계들을 발명했다. (4) 다빈치는 살아 있을 때, 결코 성공적인 요리사는 되지 못했다. 그러나, 그는 그의 생애 내내 요리에 대한 큰 흥미를 보여 주었다. (5) 나는 다빈치의 요리에 대한 비밀스런 열정에 대해 배웠다. 그러므로, 나는 결코 예전과 같은 방식으로 '최후의 만찬'을 바라보지 않을 것이라고 생각한다.

12 ③은 '의문사+to부정사' 형태의 what이 적절하다. ① 계속적 용법의 관계대명사 which, ② 인과 관계를 나타내는 접속사 because. ④ 선행사 the reason, ⑤ 부사 yet이다.

13 사람들은 다빈치가 너무 많은 시간을 음식에 낭비했고 그것이 그가 그림을 더 일찍 끝내지 못한 이유라고 불평했다.

14 각각의 선행사에 맞게 관계부사를 쓰되, the way는 how와 같이 쓸 수 없으므로, (2)에서 선행사 없이 관계부사가 이끄는 절만 쓰는 것에 유의한다.

15 저기가 사람들이 피자를 먹으러 밤새 줄을 서는 그 유명한 식당이다.

16 a place를 선행사로 하는 관계부사 where를 이용하여 한 문장으로 바꾼다.

17 be[get] used to+명사 = be[get] accustomed to+명사: ~

에 익숙하다[익숙해지다]

18 이 글은 '다빈치가 창의적인 요리사였지만 요리사로서 성공하지는 못했다'는 내용이므로, 제목으로는 '다빈치의 이루지 못한 꿈'이 적절하다. Jack of all trades: 팔방미인

19 stop at cooking: 요리를 만드는 것에 멈추지 않다, stop cooking: 요리하는 것을 멈추다. 요리를 멈춘 것이 아니라 요리를 만드는 것에 멈추지 않고 그 이상을 했다는 의미가 적절하다.

20 ④ Because da Vinci wanted to cook much more quickly and easily. 나머지는 모두 대답할 수 없다.

21 '그는 요리를 향한 그의 열정을 추구할 또 다른 기회를 얻게 되어 행복했다.'라고 하고 있다.

22 'too ~ to … = so ~ that 주어 can't …'. use의 주어로 일반 사람을 나타내는 people을 쓰는 것이 적절하다.

서술형 실전문제 p.52~53

01 turns off by itself
02 inconvenience
03 I'm not satisfied with the phone.
04 (1) where (2) when (3) how (4) why (5) when
05 (1) In other words (2) However (3) In addition
    (4) Thus (5) For example
06 As a result
07 twenty-years-old → twenty-year-old
08 Because customers were unhappy with his dishes.

02 '당신을 귀찮게 하거나 악영향을 주는 어떤 것에 의해 일어나는 문제들'은 'inconvenience(불편, 애로)'이다.

03 'I don't like ~', 'I'm not satisfied with ~'는 모두 불만족을 표현하는 말이다.

04 각각의 선행사가 (1) 장소, (2) 시간, (3) 방법, (4) 이유, (5) 시간 등이다.

05 (1) 다빈치는 늘 독특하고 창의적인 음식을 만들었다. 즉, 그는 실험적 요리사였다. (2) 다빈치는 성공적인 요리사가 되고 싶었다. 그러나, 사람들은 그를 요리사로 여기지 않았다. (3) 다빈치는 채소를 으깨는 장치를 고안했다. 게다가, 그는 파스타를 뽑아내는 기계를 발명했다. (4) 다빈치는 요리에 관심이 있었다. 그래서 그는 <최후의 만찬> 테이블에 무슨 음식을 놓을지 오래 생각했다. (5) 다빈치는 다양한 분야에서 그의 재능으로 알려졌다. 예를 들어, 그는 화가이자, 건축가, 수학자, 그리고 음악가이다.

06 앞 문장에 대한 결과가 이어지고 있으므로 As a result가 적절하다.

07 twenty-year-old처럼 하이픈(-)으로 연결되어 뒤에 나오는 명

사를 수식하는 경우 형용사처럼 쓰이는 것이므로 복수형 years라고 하지 않는다.

08 '다빈치는 기꺼이 그 작업을 맡았는데, 그가 항상 음식에 흥미를 가졌기 때문이었다.'라고 하고 있다.

창의사고력 서술형 문제 p.54

|모범답안|

01 (1) drawing, I don't like the color.
    (2) steak, It's too rare.
02 (1) This is not the place where I eat the apple.
    (2) This is the day when I don't eat the apple.
    (3) The witch asked the mirror how she could make Snow White eat the apple.
02 (A) an artist   (B) using technology   (C) technical
    (D) my first exhibition

02 보기의 단어들을 적절히 조합하여 그림과 어법에 맞게 영작한 답이면 된다.

단원별 모의고사 p.55~58

01 provide   02 crush   03 ④   04 ⑤
05 throughout   06 fix
07 I'll learn how I should act.
08 I will make sure that I'll do my best.
09 It's because he wants to become an actor.
10 ②   11 It sometimes turns off by itself.
12 It would take a few hours.   13 ③
14 ④   15 ④   16 ④
17 (1) However, it was so painful that the dog ran away.
    (2) Thus, Sumi asked for a lot of side dishes.
18 ③   19 He made simple but artistic dishes.
20 ⑤   21 ③   22 ④

01 surely: 확실히 – certainly: 확실하게, supply 제공하다 – provide 제공하다

02 '어떤 것을 세게 눌러서 깨지거나 손상되게 하다'는 'crush(으깨다, 쭈그러뜨리다)'가 적절하다. 그 승용차는 트럭에 깔려 완전히 쭈그러졌다.

03 • 우리는 평생 행복을 추구한다. • 나는 그가 불평하는 것을 들어본 적이 없다. pursue: 추구하다, 추진하다. complain: 불평하

다, determine: 결정하다, provide: 제공하다, decorate: 장식하다

04 put ~ in charge of: ~에게 …의 책임을 맡기다, of all time: 역대, 지금껏

05 throughout: ~ 동안 내내

06 fix: 수리하다. 망가지거나 제대로 작동하지 않는 것을 수리하다. 수리할 사람을 보내 주시겠습니까?

07 의문사+to부정사 = 의문사+주어+should+동사원형

08 'I promise ~'와 'I will make sure that ~'은 모두 다짐을 말하는 표현으로 쓸 수 있다.

09 소년은 'I want to go to an arts high school. I want to become an actor.'라고 하고 있다.

10 '제가 좀 봐도 될까요?'라는 뜻의 주어진 문장은 ②번 다음 문장인 '불편을 드려 죄송합니다. 고치는 데 몇 시간 정도 걸릴 거예요.'의 앞에 들어가는 것이 자연스럽다.

11 'I bought this phone only a week ago, but it sometimes turns off by itself.'라고 하고 있다.

12 'It'll take a few hours to fix it.'이라고 하고 있다.

13 'Sam이 아침식사를 하지 않은 것'과 '배고픔을 느끼지 않는 것'은 '역접' 관계로서 '접속부사' however가 쓰였다. 이것을 한 문장으로 바꾸면, '역접'의 '접속사' Though를 활용한 ③번 문장이 가장 적절하다.

14 '학생들이 환자와 PC방에서 밀접한 접촉을 가진 것'이 원인이고, '그들이 바이러스에 감염된 것'이 결과이므로, '순접'의 '인과 관계'를 나타내는 접속사 Because, As, Since 등으로 한 문장을 만드는 것이 적절하다. ②와 ③은 보기의 문장과 내용이 조금 바뀌었으므로, 유의하도록 한다.

15 선행사가 the way일 때, how는 같이 사용하지 않는다.

16 '선행사'가 the day일 때, 전치사는 in이 아니라, on을 쓰는 것이 적절하다.

17 (1) 고슴도치는 그저 그 개와 잘 지내고 싶었을 뿐이었다. 그렇지만, 너무 아파서 그 개는 도망을 갔다. (2) 오늘은 수미의 부모님이 급식 당번을 하는 날이다. 그래서, 수미는 반찬을 많이 달라고 했다.

18 '조각가'가 아니라 '과학자'로 소개하고 있다.

19 '그가 부엌을 책임지게 되었을 때, 다빈치는 메뉴를 완전히 바꿔 버렸다. 그는 약간의 당근 조각을 곁들인 생선과 같이 단순하지만 예술적인 음식을 만들었다.'라고 하고 있다.

20 a special moment(시간)를 선행사로 하는 관계부사 when이 적절하다.

21 주어진 문장의 Thus가 ③번 앞 문장에서 언급하고 있는 내용의 결과를 이끌고 있으므로 ③번이 적절하다.

22 'I entered Korea Art College.'라고 언급되었다.

Lesson

7

Wit and Wisdom

시험대비 실력평가 p.62

01 ⑤　　02 official　　03 ④　　04 ①
05 ⑤　　06 ②

01 유의어 관계이다. wit: 기지, 재치, humor: 유머, 해학, palace: 궁전, court: 대궐, 궁궐

02 '어떤 조직에서 권력 있는 직책에 있는 사람'은 'official(고위 공무원, 관리)'이 적절하다. 그는 부시 대통령 재임 시절 백악관 공무원이었다.

03 ① in one's place: ~의 입장에, ~의 상황에. 당신이 내 입장이 되면 어떤 기분이 들지 생각해 보세요. ② make sense: 타당하다, 말이 되다. 정부가 특정 음식에 세금을 부과한다는 것은 말이 안 돼. ③ come up with: 찾아내다, 떠올리다. 그의 시를 보고 무엇이 떠오르니? ④ a number of: 많은. 공원에는 꽤 많은 사람들이 있었습니다. the number of: ~의 수 ⑤ focus on: ~에 집중하다. 돈보다 일을 잘하는 데 집중하다 보면 돈은 저절로 들어온다.

04 wisdom: 지혜, 슬기, 현명함. 이 직업에서는 솔로몬의 지혜를 발휘할 필요가 있다.

05 ① certainly: 틀림없이, 분명히. 나는 분명히 그곳에 다시 갈 것이다. ② speechless: (화나거나 놀라서) 말을 못 하는. Laura는 놀라서 아무 말도 못했다. ③ correct: 맞는, 정확한. 정확한 잔액을 확인하려면 하루나 이틀 정도 기다려야 한다. ④ punish: 처벌하다, 벌주다. 우리 부모님은 내게 TV를 못 보게 하는 것으로 벌을 주고는 하셨다. ⑤ provide (필요품을) 주다, 공급[지급]하다. 봄 날씨가 추우면 해충의 수가 자연스럽게 억제될 것이다.

06 wit: 기지, 재치. 이 소설은 작가의 재치가 넘친다. worm: 벌레. 일찍 일어나는 새가 벌레를 잡는다.

서술형 시험대비 p.63

01 (1) court　(2) journey　(3) match　(4) pumpkin
02 (1) valueless　(2) wisdom
03 (1) check　(2) speechless　(3) hand　(4) place
04 (1) I can't tell one twin from the other.
　(2) Citizens feel secure taking out their wallets on the streets.
　(3) I want freedom for the full expression of my personality.

(4) Each exercise focuses on a different grammar point.

01 (1) court: 대궐, 궁궐, 왕이나 여왕이 살며 일하는 장소 (2) journey: 여행, 여정, 한 장소에서 다른 장소로 여행하는 일 (3) match: 경기, 시합, 두 팀이나 사람 사이에 조직되어 있는 스포츠 행사 (4) pumpkin: 주황색 껍질이 두껍고 둥글고 큰 채소

02 (1) '명사+less'로 형용사가 되는 어휘들이다. care: 주의, 조심 – careless: 부주의한, value: 가치 – valueless: 가치 없는 (2) '동사 - 명사' 관계이다. punish: 처벌하다 – punishment: 처벌, wise: 지혜로운, 현명한 – wisdom: 지혜

03 (1) check out: 확인하다 (2) speechless: (화나거나 놀라서) 말을 못 하는 (3) hand in: 제출하다 (4) in one's place: ~의 입장에

04 (1) the other: (둘 중) 다른 하나. other를 추가한다. (2) take out: 가지고 나가다. take를 추가한다. (3) expression: 표현. expression을 추가한다. (4) focus on: ~에 집중하다. on을 추가한다.

교과서

Conversation

핵심 Check p.64~65

1 Do you mean it's better to hand it in even though it's late?
2 I wish I could dance like you.

교과서 대화문 익히기

Check(√) True or False p.66

1 F　2 T　3 T　4 F

교과서 확인학습 p.68~69

Listen & Speak 1 A-1

look tired / to study / Good for / gets tired / Do you mean / what I mean

Listen & Speak 1 A-2

have to / a leg / Do you mean, one, legs / meaning, you do well

Listen & Speak 2 A-1	

is good at / too / good singers / What a, I wish I could

Listen & Speak 2 A-2	

can't believe, to say, Thanks to, I wish I could, to start

Communicate A	

look, good / Do you mean / I wish I could / live for today / Do you mean, focus on / why, called / as wise as

Progress Check 1	

look worried, wrong / hand in / better late than never / Do you mean, hand it in / what

Progress Check 2	

play the guitar / it / too / in / What a, I wish, could

Progress Check 3	

what to do, Another, what that means

 시험대비 기본평가　　　　　　　　　　p.70

01 ②

02 Do you mean I have to break one of my legs?

03 (C) – (B) – (D) – (A)

01 앞에서 '일찍 일어나는 새가 빨리 지쳐.'라고 하는 것으로 보아 '일찍 일어나는 게 싫다'는 뜻으로 ②번이 가장 적절하다.

02 'Do you mean ~?'은 이해를 확인하기 위해 쓰는 표현이다. 'one of+복수 명사'는 '~ 중의 하나'라는 의미이다.

03 주어진 '무슨 문제 있니?'라는 질문에 (C)에서 '과학 보고서를 냈어야 했는데, 내지 않았다'고 문제를 언급하고, (D)에서 'Do you mean ~?'으로 (B)에서 말한 'It's better late than never.'에 대해 '이해를 확인'하는 질문을 하고 있으므로, (B) 다음에 (D)가 이어지고, (A)에서 (D)의 질문에 대한 답을 하고 있으므로 (D) 다음에 (A)가 이어지는 순서가 적절하다.

시험대비 실력평가　　　　　　　　　　p.71~72

01 ③	02 ①	03 ⑤

04 Do you mean I have to break one of my legs?

05 ⑤	06 ①	07 Time flies.
08 ③	09 (B) – (C) – (A) – (D)	10 ③
11 why	12 ④	

01 '내가 내 다리 한 쪽을 부러뜨려야 한다는 말이야?'에 '행운을 빌어!'로 답하는 것은 어색하다. A와 B를 서로 바꾸는 것이 적절하다.

---

02 뒤에서 '내 다리 한 쪽을 부러뜨려야 한다는 말이야?'라는 말로 보아 'Break a leg!'이 가장 적절하다.

03 an expression을 뒤에서 수식하는 현재분사 meaning이 적절하다.

04 'Do you mean ~?'은 이해를 확인하는 표현이다.

05 빈칸에는 'I wish ~' 가정법이 들어가야 하는데 현재 사실과 반대되는 바람이나 소원을 말하는 것이 문맥에 맞으므로 가정법 과거로 쓰는 것이 자연스러우므로 'I could go back to'가 적절하다.

06 '시간이 참 빠르다'고 한 후 '작별 인사를 해야 할 시간이라는 게 믿어지지 않는다'고 하면서 '선생님들과 친구들 덕분에, 이곳에서 정말 행복했다'고 하는 것이 자연스럽다.

07 Time flies: 세월은 유수와 같다, 시간이 쏜살같다.

08 밑줄 친 문장은 이해를 확인할 때 쓰는 표현이다.

09 좀 피곤해 보인다는 주어진 문장에 이어, (B)에서 '아주 일찍 일어났다'고 이유를 설명하고, (C)에서 일찍 일어난 것에 대해 잘 했다고 말하자, (A)에서 반론을 제시하고, (D)에서 그 말에 대한 이해를 확인하는 질문을 한 후, '그렇다'는 말로 마무리하는 순서가 자연스럽다.

10 뒤에서 'Yes, exactly.'라고 하는 것으로 보아 이해를 확인하는 것이 적절하다.

11 That's why ~: 그것이 ~한 이유이다.

12 Anna가 왜 오늘을 위해 사는지는 대화를 통해 알 수 없다.

서술형 시험대비　　　　　　　　　　p.73

01 I wish I could forget about it

02 You're as wise as my grandma.

03 It's because today is a gift. 또는 Today is called the present because today is a gift.

04 I wish I could play the guitar.

05 She learned how to play the guitar from her dad.

06 (1) hand in it → hand it in

　　(2) finish that → finish what

01 'I wish ~' 가정법 과거로 현재 사실과 반대되는 바람이나 소원을 말할 때 쓰는 표현이며 '~하면 좋을 텐데' 정도의 뜻이다.

02 as ~ as 동등 비교를 쓴다.

03 "어제는 역사, 내일은 미스터리, 그리고 오늘은 현재이다. 그게 바로 오늘을 선물이라 부르는 이유." 라고 하고 있다.

04 'I wish+가정법 과거'는 현재 사실과 반대되는 바람이나 소원을 말할 때 쓰는 표현이다.

05 소녀는 '아버지께 배웠어.'라고 하고 있다.

06 (1) 목적어가 대명사이므로 '타동사+대명사 목적어+부사'의 순서로 써야 한다. (2) finish와 started의 목적어 역할을 할 수 있

는 what이 적절하다.

교과서 Grammar

p.74~75
핵심 Check

1 (1) whose (2) of which
2 (1) If I were a dog, I would sleep all day long.
  (2) If she lived in New York, she would eat only hamburgers.

시험대비 기본평가
p.76

01 ③

02 (1) is → were[was] (2) will → would
  (3) has → had (4) will → would

03 Cathy heard of a man whose wife wrote novels.

04 ④

01 내용상 '영화관의 영화'가 아니라, '영화관에서 영화가 상영되고 있었다'는 것이므로, 장소의 선행사 뒤에 관계부사 where를 쓰는 것이 적절하다. 소유격 whose 뒤에 정관사 the가 오는 것도 어법상 어색하다.

02 문제에서 모든 문장이 가정법 문장이라고 했고, 모든 문장의 구조는 '가정법 과거' 형태이므로, 조건절의 동사를 과거로, 주절의 조동사도 과거형으로 고치는 것이 적절하다. (1)은 현대 영어에서 was도 가능하다.

03 두 문장의 공통되는 명사 중 소유격 부분을 관계대명사 소유격으로 전환하여, 하나의 문장으로 영작한다.

04 주절에 조동사의 과거형이 나왔으므로, 가정법 문장이다. If절에 know의 과거동사를 쓰면 되고, 현재완료시제로는 가정법을 쓰지 않는다.

시험대비 실력평가
p.77~79

01 ①   02 ⑤

03 Oliver has a bike whose color is red.

04 If I were she, I would not give up.

05 I wish I could draw well like Bob.

06 They are going to buy a house of which the scenery is beautiful.

07 ②   08 ④   09 ④   10 ③
11 ②   12 ④   13 ③   14 ④
15 ⑤   16 ④

01 '금발머리 아가씨가 전망 좋은 카페에서 당신을 기다리고 있었다.'는 문장이다. 사람이 선행사인 경우 소유격 관계대명사는 whose만 가능하다.

02 가정법 문장이라면 he'll을 he would로, 직설법 문장이라면 were를 is로 쓰는 것이 적절하다.

03 관계대명사의 소유격이 있으므로 선행사 a bike 뒤에 whose color를 배열하는 것이 적절하다.

04 가정법 과거 시제의 문장이다. If I were she로 시작하고 주절에 조동사의 과거형 would를 쓴다. 구어체에서는 If I were her를 많이 쓴다.

05 가정법 중에서 I wish 가정법이 사용된 문장이다. 직설법으로는 'Bob처럼 그림을 잘 그리지 못한다'는 내용이므로, I wish절에 동사의 과거시제를 가정법과 마찬가지로 쓴다.

06 집을 구입할 것이고, 그 집의 풍경이 아름답다는 내용이므로, 관계대명사의 소유격을 써야 하는데, of which가 나왔다. of which 뒤에 the scenery를 쓰는 것에 유의하여 배열한다. of which the scenery 대신 the scenery of which도 가능하다.

07 ⓐ, ⓒ, ⓔ는 whose, ⓑ, ⓓ는 of which, ⓕ는 in which 또는 where를 써야 한다. 사람이 선행사일 때 소유격 관계대명사는 whose만 쓰며, 사물이 선행사일 때는 whose와 of which 둘 다 가능하지만 of which를 쓸 때는 뒤에 정관사가 온다.

08 ④를 제외한 나머지는 모두 가정법의 주절에서 실현 불가능한 가정 상황에서의 '가능'을 나타내는 조동사이다. ④에 쓰인 could는 can의 과거시제 역할로 사용되었다.

09 ④는 의문사의 소유격으로 쓰였다. 앞에 선행사가 없는 것이 특징이다. 그 외에는 모두 선행사 뒤에 쓰인 관계대명사의 소유격 whose이다.

10 ①은 가정법 과거가 현재 사실의 반대인데, 가정법과 직설법 모두 not이 있다. ②와 ④는 직설법과 같은 뜻이 되려면, 가정법 과거완료시제가 필요하다. ⑤는 직설법으로는, '스마트폰이 없어서 한 대 갖고 싶어 한다'는 내용인데, 가정법으로는 '갖고자 한다면 얻을 수 있다'는 내용으로 같은 뜻이 아니다.

11 ② '주최자가 알려지지 않은 행사'라는 의미로서, 선행사 the event 뒤에 소유격이 적절히 쓰였다. ① of which cover → whose cover 또는 of which the cover, ③ the → 삭제, ④ of which the name → whose name, ⑤ water of which → the water of which 또는 whose water

12 주절은 가정법 과거완료 문장이고, If절은 가정법 과거 시제 형태인데, 해석을 해보면 '버스를 놓친다면, 지각하지 않았을 것이다'가 되어, 의미상으로도 부적절하다. 가정법 과거 시제를 활용하여, 알맞게 고쳐본다면, 'If Angelina missed the bus, she would be late for school.'이 된다.

13 'I wish 가정법 과거'는 직설법 현재 시제의 반대 의미이므로, was not을 is not으로 고치는 것이 적절하다.

14 '그의 기타가 부서진 그 소년이 당혹스러워 보였다.'라는 문장이다. 관계대명사의 소유격 whose를 사용해서 하나의 문장으로

만드는 것이 적절하며, of which는 선행사가 사람인 경우에는 쓰지 않는다. whose 뒤에 정관사 the를 함께 쓸 수 없다.

15 '코로나 바이러스 위기 때 매출 피해가 가장 컸던 소기업들에 대한 도움이 더 필요하다.'라는 문장이다. 관계대명사의 소유격 whose를 사용해서 하나의 문장으로 만드는 것이 적절하며, of which를 이용할 때는 of which 뒤에 정관사 the를 쓴다. whose 뒤에 정관사 the를 함께 쓰지 않는다. ④의 경우, who are needed보다는 who need로 하면, 의미는 비슷해지나 문제가 요구하는 범위를 많이 벗어난다.

16 '~가 없다면'이라는 가정법 표현은 'If there were no ~'로 나타내며, without 또는 'If it were not for ~'로 대체할 수 있다. 'If it were not for'는 if를 생략해서 'Were it not for ~'로 표현 가능하다.

01 (1) were you, I would give sweets to the person who pulled
  (2) would be great if there were a man as wise
  (3) two pots whose neckswere really narrow
  (4) them was a man whose name was

02 (1) If it were not for
  (2) Were it not for
  (3) But for
  (4) As there is his wisdom, we can

03 exercised regularly, she could stay

04 (1) the → 삭제   (2) legs → the legs
  (3) who → whose   (4) whose → who
  (5) who → whose   (6) which → of which

05 legs of which are four waved at

06 whose eyes are tired is massaging with a warm

07 (1) I have a friend whose mother is a very famous magician.
  (2) This is the magazine the cover of which is black and white.
  (3) My little brother is an actor whose film you watched.

08 (1) am → were   (2) am → were[was]
  (3) are → were   (4) can → could
  (5) will → would   (6) will → would
  (7) be → have been

01 가정법과 '가주어-진주어' 구문, 소유격 관계대명사 whose 등에 유의하여, 주어진 단어들을 적절히 배열한다.

02 '그의 지혜가 없다면, Persia와 문제가 생길 수도 있다.'는 내용으로 직설법으로 표현하면, '그의 지혜가 있기 때문에, Persia와 문제가 생길 리 없다.'가 된다. 가정법 과거를 전제로, 'Without

= But for = If it were not for = Were it not for = If there were no'를 기억해 두는 것이 좋다.

03 '그 숙녀가 규칙적으로 운동을 하지 않기 때문에 건강이 좋지 않다.'라는 직설법 문장을 가정법으로 표현하면, '그 숙녀가 규칙적으로 운동을 하면, 건강이 좋을 것이다.'가 된다. If절에는 과거 동사, 주절에는 조동사의 과거형에 유의하여 영작한다.

04 어법상 어색한 단어를 하나만 찾아야 하므로, 관계대명사의 소유격을 쓰는 여러 가지 상황에서 하나의 오류만을 찾아 적절하게 고치도록 한다. (4)는 소유격이 아니라 주격 관계대명사를 써야 하는 것에 유의한다.

05 선행사는 monster이고, 바로 뒤에 정관사 the가 있으므로, 관계대명사 소유격 whose를 쓸 수 없다. the legs of which 표현을 떠올리는 것이 중요하다. 과거 시제이므로 waved의 어형 변화에도 유의한다.

06 그녀의 눈이 피로해진 것은 'her eyes are tired'라고 표현한다. 소유격 관계대명사 whose를 활용하여, 'whose eyes are tired'까지 표현하고, 진행형이므로 massage를 massaging으로 표현하는 것에 유의한다.

07 (1), (3)은 선행사가 사람이므로 관계대명사 whose를 쓴다. (2)는 'This is the magazine of which the cover is black and white.'로도 영작이 가능하지만, 주어진 단어에 cover of가 있으므로, the cover of which로 표현하는 것에 유의한다.

08 문제에서 각 문장이 가정법이라고 했으므로, (1), (2), (3) if절의 be동사 또는 I wish 뒤에 오는 be동사를 were로 바꾸는 것이 적절하다 (4), (5), (6) 가정법 과거 문장의 주절에는 조동사의 과거형을 쓴다. (7) 내용상 시제가 '가정법 과거완료'이므로, 주절에 '조동사+have+p.p.'가 와야 한다.

Reading 교과서

1 F   2 T   3 F   4 T

1 T   2 F   3 F

01 Tales   02 a number of, court
03 was, whose name   04 for, with
05 Thus, to have, near   06 Punishment

07 To test, asked them strange questions

08 came up with

09 a hair, should I do to   10 be punished

11 punish   12 turned to

13 would, do if, were in my place

14 If, were you, would give   15 talking about

16 crazy   17 What made you

18 who, must be, else, such a thing

19 so, to have, as wise as   20 Potful, Wisdom

21 with a strange favor

22 a lot of, I've been asked, to bring, a potful of

23 makes no sense, put, in   24 a potful of

25 won't be   26 a few

27 as much time as   28 A few, whose, one

29 take, to return, out of it   30 not to break

31 speechless   32 left for

33 would be, if there were, as wise as

34 what was

35 the other, for yourself   36 the other, as big as

37 can't be taken, without breaking

38 over, as big as   39 a potful of

교과서 확인학습 B

p.86~87

1 Tales of Birbal

2 Akbar, the third Mogul emperor, had a number of wise officials at his court.

3 Among them was a man whose name was Raja Birbal.

4 He was famous for his quick wit and was very wise with his words.

5 Thus, the emperor always liked to have Birbal near him.

6 Sweet Punishment

7 To test his officials' wisdom, Akbar often asked them strange questions.

8 One day, he came up with an interesting question.

9 Akbar: Someone pulled a hair from my head today. What should I do to him?

10 Official 1: He should be punished, of course.

11 Official 2: Yes, punish him!

12 Akbar turned to Birbal.

13 Akbar: What would you do if you were in my place, Birbal?

14 Birbal: If I were you, I would give him sweets.

15 Official 3: What's he talking about?

16 Official 4: Birbal's crazy!

17 Akbar: What made you say so?

18 Birbal: The person who pulled your hair must be your grandson. No one else could do such a thing.

19 Akbar: You are indeed correct, Birbal. I'm so glad to have someone as wise as you near me.

20 A Potful of Wisdom

21 One day, the king of Persia sent an official with a strange favor.

22 Persian Official: I hear you have a lot of wise men in your country. I've been asked by my king to bring him a potful of wisdom.

23 Official 5: That makes no sense! How can we put wisdom in a pot?

24 Akbar: Can you bring him a potful of wisdom, Birbal?

25 Birbal: It won't be a problem.

26 Could you please wait a few weeks?

27 Persian Official: Of course! Take as much time as you need.

28 A few weeks later, Birbal came back with two pots whose necks were really narrow. He offered one to the Persian official.

29 Birbal: You can take this pot of wisdom to your king. Please ask him to return the pot to us after he takes the wisdom out of it.

30 Birbal: The pot is very precious, so please be careful not to break it. We only have two pots of wisdom.

31 The Persian official looked inside the pot and became speechless.

32 He thanked Birbal and left for his country.

33 Persian Official: It would be great if there were a man as wise as Birbal in our country.

34 After the Persian official left, Akbar asked Birbal what was inside the pot.

35 Birbal: Here is the other pot. You can see for yourself.

36 Akbar looked inside the other pot and found a pumpkin just as big as the pot.

37 Akbar: I see! The pumpkin can't be taken out without breaking the pot. How did you do it?

38 Birbal: I put the pots over pumpkin flowers and waited until the pumpkins grew as big as the pots.

39 Akbar: Hahaha! This certainly is a potful of wisdom!

01 ②   02 ④   03 ⑤   04 ③
05 ①   06 ④   07 speechless
08 ①   09 can't take out → can't be taken out
10 (A) were (B) who (C) wise   11 ③
12 ⑤   13 What made you say so? 14 ②
15 ①   16 ③   17 ⑤   18 ④
19 Birbal asked him to ask his king to return the pot and be careful not to break it.
20 It would be great if there were a man as wise as Birbal in our country.
21 ③

01 '황제의 머리카락을 잡아당긴 사람에게 사탕을 주라'고 했으므로 보통 사람들의 생각으로는 '정신이 나갔다'고 하는 것이 적절하다. ① reasonable: 분별 있는, 사리를 아는 ③ sensible: 분별 있는, 사리를 아는 ④ fair: 공정한, 올바른 ⑤ logical: 논리적인

02 여기서는 '~해야만 한다'는 뜻의 should가 아니라 '~임에 틀림없다'는 뜻의 must가 적절하다.

03 신하들은 '처벌해야 한다'고 말했다. punish: 처벌하다, praise: 칭찬하다

04 뒤에 명사가 나오며 완전한 절이 이어지므로 소유격 관계대명사 whose가 적절하다.

05 'a lot of'는 many와 much 둘 다로 쓰일 수 있지만 뒤에 복수 명사인 men이 나오는 것으로 보아 many로 쓰인 것이다. 'a deal of'는 much의 뜻으로만 쓰인다.

06 ④번은 Birbal을 가리키지만, 나머지는 모두 the king of Persia를 가리킨다.

07 일시적으로 말할 수 없는, speechless: (충격 따위로) 말이 안 나오는

08 주어진 문장의 for yourself(직접)에 주목한다. ①번 앞에서 '또 다른 항아리가 있습니다.'라고 한 후 이어지는 문장에서 Akbar가 '또 다른 항아리 안을 보고 꼭 항아리만큼 큰 호박을 발견했다.'라고 하고 있으므로 ①번이 적절하다.

09 호박이 무엇을 꺼내는 '능동'이 아니라 꺼내지는 '수동'이 적절하므로 조동사가 있는 문장의 수동태로 '조동사+be+p.p.' 형태로 고쳐야 한다.

10 (A) 가정법 과거의 문장이므로 were가 적절하다. 구어체에서는 was를 쓰기도 한다. (B) 선행사가 The person으로 사람이므로 who가 적절하다. (C) 'as ~ as' 구문에서는 원급을 사용하므로 wise가 적절하다.

11 악바르의 손자가 왜 그의 머리를 당겼는지는 대답할 수 없다. ① To test their wisdom. ② No. ④ His Grandson. ⑤ He was glad to have someone as wise as Birbal near him.

12 ① 난 창의적인 생각들이 떠오르지 않아. ② 저는 무언가 핑계를 만들어야만 합니다. ③ 당신이 이것보다 더 좋은 아이디어를 제안해줬으면 좋겠어요. ④ 노래 한 곡 쓰는 데 시간이 얼마나 걸리나요? ⑤ 그 돈을 얼마나 빨리 마련해 주실 수 있으세요?

13 사역동사 make를 이용하여 'made+목적어+동사원형'의 형태로 쓴다.

14 뒤에서 '몇 주만 기다려 주시겠습니까?'라고 하고 있으므로 '문제될 것이 없사옵니다.'가 가장 적절하다.

15 'as ~ as' 구문에서는 원급을 사용하므로 much time이 적절하다. time이 셀 수 없는 명사이므로 much가 수식하도록 한다.

16 ⓐ와 ①, ②, ⑤: 명사적 용법 ③: 부사적 용법, ④: 형용사적 용법

17 ⓑ leave for: ~로 (향해서) 떠나다 ① be worried about: ~에 대해 걱정하다 ② look up to: ~을 존경하다 ③ think of A as B: A를 B로 여기다 ④ be tired of: ~에 싫증나다 ⑤ care for: 좋아하다, 돌보다

18 두 개 중의 처음 하나는 one으로 쓰고 나머지 두 번째 하나는 the other로 쓴다.

19 '왕께서 이 항아리에서 지혜를 꺼내신 후에는 항아리를 우리에게 돌려달라 전해 주십시오.', '그 항아리는 매우 귀중한 것이니, 그것을 깨지 않도록 조심해 주십시오.'라고 하고 있다.

20 현재 사실과 반대되는 말을 가정하는 가정법 과거(If+주어+동사의 과거형, 주어+조동사의 과거형+동사원형)를 이용하여 배열한다.

21 '우리는 오직 두 개의 지혜의 항아리만 갖고 있습니다.'라고 말하고 있다.

01 in my place
02 If I were you, I would give him sweets.
03 His grandson pulled Akbar's hair.
04 How can we put wisdom in a pot?
05 **한 항아리만큼의 지혜를 자신의 왕께 가지고 가는 것**
06 He was asked to bring a potful of wisdom by his king.
07 to return
08 It is not great as there is not a man as wise as Birbal in our country.
09 There was a pumpkin as big as the pot.
10 (A) a pumpkin (B) became speechless
11 Thus
12 Among them was a man whose name was Raja Birbal.
13 He was famous for his quick wit.

01 in one's place: ~의 처지에서, ~의 입장에서

02 현재 사실과 반대되는 말을 가정하는 가정법 과거(If+주어+동사의 과거형, 주어+조동사의 과거형+동사원형)를 이용한다.

03 마지막 문장에서 '과연 그대의 말이 맞소, 비르발.'이라고 하고 있다.

04 '지혜를 항아리에 넣을 수 없다.'라는 평서문을 같은 뜻의 의문문으로 바꾸면 '어떻게 지혜를 항아리에 넣을 수 있는가?'라고 할 수 있다. 이러한 의문문을 수사의문문이라고 한다.

05 앞 문장에서 '저의 왕으로부터 한 항아리만큼의 지혜를 왕께 가지고 오라는 명을 받았습니다.'라고 하고 있다.

06 '저는 저의 왕으로부터 한 항아리만큼의 지혜를 왕께 가지고 오라는 명을 받았습니다.'라고 하고 있다.

07 ask의 목적격 보어로 to부정사가 적절하다.

08 가정법 과거(If+주어+동사의 과거형, 주어+조동사의 과거형+동사원형)는 현재 사실과 반대되는 말을 가정하는 것으로 as나 because, since 등을 이용하여 같은 뜻의 말로 바꿔 쓸 수 있다.

09 '악바르는 또 다른 항아리 안을 보고 꼭 항아리만큼 큰 호박을 발견했다.'라고 하고 있다.

10 비르발은 호박이 들어 있는 항아리를 페르시아의 신하에게 주었고 그가 항아리 안을 들여다보고는 말을 잃었다.

11 앞 문장의 내용에 대한 결과가 이어지고 있으므로 Thus가 적절하다.

12 앞 문장과의 연결성을 높이기 위해서 전치사구가 앞으로 이동하면서 다음에 나오는 주어와 동사의 어순도 바뀌어 '동사+주어'가 되었다. a man을 수식하는 소유격 관계대명사 whose를 이용한다. 소유격 관계대명사는 그 다음에 명사가 이어지며 완전한 절을 이끈다. among them: 그들 중에

13 '그는 재빠른 재치로 유명했으며'라고 하고 있다.

영역별 핵심문제 p.95~100

01 ①　　02 (h)onesty, (w)isdom (1) wisdom
(2) honesty　03 favor　04 worthless, priceless
05 ③　　06 ⑤　　07 What a family!
08 ④　　09 (A) is (B) too (C) wish
10 Everyone in her family dances well.
11 He wishes he could dance like the girl.
12 ②　　13 ③　　14 ④
15 (1) If I were Birbal, I could answer the difficult question of the king.
　(2) If Bentley wore a skirt, he would look like a girl.
　(3) If there were a kettle, I could boil and drink my tea.

---

　(4) If Michelle didn't have the glasses, it would not be easy for her to read the books.

16 ①　　17 ⑤　　18 ④　　19 ②
20 What would you do if you were in my place
21 It doesn't make sense. 또는 That makes no sense.
22 ①　　23 ③　　24 ⑤
25 keep in touch
26 If I could turn back time, I would spend more time with you.
27 He still remembers the time when Jaeha and he went camping together.

01 <보기>와 ①: 대궐, 궁궐 ① 그들은 종종 궁궐에서 공연을 했다. ② 죄수들은 경찰의 호위 하에 법원으로 이송된다. ③ 그들은 잔디밭에 테니스 코트를 그렸다. ④ 너는 기회를 얻도록 노력해야 한다. ⑤ 법정은 그에게 유죄 판결을 내렸다.

02 (1) wisdom: 지혜, 슬기, 현명함. 그녀는 아주 지혜로운 여성이다. (2) honesty: 정직 ,정직이 없다면 존엄성은 어디에 있는가?

03 '누군가를 돕기 위해 또는 그에게 친절하기 위해 당신이 해주는 어떤 것'이라는 의미로 'favor(청, 부탁)'이 적절하다. 부탁 좀 들어주시겠어요?

04 (1) worthless: 가치 없는. worth에 less를 붙여 형용사가 된 어휘이다. 하잘것없어 보이는 물건도 다 쓸모가 있다. (2) priceless: 매우 소중한. price에 less를 붙여 형용사가 된 어휘인데 '너무 소중해서 값을 매길 수 없는, 그래서 매우 소중한'이라는 뜻이다. 많은 소중한 예술 작품들이 갤러리에서 도난당했다.

05 • find out: 찾아내다, 알아보다. 그들에게 전화해서 언제 올 건지 알아봐. • turn out: 판명되다, 밝혀지다. 그 보도는 틀린 보도로 판명되었다. • figure out: 알아내다. 난 이걸 어떻게 하는 건지 알 수가 없어.

06 기타를 정말 잘 친다는 칭찬의 말에 이어, 고맙다며 아버지께 배웠다고 말하고(D), 아버지도 기타를 치시는지 추가 질문하자(B), 유명한 밴드에 계셨다고 답하고(C), 너처럼 기타를 칠 수 있다면 좋겠다고 바람을 말하는(A) 문장으로 이어지는 것이 적절하다.

07 'What+a+명사'의 순서로 감탄문이다.

08 무슨 문제 있느냐는 질문에 '과학 보고서를 제때에 냈다.'고 대답하는 것은 어색하다.

09 (A) Everyone이 주어이므로 is, (B) 긍정문이므로 too (C) 뒤에 있는 조동사의 과거형 could로 보아 가정법으로 쓰이는 wish가 적절하다.

10 소녀는 'Everyone in my family is good at dancing.'이라고 하고 있다.

11 소년은 'I wish I could dance like you.'라고 하고 있다.

12 'Sammy는 꼬리가 매우 짧은 토끼를 갖고 있다'는 문장이다. 관계대명사의 소유격 whose를 사용해서 하나의 문장으로 만드는 것이 적절하다.

13 <보기>의 if는 가정법 과거를 이끄는 종속접속사로 쓰였다. ③ 외에 나머지는 모두 간접의문문의 명사절을 이끄는 접속사로서 '~인지'라는 뜻이다.

14 '과거시제의 직설법 문장'을 가정법으로 고치면 '가정법 과거완료'가 된다. If절에 'had+p.p', 주절에 '조동사 과거+have+p.p.'를 쓰되, 직설법과 반대되도록 not을 쓴다. 'I wouldn't have had to pay the late fee'는 '연체료를 내야만 하지 않았을 텐데'라는 뜻이다.

15 직설법 현재 문장을 가정법으로 바꿀 때, 종속절에는 동사의 과거형을, 주절에는 '조동사의 과거형+동사원형'을 쓰는 것에 유의하여, 문장을 전환한다. (4)에서 'it is easy'는 가정법으로 바꾸면 조동사 would를 활용하고, 내용이 반대가 되므로 'it would not be easy'로 바뀌는 것에 유의한다.

16 관계대명사의 소유격을 활용한 문장을 찾는다.

17 가정법 과거에 맞게 동사의 과거형을 쓰되, 이 예문의 경우 비인칭 주어 it과 동사 rained를 사용하는 것에 유의한다.

18 (A)와 (B)는 가정법 과거 형태의 문장들이다. If절에는 동사의 과거형을, 주절에는 조동사의 과거형을 쓰는 것이 적절하다. (C)는 주절에 will이 있으므로, 직설법 현재 is가 적절하다.

19 황제의 머리카락을 잡아당긴 손자에게 사탕을 주겠다는 이야기로 '달콤한 처벌'이 적절하다. ④ Harsh: 모진, 가혹한

20 가정법 과거(If+주어+동사의 과거형, 주어+조동사의 과거형+동사원형)로 쓴다. in one's place: ~의 처지에서, ~의 입장에서

21 황제의 머리에서 머리카락을 잡아당긴 사람에게 사탕을 주겠다는 비르발의 말에 '그건 말이 안 된다.'는 의미로 말한 것임을 유추할 수 있다.

22 ⓐ와 ①: 요청, 부탁, ② (시스템, 계획, 방식 등을) 선호하다, ③ 호의, ④ (호의·친절·애정을 나타내는) 선물, 기념품, ⑤ 도움, 조력

23 각각 ① a lot of, ② no sense, ④ a few, ⑤ much가 적절하다. ③ matter: (관심·고찰의) 문제

24 '필요한 만큼 얼마든지 시간을 가지시오.'라고 하고 있다.

25 keep in touch: (~와 편지·전화로) 연락하고 지내다[연락하다]

26 현재 사실과 반대되는 말을 가정하는 가정법 과거(If+주어+동사의 과거형, 주어+조동사의 과거형+동사원형)로 쓴다.

27 '우리가 함께 캠핑을 갔던 때가 생각나.'라고 하고 있다.

단원별 예상문제 p.101~104

01 ③ 02 ③ 03 ⑤
04 (1) sense (2) wisdom (3) (p)rovides 05 ①
06 you should always live for today
07 He lost his soccer match last week. 08 ②
09 ⑤ 10 ⑤
11 (1) ⓑ (2) ⓓ (3) ⓑ (4) ⓑ (5) ⓐ (6) ⓓ (7) ⓒ
   (8) ⓑ (9) ⓒ
12 ④ 13 ⑤
14 Mike knew her phone number, he could call her
15 Tom had caught the school bus this morning, he would not have been late for school again
16 wish I were[was] as wise as Birbal
17 ⑤ 18 ② 19 How can we do that?
20 ① 21 my line
22 If I could turn back time, I would do more things together with you.
23 ④
24 She[Minji] cannot believe (that) it is time to say goodbye.

01 ③번은 동의어 관계이다. 나머지는 모두 반의어 관계이다. valuable: 귀중한, precious: 귀중한 ① hopeful: 희망이 있는, hopeless: 희망 없는 ② valueless: 가치가 없는, priceless: 대단히 귀중한 ④ powerful: 유력한, powerless: 무력한 ⑤ useful: 쓸모 있는, useless: 쓸모 없는

02 ① correct: 맞는, 정확한. 정확한 암호를 입력할 수 있는 마지막 기회입니다. ② offer: 내놓다, 제공하다. 그 식당에서는 전통 가정식 요리를 제공한다. ③ punish: 처벌하다. 부모들은 적절한 방법으로 아이들을 벌주어야 한다. ④ emperor: 황제. 그는 로마의 황제가 되기를 원했다. ⑤ a potful of: 한 항아리만큼의. 저는 저의 왕으로부터 한 항아리만큼의 지혜를 왕께 가지고 오라는 명을 받았습니다.

03 priceless: 값을 매길 수 없는, 대단히 귀중한. 그 화재로 대단히 귀중한 골동품들이 소실되었다. ① 가치 없는 ② 가치 없는 ③ 소용없는, 쓸모 없는 ④ 값이 싼 ⑤ 값을 헤아릴 수 없는

04 (1) make sense: 이해가 되다, 타당하다 (2) wisdom: 지혜 (3) provide: 제공하다

05 ①번 뒤에 이어지는 내용으로 보아 주어진 문장은 ①번 앞 문장의 질문에 대한 답으로 적절하다.

06 live for today: 오늘을 위해 살다

07 Anna의 '지난주에 진 게임 말이니?'라는 물음에, 수호가 '응.'이라고 대답하고 있다.

08 뒤에서 '늦었더라도 내는 게 낫다는 뜻이야?'라고 하고 있으므로

'It's better late than never.(늦더라도 안 하는 것보다는 낫지.)'가 적절하다.

09 빈칸을 중심으로 앞과 뒤의 내용이 상반되므로 양보절을 이끄는 even though가 가장 적절하다.

10 소년이 과학 보고서를 낼 것인지는 대화에 나와 있지 않다.

11 (1), (3), (4), (8)은 소유격 관계대명사 whose가 적절하다. (2), (6)은 내용상 소유격이 필요한데, 정관사 the가 있으므로 of which를 쓴다. (5), (7)은 주격 관계대명사이며, (9)는 전치사 on의 목적어 자리에 쓰는 관계대명사이다.

12 가정법 과거 문장들이다. ① win → won ② occurrs → occurred ③ will → would ⑤ look → looked

13 관계대명사의 소유격을 응용한 문장들이다. ① the 생략 ② colors → the colors ③ the works of whom → whose works ④ the doctors → doctors 또는 whose → of which *fake: 가짜인

14 직설법에서 '그녀에게 전화하고 싶지만 할 수 없고, 그녀의 번호를 모른다.'라고 했으므로, 가정법 과거 시제 '전화번호를 안다면 그녀에게 전화할 수 있을 텐데.'라고 표현하는 것이 적절하다.

15 직설법에서 '스쿨 버스를 놓쳐서 오늘 아침에 또 지각했다.'라고 했으므로, 가정법 과거완료 시제 '스쿨 버스를 탔다면, 다시 지각하지 않았을 텐데.'라고 표현하는 것이 적절하다. if절에는 had caught를, 주절에는 조동사 과거형 would 뒤에 not have been을 쓰는 것에 유의한다.

16 직설법에서 'Birbal만큼 지혜롭지 않은데, Birbal처럼 지혜롭고 싶다.'고 했으므로, 가정법으로는 'Birbal처럼 지혜로우면 좋을 텐데'를 표현하는 I wish 가정법이 적절하다.

17 옳은 문장은 ⓐ, ⓓ, ⓔ, ⓕ, ⓗ 5개이다. ⓑ of which branches → whose branches 또는 of which the branches, ⓒ of whom → whose, ⓖ whose the title → whose title 또는 of which the title

18 황제가 그린 선보다 더 '긴' 선을 그림으로써 황제가 그린 선을 건드리지 않고 더 짧게 만들었다는 내용의 글이므로 '더 짧은 선'이 적절하다.

19 '그것을 할 수 없다.'라는 평서문을 같은 뜻의 의문문으로 바꾸면 '어떻게 그것을 할 수 있는가?'라고 할 수 있다. 이렇게 부정의 뜻을 갖는 평서문을 긍정의 의문문으로 쓸 수 있고 이러한 의문문을 수사의문문이라고 한다.

20 ⓐ와 ①: 대과거 용법 ② 경험 용법 ③ 완료 용법 ④, ⑤ 계속 용법

21 위 글의 소유대명사 mine은 'my line'을 의미한다.

22 현재 사실과 반대되는 말을 가정하는 가정법 과거(If+주어+동사의 과거형, 주어+조동사의 과거형+동사원형)로 바꿔 쓴다.

23 주어진 문장의 also에 주목한다. ④번 앞 문장의 내용에 추가되고 있으므로 ④번이 적절하다.

24 '작별 인사를 해야 할 시간이라는 게 믿어지지 않아.'라고 하고 있다.

서술형 실전문제
p.105~106

01 warm → worm

02 Because he got up very early to study for the exam.

03 Are you saying (that) you don't like to get up early?

04 (1) If Mina paid more attention to cooking, she would not burn the food.
(2) If you had not lied, your nose would not have grown longer.
(3) A lot of families whose kids are under 12 visited the zoo.

05 Birbal came back with two pots whose necks were really narrow.

06 One[A 또는 The] pot whose neck was really narrow was offered to the Persian official by Birbal.

07 악바르 황제가 그린 선을 건드리지 않은 채 더 짧게 만드는 것

08 I wish I were[was] as wise as Birbal.

09 (A) without touching it (B) a longer line

01 warm: 따뜻한, worm: 벌레

02 소녀의 '피곤해 보인다.'는 말에 소년이 '시험 공부 하려고 아주 일찍 일어났거든.'이라고 하고 있다.

03 'Do you mean ~?'은 이해를 확인하는 표현으로 'Are you saying ~?'으로 바꿔서 말할 수 있다.

04 (1) 그림에서 이미 불타고 있으므로, 현재 사실의 반대를 가정하는 가정법 과거 문장이다. If절에 과거동사 paid attention을 쓰되, more를 삽입하는 것에 유의한다. (2) 과거 사실에 대한 반대 가정이므로, 가정법 과거완료 문장을 사용하는 것이 적절하다. 'would not have p.p.' 형태에 유의한다. (3) 관계대명사의 소유격을 사용하는 문장이다.

05 소유격 관계대명사 whose를 이용하여 'Their necks'를 'whose necks'로 바꿔 한 문장으로 만든다.

06 '비르발은 목이 매우 좁은 두 항아리를 들고 돌아왔다. 그는 하나를 페르시아의 신하에게 줬다.'라고 하고 있다.

07 '악바르 황제가 그린 선을 건드리지 않은 채 더 짧게 만드는 것'

을 가리킨다.

08 'I wish+가정법'과 동등 비교 'as ~ as' 구문을 이용한다.

09 악바르 황제가 땅에 선을 그린 뒤 그의 신하들에게 그 선을 '건드리지 않은 채' 더 짧게 만들어 보라고 했을 때, 비르발은 악바르가 그린 선 옆에 '더 긴 선'을 그림으로써 그 선을 짧게 만들었다.

창의사고력 서술형 문제   p.107

|모범답안|

01 (1) The evil queen whose apples didn't work was angry at the mirror.

(2) Snow White whose appetite was gone rejected the apples.

(3) The witch whose plan failed was angry.

02 (1) You're good at drawing. I wish I could draw well like you.

(2) You're good at playing soccer. I wish I could play soccer well like you.

(3) You're good at dancing. I wish I could dance well like you.

(4) You're good at speaking English. I wish I could speak English well like you.

03 (A) seven times (B) disappointed (C) give up
   (D) eight (E) tried

01 *reject: 거부하다 *appetite: 입맛

단원별 모의고사   p.108~112

01 present   02 emperor   03 leave

04 (1) The king spent a lot of time at his court.

(2) His parents punished him for lying.

(3) Her books are full of her wit and wisdom.

05 ⑤   06 famous   07 ⑤   08 ④

09 ①   10 it's an expression meaning I hope you do well   11 He can't forget about the game he lost last week.   12 (A) past (B) today

13 ①   14 ④   15 ④   16 would be great if there were a man as wise as Birbal in our country   17 breaking the pot, the pumpkin could not be taken out   18 ①, ⑤   19 ④

20 whose goal is to become a diplomat is studying foreign languages very hard

---

21 came to question the lady whose purse was stolen outside the department store

22 ②   23 목이 매우 좁은 항아리에 꼭 항아리만큼 큰 호박을 넣은 것

24 (1) Please ask him to return the pot to us after he takes the wisdom out of it.

(2) The pumpkin can't be taken out without breaking the pot.

25 ②not to break, ③were / ② to부정사의 부정은 not 이나 never를 to부정사 앞에 쓴다. ③ 가정법 과거이므로 be동사의 과거형 were를 써야 한다.

26 ④   27 had drawn

28 the line that Emperor Akbar drew

---

01 precious: 귀중한, 값비싼 – valuable: 귀중한, gift: 선물 – present: 선물

02 '제국의 통치자인 남자'는 'emperor(황제)'가 적절하다.

03 '어떤 장소나 사람에게서 멀어져 가다'는 'leave(떠나다)'가 적절하다. 떠나실 때 문 좀 잠가 주시겠어요?

04 court: 궁정, 궁궐, punish: 벌을 주다, wit: 기지, 재치, wisdom: 지혜

05 past: 과거, pull: 끌다, 당기다, 끌어당기다 • 결코 과거를 지워 버릴 수는 없다. • 의자를 식탁 더 가까이로 당겨 와. place: 장소, 입장, push: 밀다, future: 미래, invent: 발명하다, shake: 흔들다

06 '매우 잘 알려진'을 나타내는 말은 'famous'이다.

07 밑줄 친 문장은 바람·소원을 나타낼 때 쓰는 표현이다.

08 ⓐ와 ④: 동명사, 나머지는 모두 현재분사이다.

09 ① 행운을 빌어! ② 서둘러! ③ 슬퍼하지 마! ④ 무심코 비밀을 누설하지 마! ⑤ 원예의 재능이 있다면 좋을 텐데!

10 mean을 현재분사 meaning으로 바꿔 an expression을 수식하도록 영작한다.

11 수호는 지난주에 진 축구 시합을 잊을 수 있으면 좋겠다고 했다.

12 Anna는 수호가 과거는 잊고 오늘을 살기를 원한다.

13 'look+형용사'가 되어야 하는데 well이 형용사로 쓰이면 '건강한'이라는 뜻으로 어색하므로 well을 good으로 고치는 것이 적절하다.

14 주어진 문장은 'Brian이 컨디션이 좋다면, 다른 선수들보다 두 배의 버저비터를 해낼 텐데.'라는 가정법 과거 문장이다. 직설법으로는 반대의 현재시제이므로, As가 이끄는 종속절과 주절에 모두 현재시제가 있는 ④가 정답이다. 'Brian이 컨디션이 좋지

21

않아서, 다른 선수들보다 두 배의 버저비터를 성공하지 않는다.'

15 ④의 whose는 의문형용사이다. 나머지는 모두 관계대명사의 소유격이다.

16 주어진 문장은 '우리나라에 Birbal과 같은 지혜로운 사람이 아무도 없어 안 좋다.'는 내용이다. 가정법을 활용하면 '우리나라에 Birbal같은 지혜로운 사람이 있다면 좋을 텐데.'가 된다.

17 주어진 문장은 '호박을 꺼내려면 항아리를 깨야 한다.'는 내용이다. 가정법을 이용해서 표현하면, '항아리를 깨지 않으면, 호박이 꺼내질 수 없을 텐데.'가 된다.

18 ① 주격 관계대명사의 자리이다 of which를 of가 없는 which 또는 that으로 바꾸는 것이 적절하다. ⑤ 선행사가 the professor로 사람일 때, 소유격 관계대명사는 whose만 가능하다. the opinion of whom을 whose opinion으로 바꾸는 것이 적절하다.

19 '그 선수가 너무 작지 않으면, 올림픽 국가 대표팀에 선발될 것이다'라는 문장이며, '그의 키 문제가 아니라면'과 같은 표현으로 대체할 수 있다. If it were not for = Were it not for = Without ④ 'Had it not been for'는 'If it had not been for'에서 if를 생략하고 도치된 표현으로서 가정법 과거완료시제에 사용하므로, 적절하지 않다.

20 내용상 '목표가 외교관인 그 학생은 외국어들을 매우 열심히 공부하고 있다.'는 내용이다. student가 선행사이므로, 사람을 선행사로 하는 소유격 관계대명사 whose를 이용하여, 두 문장을 연결하는 것이 적절하다. *diplomat: 외교관

21 내용상 '지갑을 도둑맞은 여성에게 경찰이 질문하러 왔다'는 내용이다. lady가 선행사이므로, 사람을 선행사로, 소유격 관계대명사 whose를 활용한다.

22 뒤에 weeks라는 복수 명사가 나오므로 A few가 적절하다. little과 a little은 복수 명사와 함께 쓰이지 않는다.

24 비르발이 '항아리에서 지혜를 꺼내신 후에는 항아리를 우리에게 돌려달라'고 했는데 악바르가 보니 '항아리를 깨지 않고는 호박을 꺼낼 수가 없기' 때문이다.

26 악바르 황제가 그린 선보다 더 '긴' 선을 그림으로써 황제가 그린 선을 더 짧게 만들었다고 하는 것이 적절하다.

27 악바르 황제가 그린 것이 비르발이 그린 것보다 앞선 시제이므로 과거완료로 나타내는 것이 적절하다.

28 '악바르 황제가 그린 선'을 가리킨다.

교과서 파헤치기

Lesson 6

단어 TEST Step 1

p.02

01 독특하게	02 계산서	03 으깨다
04 불행하게도	05 확실히, 분명히	
06 진가를 알아보다, 고마워하다		07 환상적인
08 수리하다	09 웅장한, 위대한	10 일어나다
11 완전하게	12 불편, 애로	13 추구하다, 추진하다
14 고객, 소비자	15 발명가	16 이유
17 창의적인, 창조적인		18 역할, 배역
19 사실적인	20 덜 익은, 살짝 익힌	21 만족한
22 솔직하게, 솔직히	23 불평하다	24 열정, 흥미
25 끝마치다	26 지불하다, 지급하다	
27 획기적인	28 ~ 동안 내내	29 제공하다
30 서류	31 한 조각, 일부	32 신선한
33 기꺼이	34 성공적인	35 작성하다
36 겁주어 쫓아내다	37 ~이기 때문에, ~이므로	
38 결과적으로	39 역대, 지금껏	40 내붙이다, 게시하다
41 ~에 익숙하다	42 최선을 다하다	
43 ~의 책임을 지다, ~을 떠맡다		

단어 TEST Step 2

p.03

01 passion	02 appreciate	03 check
04 throughout	05 rare	06 pay
07 fix	08 form	09 surely
10 inconvenience	11 completely	12 gladly
13 pursue	14 reason	15 role
16 happen	17 complain	18 decorate
19 fantastic	20 meal	21 fresh
22 honestly	23 creative	24 crush
25 innovative	26 slice	27 successful
28 unfortunately	29 grand	30 customer
31 uniquely	32 supper	33 provide
34 satisfied	35 be used to	36 fill out
37 not anymore	38 as a result	39 of all time
40 do one's best	41 feel like -ing	42 put up
43 scare away		

단어 TEST Step 3

p.04

1 role, 역할, 배역   2 rare, 덜 익은, 살짝 익힌
3 meal, 식사   4 provide, 제공하다
5 supper, 만찬, 저녁 식사   6 throughout, ~동안 내내
7 check, 계산서   8 appreciate, 진가를 알아보다

9 crush, 으깨다   10 customer, 고객, 소비자
11 decorate, 장식하다, 꾸미다   12 fix, 수리하다
13 form, 서류   14 inventor, 발명가
15 complain, 불평하다   16 pursue, 추구하다, 추진하다

대화문 TEST Step 1

p.05~06

Listen & Speak 1 A-1

draw, did, it / look so real, feel like having a bite of / I'm not satisfied with, unique / so, fantastic drawing

Listen & Speak 1 A-2

How can, help / bought, only a week ago, sometimes turns off by itself / have a look at, inconvenience, take, few hours to fix / I'm not satisfied with, like, one / course, fill out, form

Listen & Speak 2 A-1

did, buy / myself / better than any other jam / should sell it / would, to buy / I promise I'll be

Listen & Speak 2 A-2

thought, were interested in / not anymore, want to become / Are, sure / how to act, I promise I'll do my best

Communicate A

your meal / good, fresh / about / I'm not satisfied with, rare / Would, like, to bring, another one / be going, have, check / won't have to pay for / I promise we'll provide, with, experience

Progress Check 1

How can I / got, as, I'm not satisfied with / in different colors / one in blue / do, get one

Progress Check 2

take, classes / interested in / not anymore, chef / hard work / worry, I promise I'll do / then

Progress Check 3

on / Have, finished / I promise I'll finish

대화문 TEST Step 2

p.07~08

Listen & Speak 1 A-1

B: Wow! Did you draw this?

G: I did. Do you like it?

B: Yes, the bread and the milk look so real. I feel like having a bite of the bread.

G: Thanks, but I'm not satisfied with it. It's not unique.

B: I don't think so. I think it's a fantastic drawing.

M: Hello, ma'am. How can I help you?

W: I bought this phone only a week ago, but it sometimes turns off by itself.

M: Oh, I see. May I have a look at it? (Pause) We're sorry for the inconvenience. It'll take a few hours to fix it.

W: I'm not satisfied with the phone. I'd like a new one.

M: Of course. I just need to fill out this form.

G: Wow, I like this blueberry jam. Where did you buy it?

B: I made it myself.

G: Really? This is better than any other jam I've ever had. You should sell it.

B: Do you think people would want to buy this?

G: Of course. I promise I'll be your first customer.

B: Mom, I want to go to an arts high school. I want to become an actor.

W: What? I thought you were interested in science.

B: I was but not anymore. I want to become a movie star.

W: Are you sure you want to be an actor?

B: Yes, I'll learn how to act. I promise I'll do my best.

Man: Are you enjoying your meal?

Woman: Well, the bread was good, and the salad was fresh.

Man: How about your steak?

Woman: Honestly, I'm not satisfied with the steak. It's too rare for me.

Man: I'm sorry. Would you like me to bring you another one?

Woman: That's O.K. I need to be going. Let me just have the check, please.

Man: I'm really sorry. You won't have to pay for the steak.

Woman: O.K. Thanks.

Man: I promise we'll provide you with a better experience next time you visit.

M: Hello, ma'am. How can I help you?

W: I got this hat as a gift yesterday, but I'm not satisfied with the color.

M: Oh, I see. We have this hat in different colors.

W: Do you have one in blue?

M: Yes, we do. I'll get one for you.

W: Thanks.

B: Mom, I want to take cooking classes.

W: What? I thought you were interested in sports.

B: I was but not anymore. I want to become a chef.

W: Are you sure? Cooking is hard work.

B: Don't worry. I promise I'll do my best.

W: O.K., then.

G: Dad, I want to watch a movie on TV now.

M: Have you finished your homework?

G: No, but I promise I'll finish it after I watch TV.

01 Vinci the Cook

02 known as, greatest, time

03 also, inventor, musician

04 few, however, that, creative

05 In, worked as, at

06 took charge, changed, completely

07 simple, artistic, like, slices

08 dishes, even decorated with

09 because, used, with, servings

10 As, result, lost, job

11 few, later, opened, with

12 create, where, try, innovative

13 put up, uniquely written

14 believed, appreciate, creative cooking

15 Unfortunately, never happened

16 In, early, work for

17 different roles, such as

18 put in charge of

19 another chance, pursue, passion

20 stop at cooking creative

21 much more quickly, easily

22 Thus, invented, machines

23 created, crush vegetables, pull

24 device, scare, away from

25 innovative, most, too, to

26 grand, based on, wall

27 took, because, been interested

28 spent, kinds, what, put

29 wasted, over, reason, complained

30 Although, successful, interest, throughout

31 not only, but also

32 that, secret, same way

01 the Cook

02 is known as, greatest painters of all time

03 also, inventor, scientist

04 few, however, creative cook

05 twenty-year-old, as a cook

06 took charge of, changed, completely

07 but, like, a few carrot slices

08 were even decorated with

09 however, were used to, with, servings

10 As a result   11 A few, later

12 to create, where, innovative

13 put up, beautifully painted, uniquely written

14 would, appreciate, creative

15 Unfortunately, happened   16 early, to work

17 was given, roles, such as

18 was, put in charge of

19 to be given another, to pursue, passion

20 stop at   21 much more

22 Thus, invented   23 that, crush

24 that, scare, away from

25 were too, too, to use

26 to make, which was based on

27 took on, had, been interested in

28 a lot of, cooking, what to put

29 for over, why, to

30 Although, interest in, throughout

31 not only, but also, creative cook

32 Now that, secret passion, the same way

1 요리사 다빈치

2 레오나르도 다빈치는 역대 가장 위대한 화가들 중의 한 명으로 알려져 있다.

3 그는 또한 위대한 발명가, 과학자, 그리고 음악가였다.

4 하지만, 극히 소수의 사람들만이 또한 그가 창의적인 요리사였다는 것을 안다.

5 1473년, 스무 살의 레오나르도 다빈치는 이탈리아 플로렌스에 있는 음식점에서 요리사로 일했다.

6 그가 부엌을 책임지게 되었을 때, 다빈치는 메뉴를 완전히 바꿔 버렸다.

7 그는 약간의 당근 조각을 곁들인 생선과 같이 간단하지만 예술적인 음식을 만들었다.

8 몇몇 음식들은 심지어 꽃으로 장식되었다.

9 하지만, 손님들은 많은 양의 고기 요리에 익숙했었기 때문에 불만족스러워했다.

10 그 결과, 다빈치는 그의 직업을 잃었다.

11 몇 년 후, 다빈치는 그의 친구인 산드로 보티첼리와 함께 음식점을 열었다.

12 그는 사람들이 그의 획기적인 음식을 먹어 볼 수 있는 장소로 만들기를 원했다.

13 그들은 아름답게 그려진 간판을 내걸었고 독특하게 써진 메뉴를 만들었다.

14 다빈치는 사람들이 곧 그의 창의적인 요리의 진가를 알아볼 것이라고 믿었다.

15 불행히도, 그런 일은 결코 일어나지 않았다.

16 1480년대 초반에, 다빈치는 밀라노에서 루도비코 스포르차를 위해 일하기 시작했다.

17 그는 음악가, 화가, 그리고 공학자와 같은 많은 역할들을 부여받았다.

18 그는 또한 주방을 책임지게 되었다.

19 그는 요리를 향한 그의 열정을 추구할 또 다른 기회를 얻게 되어 행복했다.

20 다빈치는 창의적인 요리를 만드는 것에 멈추지 않았다.

21 그는 훨씬 더 빠르고 쉽게 요리하고 싶어했다.

22 따라서, 그는 그의 주방에서 사용할 새로운 기계들을 발명하였다.

23 그는 채소를 으깨고 스파게티를 뽑는 기계들을 만들었다.

24 그는 심지어 개구리를 겁주어 물탱크에서 쫓아낼 수 있는 기구도 만들었다.

25 확실히 그것들은 모두 매우 획기적이었지만, 그것들 중 대부분은 사용하기에 너무 크거나 너무 어려웠다.

26 1495년, 스포르차는 다빈치에게 웅장한 그림을 밀라노에 있는 교회의 벽에 그려 달라고 부탁했는데, 그것은 예수의 최후의 만찬을 바탕으로 한 것이었다.

27 다빈치는 기꺼이 그 작업을 맡았는데, 그가 항상 음식에 흥미를 가졌기 때문이었다.

28 그는 그림 속 식탁 위에 어떤 음식을 올릴지 결정하기 위해 모든 종류의 음식을 요리하느라 많은 시간을 썼다.

29 "다빈치는 1년 넘게 부엌에서 시간을 낭비해 오고 있습니다. 그것이 그가 아직도 그림을 끝내지 못한 이유입니다."라고 교회 사람들이 스포르차에게 불평을 했다.

30 다빈치는 결코 성공적인 요리사는 되지 못했지만 그는 그의 생애 내내 요리에 대한 큰 흥미를 보여 주었다.

31 그는 훌륭한 화가일 뿐만 아니라 창의적인 요리사였다.

32 이제 여러분은 요리에 대한 그의 비밀스런 열정을 모두 알게 되었기 때문에 〈최후의 만찬〉을 절대 같은 식으로는 보지 않을 것이다.

1 Da Vinci the Cook

2 Leonardo da Vinci is known as one of the greatest painters of all time.

3 He was also a great inventor, scientist, and musician.

4 Very few people, however, know that da Vinci was also a creative cook.

5 In 1473, twenty-year-old da Vinci worked as a cook at a restaurant in Florence, Italy.

6 When he took charge of the kitchen, da Vinci changed the menu completely.

7 He made simple but artistic dishes like fish with a few carrot slices.

8 Some dishes were even decorated with flowers.

9 Customers, however, were unhappy because they were used to dishes with big servings of meat.

10 As a result, da Vinci lost his job.

11 A few years later, da Vinci opened a restaurant with his friend Sandro Botticelli.

12 He wanted to create a place where people could try his innovative food.

13 They put up a beautifully painted sign and made a uniquely written menu.

14 Da Vinci believed that people would soon appreciate his creative cooking.

15 Unfortunately, that never happened.

16 In the early 1480s, da Vinci began to work for Ludovico Sforza in Milan.

17 He was given many different roles, such as a musician, a painter, and an engineer.

18 He was also put in charge of the kitchen.

19 He was happy to be given another chance to pursue his passion for cooking.

20 Da Vinci did not stop at cooking creative dishes.

21 He wanted to cook much more quickly and easily.

22 Thus, he invented new machines for his kitchen.

23 He created machines that could crush vegetables and pull spaghetti.

24 He even made a device that could scare frogs away from the water tank.

25 Surely, they were all very innovative, but most of them were too big or too difficult to use.

26 In 1495, Sforza asked da Vinci to make a grand painting, which was based on the last supper of Jesus, on the wall of a church in Milan.

27 Da Vinci gladly took on the project because he had always been interested in food.

28 He spent a lot of time cooking all kinds of food to decide what to put on the table in his picture.

29 "Da Vinci has wasted his time in the kitchen for over a year. That's the reason why he hasn't finished the painting yet," complained the people from the church to Sforza.

30 Although da Vinci never became a successful cook, he showed great interest in cooking throughout his life.

31 He was not only a great painter but also a creative cook.

32 Now that you know all about his secret passion for cooking, you will never look at *The Last Supper* the same way.

Write

1. an artist who uses technology

2. special moment, decided what I wanted

3. Back in, small statue using technology

4. great chance to learn, using technology

5. decided to, technical high school

6. After, graduated from, entered, learned, arts, technology

7. This year, held, exhibition

8. am, satisfied with

Link

1. the most important thing to consider, choose their career

2. come up with, design new things

3. work at a place where, use their creativity

Watch and Think Share

1. is known for using, during

2. few people, however, historian, painter, writer

3. won, Nobel Prize in Literature

Write

1. My name is Kim Jieun. I am an artist who uses technology.

2. There was a special moment when I decided what I wanted to be.

3. Back in 2030, I made a small statue using technology.

4. It was a great chance to learn about using technology for arts.

5. Thus, I decided to go to a technical high school.

6. After I graduated from high school, I entered Korea Art College and learned more about arts and technology.

7. This year, I held my first exhibition.

8. I am very satisfied with my life.

Link

1. Some people think creativity is the most important thing to consider when they choose their career.

2. They like to come up with new ideas and design new things.

3. Thus, they want to work at a place where they can use their creativity.

Watch and Think Share

1. Winston Churchill is known for using the Prime Minister of the United Kingdom during World War II.

2. Very few people, however, know that he was also a historian, a painter, and a writer.

3. He even won the Nobel Prize in Literature in 1953.

Lesson 7

01 귀중한, 값비싼   02 맞는, 정확한   03 정확하게

04 고위 공무원, 관리 05 한 항아리[냄비]의 양

06 정직   07 정말, 확실히   08 ~중에, ~의 사이에

09 깨지다, 부러뜨리다   10 여행, 여정

11 이상한   12 경기, 시합

13 지혜로운, 현명한, 슬기로운   14 기지, 재치

15 좁은   16 내놓다, 제공하다   17 대궐, 궁궐

18 황제   19 (땅속에 사는) 벌레 20 정책

21 사탕, 단것; 단, 달콤한   22 처벌하다, 벌주다

23 호박   24 되돌려주다   25 표현

26 청, 부탁   27 (화나거나 놀라서) 말을 못 하는

28 그러므로   29 지혜, 슬기, 현명함 30 현재, 지금

31 틀림없이, 분명히 32 (틀림없이) ~일 것이다

33 끌다, 당기다, 끌어당기다   34 시험

35 혼자서, 스스로   36 ~을 제출하다

37 ~을 찾아내다, ~을 떠올리다   38 ~ 덕분에

39 ~에 주력하다, 집중하다

40 ~의 처지에서, ~의 상황에서   41 타당하다, 말이 되다

42 ~로 유명하다   43 한 냄비의, 한 항아리의

01 wise   02 expression   03 favor

04 among   05 certainly   06 gift

07 honesty   08 punish   09 narrow

10 precious   11 correct   12 present

13 official   14 strange   15 indeed

16 policy   17 journey   18 worm

19 match   20 pumpkin   21 break

22 emperor   23 court   24 speechless

25 exam   26 wit   27 past

28 exactly   29 return   30 sweet

31 thus   32 wisdom   33 potful

34 offer   35 hand in   36 focus on

37 over again   38 in one's place 39 for oneself

40 come up with 41 be famous for 42 thanks to

43 make sense

1 honesty, 정직   2 present, 현재, 지금

3 precious, 귀중한, 값비싼   4 leave, 떠나다

5 emperor, 황제　6 correct, 맞는, 정확한

7 court, 대궐, 궁궐　8 pumpkin, 호박

9 journey, 여행, 여정　10 match, 경기, 시합

11 worm, 벌레　12 narrow, 좁은

13 official, 고위 공무원, 관리　14 gift, 선물

15 punish, 처벌하다, 벌주다

16 speechless, (화나거나 놀라서) 말을 못 하는

대화문 TEST Step 1　　　　　　　p.25~26

Listen & Speak 1 A-1

look tired / got up, to study / Good for, early bird, worm / gets tired / Do you mean / exactly what I mean

Listen & Speak 1 A-2

have to / a leg / Do you mean, break one, legs / expression meaning, you do well

Listen & Speak 2 A-1

dance well / Everyone, is good at / too / good singers / What a, I wish I could, like

Listen & Speak 2 A-2

can't believe, to say, Thanks to, I wish I could, back to, to start, new journey

Communicate A

wrong, look, good / thinking about / Do you mean, lost / I wish I could / live for today / Do you mean, focus on / exactly, gift, why, called / expressions, as wise as

Progress Check 1

look worried, wrong / hand in, by / better late than never / Do you mean, hand it in even though, late / what

Progress Check 2

play the guitar / it / too / in / What a, I wish, could, like

Progress Check 3

broke, what to do, Another, Honesty, policy, what that means

대화문 TEST Step 2　　　　　　　p.27~28

Listen & Speak 1 A-1

G: You look tired this morning.

B: I got up very early to study for the exam.

G: Good for you. The early bird catches the worm.

B: No. The early bird gets tired quickly.

G: Do you mean you don't like to get up early?

B: Yes, that's exactly what I mean.

Listen & Speak 1 A-2

G: I have to sing at the school's English pop song contest.

B: Wow. Break a leg!

G: What? Do you mean I have to break one of my legs?

B: No, it's an expression meaning I hope you do well.

Listen & Speak 2 A-1

B: Wow, you really dance well.

G: Thanks. I love dancing. Everyone in my family is good at dancing.

B: Really? Your parents dance well, too?

G: Yes. They're also good singers.

B: What a family! I wish I could dance like you.

Listen & Speak 2 A-2

B: Hello, everyone! Time flies. I can't believe it's time to say goodbye. Thanks to my teachers and friends, I was really happy here. I wish I could go back to my first year and live these years over again, but it's time to start a new journey to high school. I hope I can see you again. Thank you.

Communicate A

Anna: What's wrong? You don't look so good.

Suho: I'm still thinking about our soccer match last week.

Anna: Do you mean the game you lost last week?

Suho: Yes. I wish I could forget about it, but I can't.

Anna: Well, you should always live for today.

Suho: Do you mean I should forget the past and focus on the present?

Anna: Yes, exactly. People say, "Yesterday is history, tomorrow is a mystery, and today is a gift. That's why it's called the present."

Suho: Now I see. You know so many great expressions. You're as wise as my grandma.

Progress Check 1

G: You look worried. Is something wrong?

B: I had to hand in my science report by yesterday, but I didn't.

G: It's better late than never.

B: Do you mean it's better to hand it in even though it's late?

G: Yes, exactly. You should always finish what you've started.

Progress Check 2

B: Wow, you play the guitar so well.

G: Thanks. I love playing the guitar. I learned it from my dad.

B: Really? Does your father play the guitar, too?

G: Yes. He was in a famous band.

B: What a family! I wish I could play the guitar like you.

Progress Check 3

M: You broke your friend's phone, and you don't know what to do. Another friend says to you, "Honesty is the best policy." You don't know what that means exactly.

본문 TEST Step 1 p.29~31

01 Tales of

02 emperor, number, officials, court

03 Among, whose name

04 famous for, with, words

05 Thus, emoeror, have, near

06 Sweet Punishment

07 test, wisdom, asked, strange

08 One, came up with

09 pulled, hair, head, should

10 be punished, course　　　11 punish him

12 turned to

13 would, do, were, place

14 If, were you, would give　　15 talking about

16 Birbal's crazy

17 What made, say so　　18 must be, else, such

19 correct, so, wise, near　　20 Potful, Wisdom

21 sent, with, strange favor

22 been asked, bring, potful

23 makes, sense, put, in

24 bring, potful, wisdom　　25 won't be, problem

26 wait a few weeks　　27 much time as, need

28 few, back, whose, narrow

29 take, return, after, out

30 precious, careful, break, wisdom

31 official, inside, became speechless

32 thanked, left for, country　　33 be, if, were, as

34 After, left, what, inside

35 the other, for yourself

36 other, found, big as

37 be taken, without breaking

38 put, over, until, grew

39 certainly, potful of wisdom

본문 TEST Step 2 p.32~33

01 Tales of

02 a number of wise officials, court

03 Among, was, whose name　04 for, wit, with

05 Thus, emperor, to have, near

06 Punishment

07 To test, officials' wisdom, asked them strange questions

08 came up with

09 a hair, should I do to

10 be punished, course　　11 punish

12 turned to

13 would, do if, were in my place

14 If, were you, would give　　15 talking about

16 crazy　　17 What made you

18 who, must be, else, such a thing

19 indeed correct, so, to have, as wise as

20 Potful, Wisdom

21 with a strange favor

22 a lot of, I've been asked, to bring, a potful of wisdom

23 makes no sense, put, in a pot

24 a potful of　　25 won't be

26 a few weeks　　27 as much time as

28 A few, whose, narrow, one, official

29 take, to return, out of it　30 not to break

31 speechless　　32 thanked, left for

33 would be, if there were, as wise as

34 After, left, what was

35 the other, for yourself　　36 the other, as big as

37 can't be taken, without breaking

38 over, until, as big as

39 certainly, a potful of wisdom

본문 TEST Step 3 p.34~35

1 비르발 이야기

2 악바르는 무굴 제국의 제3대 황제로, 자신의 궁정에 많은 현명한 신하들이 있었다.

3 그 중 라자 비르발이라는 이름의 한 사람이 있었다.

4 그는 재빠른 재치로 유명했으며 말이 매우 지혜로웠다.

5 그래서, 황제는 언제나 비르발을 곁에 두기를 원했다.

6 달콤한 처벌

7 신하들의 지혜를 시험해 보기 위해, 악바르는 종종 그들에게 이상한 질문을 했다.

8 어느 날, 황제는 재미있는 질문이 생각났다.

9 악바르: 오늘 어떤 이가 내 머리에서 머리카락을 잡아당겼소. 이

자에게 무엇을 해야 하겠소?

10 신하 1: 당연히 처벌해야 합니다.

11 신하 2: 예, 그를 처벌하소서!

12 악바르가 비르발에게 돌아섰다.

13 악바르: 그대가 내 입장이라면 무엇을 하겠소, 비르발?

14 비르발: 소신이 폐하라면, 그에게 사탕을 주겠습니다.

15 신하 3: 저 사람은 무슨 말을 하는 건가?

16 신하 4: 비르발이 정신이 나갔어!

17 악바르: 왜 그렇게 말했소?

18 비르발: 폐하의 머리카락을 잡아당긴 사람은 폐하의 손자임이 분명합니다. 다른 그 누구도 그런 짓을 할 수 없지요.

19 악바르: 과연 그대의 말이 맞소, 비르발. 그대처럼 현명한 자를 옆에 두어 정말 기쁘오.

20 한 항아리만큼의 지혜

21 어느 날, 페르시아의 왕이 이상한 요청과 함께 신하를 보냈다.

22 페르시아의 신하: 폐하의 나라에 현명한 자들이 많다고 들었습니다. 저는 저의 왕으로부터 한 항아리의 지혜를 왕께 가지고 오라는 명을 받았습니다.

23 신하 5: 저건 말이 안 되오! 어떻게 지혜를 항아리에 넣을 수 있단 말이오?

24 악바르: 그에게 지혜 한 항아리를 가져다줄 수 있겠소, 비르발?

25 비르발: 문제될 것이 없사옵니다.

26 몇 주만 기다려 주시겠습니까?

27 페르시아의 신하: 물론이오! 필요한 만큼 얼마든지 시간을 가지시오.

28 몇 주 후, 비르발은 목이 매우 좁은 두 항아리를 들고 돌아왔다. 그는 하나를 페르시아의 신하에게 줬다.

29 비르발: 이 지혜의 항아리를 그대의 왕께 가져다 드리십시오. 왕께서 이 항아리에서 지혜를 꺼내신 후에는 항아리를 우리에게 돌려달라 전해 주십시오.

30 비르발: 그 항아리는 매우 귀중한 것이니, 그것을 깨지 않도록 조심해 주십시오. 우리는 오직 두 개의 지혜의 항아리만 갖고 있습니다.

31 페르시아 신하는 항아리 안을 들여다보곤 말을 잃었다.

32 그는 비르발에게 감사를 표한 뒤 그의 나라로 떠났다.

33 페르시아의 신하: 우리 나라에도 비르발처럼 현명한 자가 있다면 정말 좋을 텐데.

34 페르시아의 신하가 떠난 뒤, 악바르는 비르발에게 항아리 속에 무엇이 있었는지를 물었다.

35 비르발: 여기 또 다른 항아리가 있습니다. 직접 살펴보시지요.

36 악바르는 또 다른 항아리 안을 보고 꼭 항아리만큼 큰 호박을 발견했다.

37 악바르: 그렇군! 항아리를 깨지 않고는 호박을 꺼낼 수가 없구려! 어떻게 한 것이오?

38 비르발: 항아리를 호박꽃에 덮어 놓은 후 호박이 항아리만큼 클 때까지 기다렸습니다.

39 악바르: 하하하! 이건 정말로 지혜의 항아리구려!

1 Tales of Birbal

2 Akbar, the third Mogul emperor, had a number of wise officials at his court.

3 Among them was a man whose name was Raja Birbal.

4 He was famous for his quick wit and was very wise with his words.

5 Thus, the emperor always liked to have Birbal near him.

6 Sweet Punishment

7 To test his officials' wisdom, Akbar often asked them strange questions.

8 One day, he came up with an interesting question.

9 Akbar: Someone pulled a hair from my head today. What should I do to him?

10 Official 1: He should be punished, of course.

11 Official 2: Yes, punish him!

12 Akbar turned to Birbal.

13 Akbar: What would you do if you were in my place, Birbal?

14 Birbal: If I were you, I would give him sweets.

15 Official 3: What's he talking about?

16 Official 4: Birbal's crazy!

17 Akbar: What made you say so?

18 Birbal: The person who pulled your hair must be your grandson. No one else could do such a thing.

19 Akbar: You are indeed correct, Birbal. I'm so glad to have someone as wise as you near me.

20 A Potful of Wisdom

21 One day, the king of Persia sent an official with a strange favor.

22 Persian Official: I hear you have a lot of wise men in your country. I've been asked by my king to bring him a potful of wisdom.

23 Official 5: That makes no sense! How can we put wisdom in a pot?

24 Akbar: Can you bring him a potful of wisdom, Birbal?

25 Birbal: It won't be a problem.

26 Birbal: Could you please wait a few weeks?

27 Persian Official: Of course! Take as much time as you need.

28 A few weeks later, Birbal came back with two pots whose necks were really narrow. He offered one to the Persian official.

29 Birbal: You can take this pot of wisdom to your

king. Please ask him to return the pot to us after he takes the wisdom out of it.

30 Birbal: The pot is very precious, so please be careful not to break it. We only have two pots of wisdom.

31 The Persian official looked inside the pot and became speechless.

32 He thanked Birbal and left for his country.

33 Persian Official: It would be great if there were a man as wise as Birbal in our country.

34 After the Persian official left, Akbar asked Birbal what was inside the pot.

35 Birbal: Here is the other pot. You can see for yourself.

36 Akbar looked inside the other pot and found a pumpkin just as big as the pot.

37 Akbar: I see! The pumpkin can't be taken out without breaking the pot. How did you do it?

38 Birbal: I put the pots over pumpkin flowers and waited until the pumpkins grew as big as the pots.

39 Akbar: Hahaha! This certainly is a potful of wisdom!

구석구석지문 TEST Step 1 p.41

Link

1. Shorter Line
2. drew a line, asked his officials
3. Make, shorter without touching
4. Without touching
5. How, that
6. smiled
7. too easy
8. next to, that, had drawn
9. shorter than mine
10. did it
11. wish, were as wise as

Write

1. Dear
2. flies, to say goodbye
3. the time when we went
4. the movie we watched
5. playing basketball with, after school
6. for teaching me basketball skills
7. could turn back time, would spend
8. keep in touch, graduate

9. Best

Culture Project

1. When, failed, seven times, disappointed
2. from, said to, If I were, wouldn't give up
3. Fall, stand up
4. Japanese saying, Do not give up
5. tried again, finally passed

구석구석지문 TEST Step 2 p.42

Link

1. A Shorter Line
2. One day, Emperor Akbar drew a line on the ground and asked his officials.
3. Akbar: Make this line shorter without touching it.
4. Official 1: Without touching it?
5. Official 2: How can we do that?
6. Birbal smiled.
7. Birbal: That's too easy.
8. Birbal drew a longer line next to the line that Akbar had drawn.
9. Birbal: Your line is now shorter than mine.
10. Akbar: You dud it, Birbal!
11. Official 3: I wish I were as wise as Birbal.

Write

1. Dear Jaeha,
2. Time flies. I cannot believe that it is time to say goodbye.
3. I still remember the time when we went camping together.
4. I really liked the movie we watched that night.
5. I also loved playing basketball with you after school.
6. I really want to thank you for teaching me basketball skills.
7. If I could turn back time, I would spend more time with you.
8. I hope we keep in touch even after we graduate.
9. Best, Jake

Culture Project

1. When my brother failed his driving test seven times, he was very disappointed.
2. Kento, his friend from Japan, said to him, "If I were you, I wouldn't give up.
3. Fall seven times, stand up eight."
4. It's a Japanese saying that means "Do not give up."
5. My brother tried again and finally passed.

MEMO

적중100

영어 기출 문제집

정답 및 해설

미래 | 최연희